STUDIES OF HIGH TEMPERATURE SUPERCONDUCTORS

(Advances in Research and Applications)

VOLUME 27

STUDIES OF HIGH TEMPERATURE SUPERCONDUCTORS

(Advances in Research and Applications)

VOLUME 27

Pseudogap in High Temperature Superconductors

EDITOR
ANANT NARLIKAR
National Physical Laboratory
New Delhi

Nova Science Publishers, Inc.
Commack, New York

Editorial Production: Susan Boriotti
Office Manager: Annette Hellinger
Graphics: Frank Grucci and John T'Lustachowski
Information Editor: Tatiana Shohov
Book Production: Donna Dennis, Patrick Davin, Christine Mathosian and Tammy Sauter
Circulation: Maryanne Schmidt
Marketing/Sales: Cathy DeGregory

Library of Congress Cataloging-in-Publication Data
available upon request

ISBN 1-56072-684-9

6080 Jericho Turnpike, Suite 207
Commack, New York 11725
Tele. 516-499-3103 Fax 516-499-3146
e-mail: Novascience@earthlink.net
e-mail: Novascil@aol.com
Web Site: http://www.nexusworld.com/nova

Printed in the United States of America

Studies of High Temperature
Superconductors
Volume 27

ISBN 1-56072-684-9

CONTENTS

Chapter - 3
NMR STUDIES OF THE NORMAL STATE PSEUDOGAP IN HIGH TEMPERATURE SUPERCONDUCTING CUPRATES
G. V. M. Williams

Chapter - 4
SOME THEORETICAL MODELS FOR THE PSEUDOGAP IN HTSC
K. P. Sinha

Chapter - 5
THE FLUCTUATION-INDUCED PSEUDOGAP IN THE OPTICAL CONDUCTIVITY OF HIGH Tc SUPERCONDUCTORS
Francesca Federici and Andrei A. Varlamov

Chapter- 6
PSEUDOGAPS AND MAGNETIC PROPERTIES OF THE TWO DIMENSIONAL t-J MODEL
A. Sherman and M. Schreiber

CONTRIBUTORS TO VOLUME -27

K. H. Bennemann, Institute for Theoretical Physics, Freie Universitat Berlin, Arnimallee 14, D-14195 Berlin, GERMANY

X. K. Chen, Physics Department, Simon Fraser University, Burnaby, British Columbia, CANADA V5A 1S6

Francesca Federici, Theoretical Physics Group, School of Physics and Astronomy, University of Birmingham, Edgbaston, Birmingham B15 2TT, UNITED KINGDOM

J. Halbritter, Forschungszentrum Karlsruhe, Institut fur Materialforschung I, Postfach 3640, D-76021 Karlsruhe, GERMANY

J. C. Irwin, Physics Department, Simon Fraser University, Burnaby, British Columbia, CANADA V5A 1S6

J. G. Naeini, Physics Department, Simon Fraser University, Burnaby, British Columbia, CANADA V5A 1S6

J. Schmalian, Institute for Theoretical Physics, Freie Universitat Berlin, Arnimallee 14, D-14195 Berlin, GERMANY

M. Schreiber, Institut fur Physik, Technische Universitat, D-09107 Chemnitz, GERMANY

A. Sherman, Institute of Physics, University of Tartu, Riia 142, EE-2400 Tartu, ESTONIA

K. P. Sinha, Department of Physics, Indian Institute of Science, Bangalore 560012 and Jawaharlal Nehru Centre for Advanced Scientific Research, IISc Campus, Bangalore 560012, INDIA

Oleg Sushkov, School of Physics, University of New South Wales, Sydney 2052, AUSTRALIA

G. V. M. Williams, New Zealand Institute for Industrial Research, P.O. Box 3130, Lower Hutt, NEW ZEALAND

Andrei A. Varlamov, Department of Theoretical Physics, Moscow

Institute of Steel and Alloys, Leninskii Prospect 4, Moscow 117936
RUSSIA

FUTURE VOLUMES PLANNED

MICROSTRUCTURAL STUDIES OF HIGH Tc SUPERCONDUCTORS

STUDIES OF HTSC USING NUCLEAR AND SPECTROSCOPIC TECHNIQUES

SUPERCONDUCTIVITY IN ORGANIC SYSTEMS

SUPERCONDUCTIVITY IN STRONGLY CORRELATED SYSTEMS

COMMERCIAL STATUS AND FUTURE PROSPECTS OF HTSC

The Editor would welcome suggestions from the reader and potential authors for other possible areas.

Contents Of Earlier Volumes

PREFACE

For scientists working in condensed matter physics, superconductivty had always stimulated fascination and enquiry. The discovery of high T_c ceramic superconductors in 1986 unleashed a new onslaught on the mysteries surrounding the phenomenon. The onslaught came from many fronts - basic science as well as engineering and applied disciplines like materials science, metallurgy, ceramics, electrical and electronic engineering, including microelectronics. Through waves of enraptured popular imagination and swings in funding for scientific research, this academic interest originating in diverse disciplines, has maintained its focus on the subject. This book series recognises the importance of consolidating the ever theoretical and practical ideas and tools, emerging from variegated areas. To facilitate a holistic understanding of the phenomenon and also the development of optimal applications, the series provides an international rendezvous for recent discoveries and new insights bearing relevance to the subject. Given its interdisciplinary premise the "Studies of High Temperature Superconductors" is aimed at the professional scientist and engineers, as well as at graduate students of physics, chemistry, materials science, solid state electronics and engineering.

The present volume, the volume-27 of "Studies" is devoted to the normal state pseudogap discovered in high Tc cuprates, which is currently an area of great topical interest and still not fully understood. The articles written by renowned experts in the field consolidate the experimental findings and present various theoretical models to explain the occurrence of the gap, and it is hoped that the present volume would help the reader to assess the exciting status of the happenings in this frontal field.

I would like to thank Mr. Frank Columbus, the President, Nova Science Publishers, and his colleagues for their efficient cooperation.

January, 1999 Anant Narlikar

Studies of High Temperature
Superconductors
Volume 27

ISBN 1-56072-684-9

ANALYSIS OF PROPERTIES OF HIGH-T_c-SUPERCONDUCTORS

J. SCHMALIAN AND K. H. BENNEMANN

Institute for Theoretical Physics, Freie Universitat Berlin, Arnimallee 14, D-14195
Berlin, GERMANY

I. INTRODUCTION

The doping dependence of various properties of underdoped high-T_c-superconductors has been studied intensively during the last years [1]. Most remarkably, one observed that for decreasing doping concentration x the transition temperature T_c first increased and then after reaching a maximal T_c started to decrease again [2], that the d-wave symmetry order parameter Δ and the ratio $2\Delta/k_BT_c$ continue to increase for decreasing x in underdoped systems [3], that dependent on x below a characteristic temperature T^* pseudogaps appeared in the spectral density and density of states [4], and that the lifetime $\tau(x)$ of the elementary excitations deviated from $\tau^{-1} \propto \omega$ at temperatures T below T^* [5]. Furthermore, photoemission and tunneling spectroscopy show a gap around the Fermi-energy ε_F which persists above T_c for both underdoped and overdoped superconductors. In particular the tunneling spectra have characteristic dips at about 2Δ or 3Δ below ε_F [4].

Here, we attempt to explain this behaviour as due to short-range anti-ferromagnetic spin-fluctuations of frequency ω_s affecting the electronic elementary excitations and causing d-wave symmetry superconductivity. On purpose a relatively simple theory is used to see how far such an approach explains important facts and to keep physics transparent. For excitation energies $\omega \sim T \gg \omega_s$ where ω_s characterizes the spin-excitation energies, the exchange fields act quasi statically on the elementary excitations and which thus feel locally anti-ferromangetic gaps [6]. The resultant local density of states at the Fermi-energy ε_F, $\rho(0)$, decreases for $x \rightarrow 0$, since the exchange fields increase and short-range a.f. order of magnetic moments is expected. This decreases T_c, the quasi-particle scattering rates $\tau^{-1} \propto \rho(0)$, enhances the superconducting d-wave symmetry order parameter Δ and the ratio

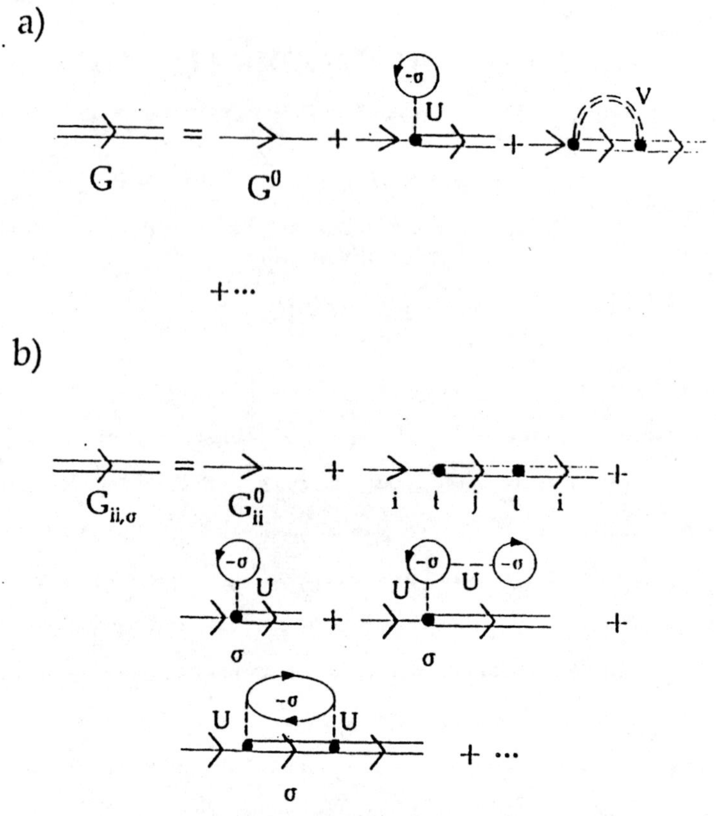

FIG. 1. Diagrammatic illustration of the quasi-particle Green's-function $G(\omega)$ and self-energies. (a) refers to the FLEX-like approximation, where V includes particle-spin-excitation, charge-- fluctuation and particle - particle interactions. $V \sim UU_{eff}$, here U is the on-site Hubbard-Coulomb interaction, U_{eff} the effective interaction due to vertex corrections. The second term on the right hand side is of the form $\frac{U}{2}(n - \sigma\mu_s)G_0G$ with $G^0 = (i\omega_n - \varepsilon_k + \mu)^{-1}$ and magnetic moment μ_s. The dispersion is given by ε_k. (b) refers to a local Green's function $G_{ii,\sigma}(\omega)$ at site i and for spin σ and dynamical mean field theory. The hopping integral t_{ij} denotes transitions from site i to site j. One solves self-consistently with respect to μ_s. Short-range a.f. order can be described via the second term, for example.

$2\Delta/k_BT_c$, and also the magnetic pseudogaps $\delta(x,T)$, for example. For $T \to 0$ and $x \to 0$ local magnetic moments $\mu_s(x)$ are expected to be formed and short-range anti-ferromagnetic order should occur which should be detrimental to superconductivity. Since the electrons cause both magnetic activity and superconductivity, one expects an interesting interplay of spin-fluctuations and superconductivity as well as normal-state electronic behaviour. For $x \to 0$ and $T \to 0$ the increasing correlation lengths cause more important effects due to interlayer coupling of the superconducting CuO_2-planes in the high-T_c-superconductors.

The basic physics underlying our approach is diagrammatically shown in Fig. 1. Note, a self-consistent calculation of the diagrams would recapture the FLEX-results, but is moreover capable of describing in a T versus x phase-diagram the occurence of local magnetic moments $\mu_s(x,t)$ and their short-range correlations [6–8]. The graphs in Fig. 1(b) describe mainly the formation of local magnetic moments and their short-range order within the dynamical mean field theory. In the appendix we briefly outline the theory given by the graphs in Fig. 1, in particular the occurence of magnetic moments μ_s and their short-range a.f. order [8]. This is characterized by a temperature $T_{sr} \propto J\mu_s^2(x)$ and energies of the order of 200 meV. Note, the occurence of $\mu_s(x,T)$ is also reflected by the change in the dependence of the spin-excitation energy ω_s on the spin-correlation length ξ.

The theory illustrated in Fig. 1 and slight extension thereof yields the phase-diagram shown in Fig. 2. T^* denotes the characteristic temperature at which a gap appears in the quasi-particle excitation spectrum and which is observed in transport measurements. At T_c^* Cooper-pair formation occurs. The anomalous Green's function $\phi(\mathbf{k},\omega) \sim \Delta(\mathbf{k},\omega)$ is zero at T_c^* and gets finite at temperatures T below T_c^*. At T_c determined by $Re\Delta(\mathbf{k},\omega = \Delta_k) = \Delta_k = 0$ phase-coherent superconductivity is present. For $T_c < T < T_c^*$ presumably a phase-disordered superconducting state is present as expected due to the relatively low density of Cooper-pairs. The superconducting state between T_c and T_c^* may correspond to the disordered local magnetic moment phase in magnetism of transition-metals. The

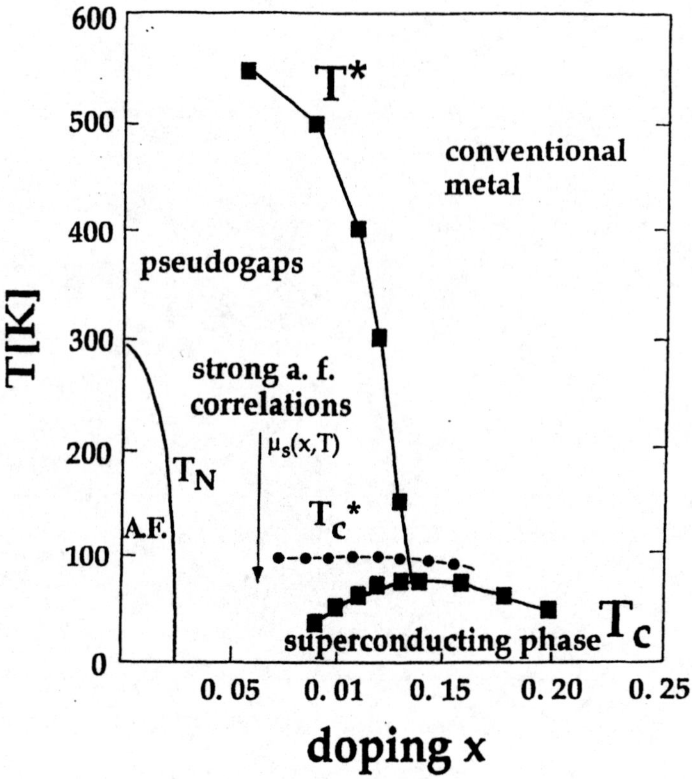

FIG. 2. Illustration of the doping dependence of the superconducting transition temperature $T_c(x)$, the characteristic temperature $T^*(x)$ below which a pseudogap appears in the spectral density, and of the Néel temperature $T_N(x)$. T_c^* refers to mean-field FLEX results for the superconducting transition temperature. At T_c^* Cooper-pairing begins. The expected occurence of local magnetic moments $\mu_s(x)$ is indicated. Short range a.f. order of the moments μ_s is expected for $T \to 0$ and $x \to 0$ and will be reflected by a characteristic temperature T_{sr} below T^* in NMR and also neutron scattering data and a gap in the density of states $N(0,x)$. One estimates $T_{sr} \propto J\mu_s^2(x)$, J is the a.f. coupling constant.

dynamical mean-field theory yields magnetic moments $\mu_s(x,T)$ on Cu-sites which increase for $x \to 0$ and $T \to 0$. For $x \to 0$ anti-ferromagnetism occurs at the Néel temperature T_N. For large doping x spin-fluctuation induced superconductivity decreases, since itinerancy increases and magnetic activity weakens, and for $x \to 0$ superconductivity disappears, since magnetic fluctuations become too stiff. Above T^* the superconductors show Fermi-liquid behaviour, below T^* marginal- and non-Fermi-liquid behaviour.

The electronic theory mainly used in the following is of FLEX type, including in an approximate way short-range anti-ferromagnetic order. Largely an effective one-band Hubbard-hamiltonian for one monolayer CuO_2 per unit cell of the high-T_c-superconductors is taken as a model. Details of the theory are described in previous publications [6,7]. As doping x decreases the magnetic moments $\mu_s(x)$ anti-ferromagnetic spin correlations become increasingly more important and must be included in FLEX calculations. Mainly as $x \to 0$ the density of states at the Fermi-surface (F.S.) $\rho(0,x)$ decreases and gaps appear affecting T_c and many other properties. In particular, the local magnetic moments $\mu_s(x)$ which occur and increase for $x \to 0$ form short-range anti-ferromagnetic order for decreasing temperature [8]. As the magnetic correlations increase, also the coupling between the CuO_2 layers gets important. Then, the interplay of charge- and spin-fluctuations may play an important role, in particular for superconductivity. The Cooper-pair formation is characterized by an energy of the order of Δ. For $x \lesssim 0.12$ we get $\Delta(T) \sim 40$ meV, for example. Magnetic interaction energies are of the order of 100 to 200 meV. Superconductivity is destroyed as $\rho(0,x) \to 0$, in particular for $\mathbf{k} \simeq (\pi,0)$, and for $\xi_s > \xi$, where ξ_s refers to the a.f. spin-correlation length and ξ to the superconducting coherence-length. Note, we have omitted for simplicity other characteristic temperatures between T^* and T_c referring to the occurence of $\mu_s(x)$, spin correlations, charge-fluctuations, etc.

In the following we discuss first the electronic properties of the effective one-band Hubbard-model. Then we present some important results of the 3-band Hubbard-model. Finally, we present some results showing how the electron-phonon coupling affects the spin-fluctuation induced superconductivity.

II. THEORY AND RESULTS

First, we analyze the doping dependence of the transition-temperature $T_c(x)$ due to spin-fluctuations [7,2]. As suggested by the penetration-depth $\lambda_L(x)$, the superfluid density $n_s(x) \sim \lambda_L^{-2}$ is relatively small in high-T_c-superconductors, in particular in underdoped ones. Hence the functional $T_c(n_s)$ is given in terms of n_s by

$$T_c \propto n_s + \cdots. \tag{1}$$

This is derived physically by assuming that at the transition temperature T_c the phase-coherence amongst the Cooper-pairs breaks up. Then, $T_c \sim \delta E$, where δE refers to the Cooper-pairing energy gained by phase-coherence. Hence, $\delta E \sim \psi_i^+ \psi_j \sim n_s$ and finally $T_c \propto n_s$. Note, ψ_i describes a Cooper-pair located at region (site) i and i and j refer to neighboring Cooper-pairs. Eq. (1) has also been derived using a Ginzburg-Landau theory as the critical temperature at which the phase coherent superconducting state breaks up into a state with phase-disordered Cooper-pairs [9]. In view of the short coherence-length one may furthermore use London's theory, yielding $n_s \propto 1/\lambda_L^2$. Thus, we get for the superconducting transition-temperature [10]

$$T_c \propto \frac{1}{\lambda_L^2(0)}, \tag{2}$$

with

$$\lambda_L^{-2} = 8\pi e^2 \sum_k v_{k,x}^2 \int_{-\infty}^{\infty} \frac{d\varepsilon}{2\pi} f(\varepsilon) Im F_k^2(\varepsilon) + \cdots \tag{3}$$

for the penetration depth. Here, $v_{k,x} = \partial\varepsilon_k/\partial k_x$ are the particle velocities, $f(\varepsilon)$ is the Fermi-function and $F_k(\varepsilon)$ is the anomalous Green's function due to the Cooper-pairs [7]. Note, the Ginzburg-Landau free-energy analysis yields

$$T_c \simeq 2.2(\phi_0^2/32\pi^3)a_\perp/\lambda_L^2 \sim \hbar^2 n_s\, d/m^*, \phi_0 = hc/2e, \tag{4}$$

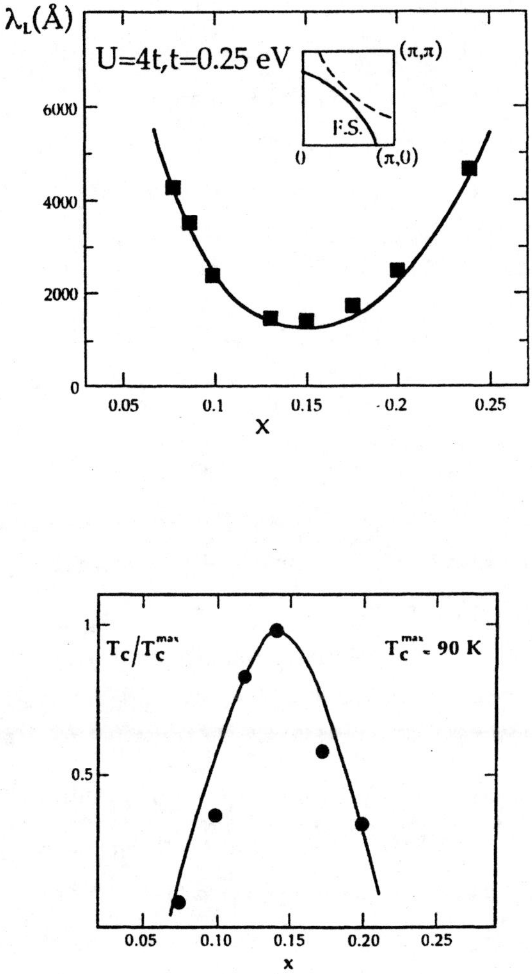

FIG. 3. Doping dependence of the superconducting transition-temperature $T_c(x)$ resulting from $T_c \; \alpha \; \lambda_L^{-2}(x, T = 0)$, where the in-plane penetration-depth λ_L is calculated using our FLEX results and a LSCO-like model Fermi-surface. For numerical reasons we calculated λ_L at temperatures $T \simeq 40$ K and extrapolated to $T \to 0$ assuming that $\lambda_L(T)$ increases linearly with T. Using $\lambda_L^2(T) = \lambda_L^2(0)/(1 - t^\alpha)$, $t \equiv T/T_c$, and $\alpha \simeq 2$ for $x < 0.1$ one gets similar results.

if phase-fluctuations of the superconducting order parameter cause the break up of global superconductivity [9]. Here, $a_\perp$ is the out of CuO_2-plane phase correlation length, d is the CuO_2-layer spacing, and m^* the effective mass of the carriers. Note, if the distance between the Cooper-pairs gets smaller than their size, then $T_c \propto n_s$ gets replaced again by the usual relationship between T_c and the order-parameter and $T_c \sim \Delta$, since due to the overlapp of the Cooper-pairs phase-coherence is present and Δ is the essential energy gain due to Cooper-pairing.

Summarizing, we conclude that for small n_s one has $T_c \propto n_s \sim \lambda_L^{-2}$. In particular for underdoped superconductors one may also approximately use $\Delta \sim \sqrt{n_s} \sim \lambda_L^{-1}$, and then

$$2\Delta/k_B T_c \sim \lambda_L. \tag{5}$$

Note, here we have neglected for simplicity other factors besides λ_L depending on x. From comparison of the calculated and experimental results for $T_c(x)$ we conclude that $a_\perp$ or d/m^* vary only weakly with x as is observed directly.

We calculated for a CuO_2 plane an in-plane penetration depth $\lambda_L(T) \equiv \lambda_{||}$ using the FLEX approximation [2,7]. Thus, we obtain the results for $\lambda_{||}$ and for $T_c(x)$ shown in Fig. 3. It is remarkable that we obtain from $T_c \propto \lambda_L^{-2}$ in fair agreement with experiment an optimal superconducting transition-temperature T_c for a doping $x \simeq 0.14$ and then $T_c(x) \rightarrow 0$ for $x \rightarrow 0.05$. Physically responsible for $T_c \rightarrow 0$ as $x \rightarrow 0$ is the increasing stiffness of the anti-ferromagnetic spin-fluctuations and the decrease of the density of states $\rho(\omega = 0, x)$. Certainly, $T_c(x) \rightarrow 0$ as $\rho(0) \rightarrow 0$ at least. From our results for $\rho(\mathbf{k}, \omega)$ and $\rho(\omega)$ we estimate $T_c \simeq 0$ for $x \gtrsim 0.05$ in fair agreement with experiments. The occurence of magnetic moments and their short-range order would speed up $T_c(x) \rightarrow 0$. Note, for $x > 0.14$ and further increasing doping x the transition temperature T_c decreases again, since itinerancy increases and the spin-fluctuation induced Cooper pairing weakens [7].

In Fig. 4 we compare results for $T_c(x)$ and for the superconducting transition temperature T_c^* obtained using mean-field theory from $\phi(\mathbf{k}, \omega) = \Delta(\mathbf{k}, \omega) = 0$ for all $\mathbf{k}, \omega$. Note, at T_c^* Cooper-pairs occur, since $\phi > 0$. As expected phase-fluctuations reduce the occurence of

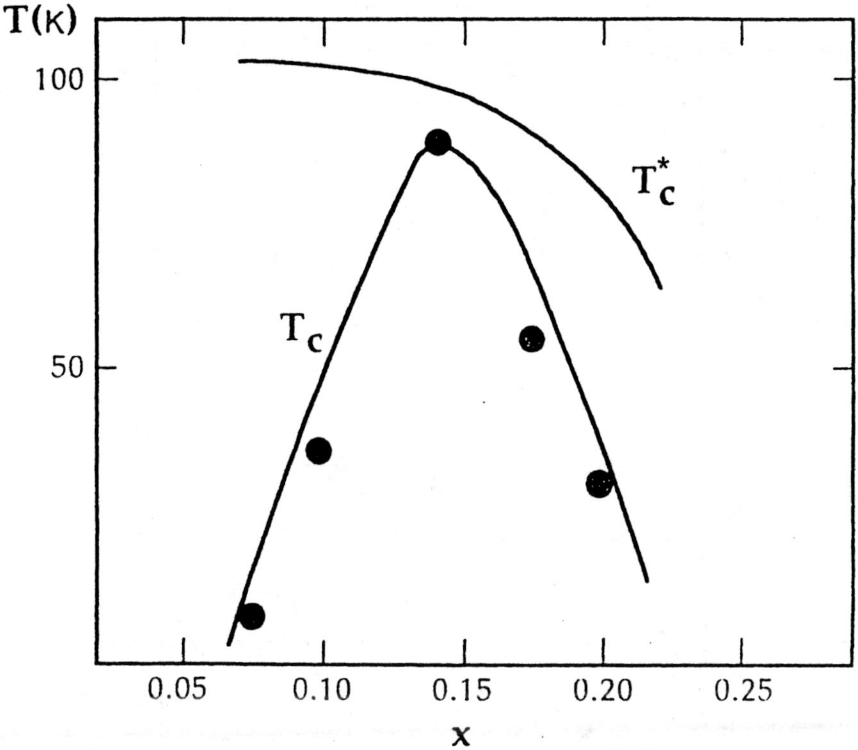

FIG. 4. Results for $T_c(x) \propto \lambda_L^{-2}$ and for comparison mean-field FLEX-results T_c^* obtained from $\Delta_k(\omega, T_c^*) = 0$ for all $\mathbf{k}, \omega$. We fit λ_L such that $T_c^{max} = 90K$ at $x = 0.14$. Note, Cooper-pairing begins at T_c^* and a phase coherent superconducting state at T_c. Between T_c and T_c^* a phase disordered Cooper-pair state exists for both over- and underdoped superconductors, but T_c is closer to T_c^* for overdoped superconductors. At temperatures T such that $T_c < T < T_c^*$ one has for the gap function $\phi(\mathbf{k}, \omega) > 0$ and coupled amplitude- and phase-fluctuations of $\phi(\mathbf{k}, \omega)$ occur. Note, improvements of FLEX should yield a decrease of T_c^* for $x \to 0$.

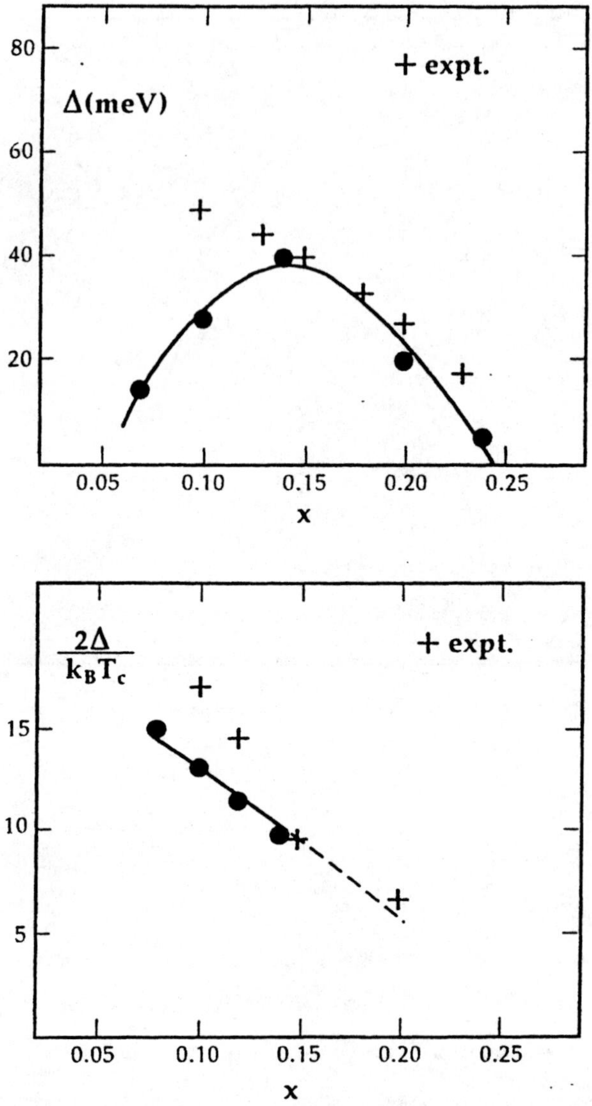

FIG. 5. Results are shown for the doping dependence of the superconducting gap $\Delta(x) \simeq a(x)\lambda_L^{-1}$ and $(2\Delta/k_BT_c) \sim a(x)\lambda_L$ and compared with experimental results.

global superconductivity and T_c^* to T_c for both over- and underdoped superconductors. [2,9] However, this reduction is strongest for underdoped superconductors. As seen, FLEX fails for $x \to 0$, since $T_c^* \to 0$ must result, of course.

Note, the gap function $\phi(\mathbf{k},\omega)$ has d-wave symmetry for $T < T_c$ as well as for $T_c < T < T_c^*$. In the range $T_c^* > T > T_c$ one has $\phi(\mathbf{k},\omega = 0) = 0$. Including interlayer coupling T_c increases and $(T_c^* - T_c)$ gets somewhat smaller for all x. Gaps in the spectral density $\rho(\mathbf{k},\omega)$ and $\rho(\omega)$ around ε_F due to dynamical a.f. spin-fluctuations will remain for $T > T_c^*$ and $T^* > T$. From $n_s \propto \lambda_L^{-2}$ we estimate for the region $T_c < T < T_c^*$ that the coherence-length ξ is of the order of the distance between the Cooper-pairs.

Whether actually at temperatures T such that $T_c < T < T_c^*$ Cooper pairs with incoherent phases exist is experimentally not explicitly verified and remains an open question. Note, for $T > T_c$ effects due to $\phi(\mathbf{k},\omega)$ are only expected if one measures fast enough and locally enough such that averaging over the Cooper-pair phases is avoided. On general physical grounds one expects phase-fluctuations for $\xi \lesssim d$ and to be more important for the underdoped superconductors. For a doping $x = 0.16$ we find for LSCO-systems $n_s \sim 2 \cdot 10^{14}$ cm^{-2} and that nearly 60% of the charge carriers are paired, while for $x = 0.09$ we get $n_s \sim 0.7 \cdot 10^{14}$ cm^{-2}, ($m_{\|}^* \simeq 2.2$), and only 10% of the charge carriers are paired [2]. Interestingly, $T_c \propto n_s \propto \lambda_{\|}^{-2}$ gives an immediate plausible understanding of the different T_c's observed for LSCO, YBCO and BSCCO compounds, respectively. For example, we get that the penetration-depth of $LaSrCuO_4$ is much larger than of YBCO, etc.

In Fig. 5 we show results for the doping dependence of the superconducting gap $\Delta(x)$ obtained from $\Delta \simeq a(x)\lambda_L^{-1}$ and for the ratio $(2\Delta/k_B T_c) \sim \lambda_L$. These results are compared with recent experimental ones [3,4]. Note the discrepancy between theory and experiment regarding $\Delta(x)$ which needs further analysis and experimental studies. Also in view of our results for the pairing potential V and on physical grounds we expect $\Delta(x)$ to decrease for $x \to 0$ below $x = 0.14$. In our estimate of $(2\Delta/k_B T_c)$ for the underdoped superconductors we use $a(x) \propto V(x)$ and find that the increase of $\lambda_L(x)$ is stronger than the doping dependence

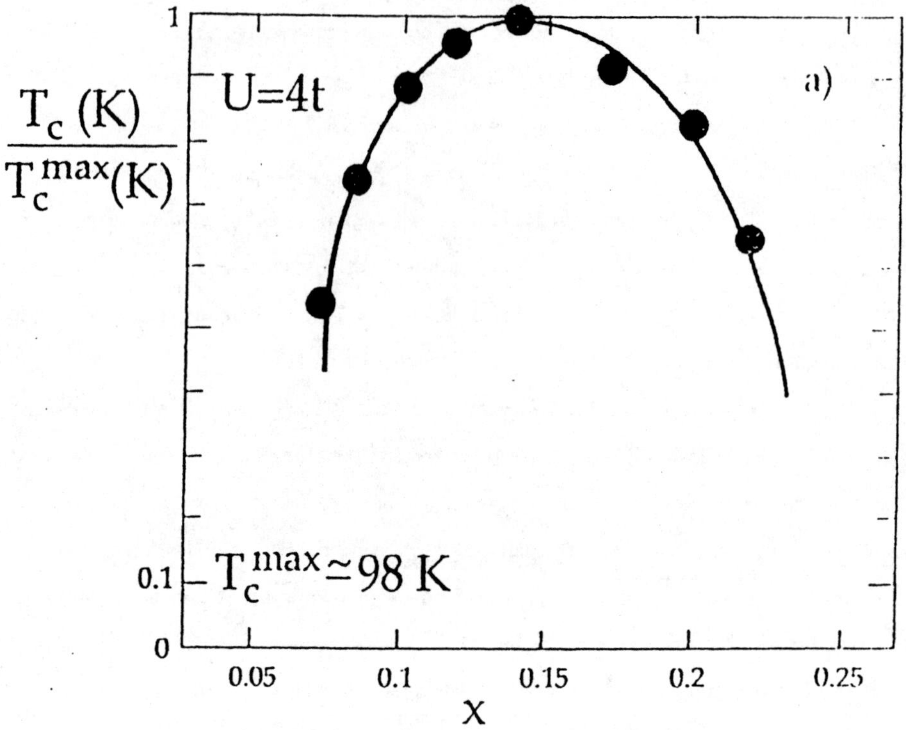

FIG. 6. Results for the superconducting transition-temperature T_c obtained within FLEX for a LSCO-like model Fermi-surface as the temperature at which the superconducting gap $\Delta \equiv \Delta_k(\omega = \Delta, T)$ in the spectral density of states $\rho(\mathbf{k},\omega)$ disappears (at $\mathbf{k} \simeq (\pi, 0)$).

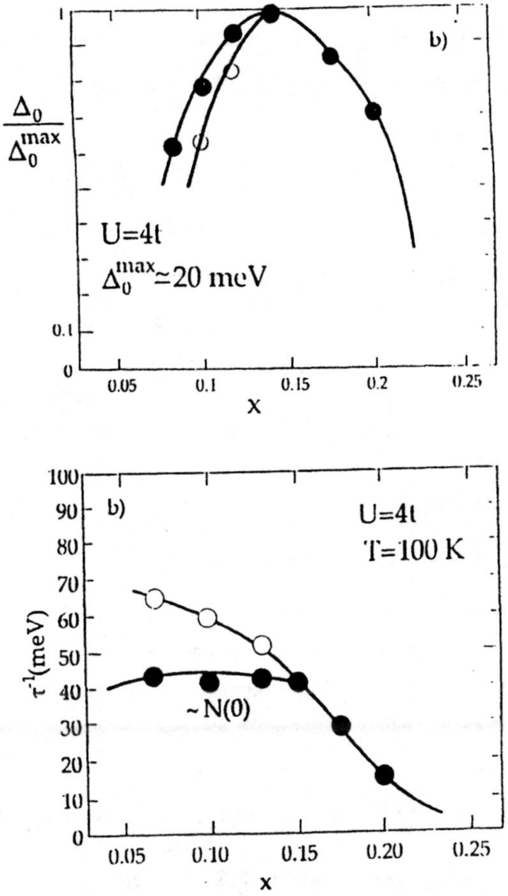

FIG. 7. The results for the gap $\Delta_0 \equiv \Delta(\omega = 0)$ were obtained from $\Delta(\mathbf{k},\omega) = \phi(\mathbf{k},\omega)/Z$, $\mathbf{k} \simeq /\pi, 0)$, and using for the renormalization function $Z(\mathbf{k},\omega)$ the shown lifetimes $\tau(x)$. The open circle results for Δ_0 are obtained if one uses for τ^{-1} values given by the open circles ($\tau^{-1} \propto N(0)$). Note, assuming $\tau_k^{-1} \propto \rho(\mathbf{k}_F, 0) \propto \rho(0)$, also for $(\pi, 0)$, resembles results obtained assuming short-range a.f. order. The open circles refer to FLEX results which give not a sufficiently strong enough reduction of $\rho(\mathbf{k}, \omega = 0)$ on the Fermi-surface. Note, the density of states behaves as $N(0,x) \to 0$ for $x \to 0$ and which tends to enhance the quasi-particle lifetime.

of $a(x)$. For the overdoped superconductors we estimate roughly that $a(x)$ decreases more strongly than $T_c(x) \sim \lambda_L^{-2}$. In a Ginzburg-Landau expansion $F = \int d^3r\{(\hbar^2/2m_{\|}^*)|\nabla\psi|^2 + \alpha|\psi|^2 + \beta|\psi|^4 + \cdots\}$ the doping dependence of $m_{\|}^*$, α and β yields the one of $(2\Delta/k_BT_c)$.

In Fig. 6 results for the transition-temperature $T_c(x)$ obtained previously by Grabowski et al. [7] from the disappearance of the superconducting gap Δ in the density of states $\rho(\omega)$ and spectral density $\rho\mathbf{k},\omega)$ at $\mathbf{k} \simeq (\pi, 0)$ or equivalently from $\Delta_k = Re\Delta(\mathbf{k}, \omega = \Delta_k) = 0$ are shown. This yields also an optimal T_c and for the doping dependence a similar behaviour as obtained from $T_c \propto \lambda_{\|}^{-2}$. Note, we use $\Delta = \Delta_k(\omega = \Delta, T) = 0$, since this reflects the essential gain in energy due to global phase-coherent Cooper-pair formation. Hence, this determination of T_c is consistent with the one using $T_c \propto n_s$. [11] Note, $\Delta(\mathbf{k}, \omega = 0) = 0$ yields an optimal T_c as a function of x due to the interplay of the lifetime τ of the quasi-particles constituting the Cooper-pairs and the lifetime ($\sim (2\Delta)^{-1}$) of the Cooper-pair [7]. At optimal doping x, again for $x \approx 0.14$, both are nearly equal. Also, as in the case of $T_c \propto \lambda_L^{-2}$ superconductivity disappears at $x \lesssim 0.06$.

In Fig. 7 we present FLEX-like results for the doping dependence of the superconducting gap $\Delta_0(x)$, where $\Delta_0(x) \equiv \Delta(\mathbf{k}, \omega = 0, x)$ and $\mathbf{k} \simeq (\pi, 0)$. The gap $\Delta(x)$ has d-wave symmetry for all x. It is

$$\Delta(\mathbf{k},\omega) = \frac{\omega(\omega - i\tau^{-1}(\mathbf{k},\omega))}{\omega^2 + \tau^{-2}(\mathbf{k},\omega)} \, \frac{\phi(\mathbf{k},\omega)}{ReZ(\mathbf{k},\omega)}, \tag{6}$$

where evidently $\tau_{\mathbf{k}}^{-1} = Im(\omega Z(k,\omega))/ReZ(k,\omega)$ is the quasi-particle scattering rate, $\phi(\mathbf{k},\omega)$ is the superconducting order-parameter and $Z(\mathbf{k},\omega)$ the Eliashberg renormalization function [7]. Taking into account the decrease of the density of states $\rho(0)$ for $x \to 0$ and the appearance of a gap at the Fermi-surface, in particular around $\mathbf{k} = (\pi, 0)$, we obtain the gap $\phi(\mathbf{k}, \omega = 0)$ and then $\Delta_0(x)$.

Note the interesting interplay of the quasi-particle scattering rate and Cooper-pairing described by Eq. (6). Interestingly, correcting the quasi-particle lifetime by using $\tau^{-1} \propto \rho(0)$ and the reduction of $\rho(0, x)$ due to a.f. spin-excitations ($\rho(\mathbf{k}_F, 0) \propto \rho(0)$) we get for τ and $\Delta(x)$ results also shown in Fig. 7. Again, we get in theory that $\Delta(x)$ decreases for $x \to 0$ as

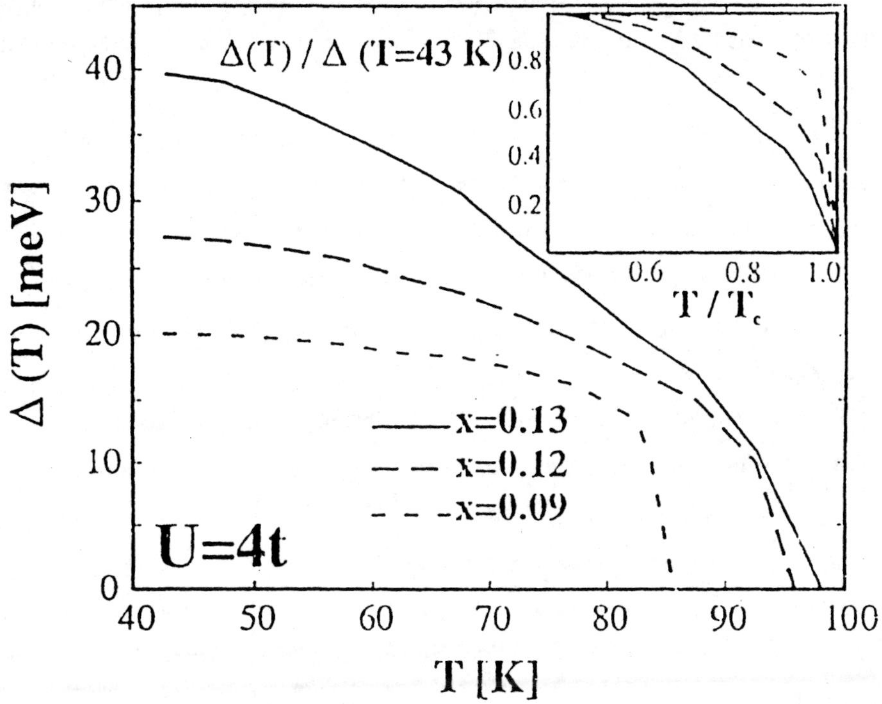

FIG. 8. Temperature dependence of $\Delta(T)$. For underdoped superconductors one gets an unusually weak T-dependence until $T \simeq T_c$. The inset shows that the gaps open faster for $x \to 0$.

expected on general grounds, but in disagreement with recent observations [3,4] As said, this decrease is somewhat softened by $\rho(0) \to 0$ for $x \to 0$. Note the remarkable enhancement of the lifetime $\tau(x)$ due to the decrease of $\rho(0)$ as a result of the reduction of the spectral density $\rho(\mathbf{k},\omega)$. [12]

In Fig. 8 FLEX-results are shown for the temperature dependence of the gap for underdoped superconductors. Note, for $x \to 0.05$ the gap $\Delta(T)$ is nearly temperature independent and $\Delta(T) \to 0$ for $T \simeq T_c$. This is in remarkable agreement with experiment [1,3,4,7]. The inset shows $(\Delta(T)/\Delta(T=43K))$ and that the gap opens more rapidly for $x \to 0$ as observed by Raman scattering experiments [7]. Note, $\Delta(0) \simeq 40$ meV for $x \simeq 0.13$ is in fair agreement with experiment.

In Fig. 9 we show results for the ratio $(2\Delta/k_BT_c)$ obtained from the results for $\Delta(x)$ and $T_c(x)$. Note the increase for $x \to 0.05$ as in the case of $(2\Delta/k_BT_c) \sim \lambda_L$. This behaviour is in sharp contrast to the B.S.C. result of $(2\Delta/k_BT_c) = 3.52$. We find much larger values for this ratio, in particular for underdoped superconductors.

Results for the spectral density $\rho(\mathbf{k},\omega)$ characterizing the elementary excitations and the other quantities were obtained from FLEX like calculations of the self-energy (N = number of lattice sites)

$$\Sigma(\mathbf{k}, i\omega_n) = \frac{T}{N} \sum_{\mathbf{k}',\omega_m} V(\mathbf{k}',\omega_m) G(\mathbf{k}-\mathbf{k}',\omega_n-\omega_m) \tag{7}$$

for real frequencies $\omega, i\omega_n \to \omega + i\gamma$. [13]. Here, formally [7]

$$V = \frac{1}{2} U(\chi_c + 3\chi_s - 2\chi) U_{eff}, \tag{8}$$

where the susceptibilities χ_c and χ_s are describing (within RPA like treatment) charge- and spin-fluctuations, respectively. The particle-hole-bubble term 2χ with $\chi = \frac{T}{N}\sum GG$ avoids double counting. G denotes the Green's function, s. Fig. 1. Vertex corrections are approximately included via replacing one U by $U \to U_{eff}$, where U_{eff} denotes an effective Hubbard U interaction. Contributions to V due to particle-particle scattering may be added straightforwardly. Using Eqs. (7) and (8) magnetic (pseudo)gaps appear in the spectral density $\rho(\mathbf{k},\omega)$ and in the density of states $\rho(\omega)$ for $T < T^*$.

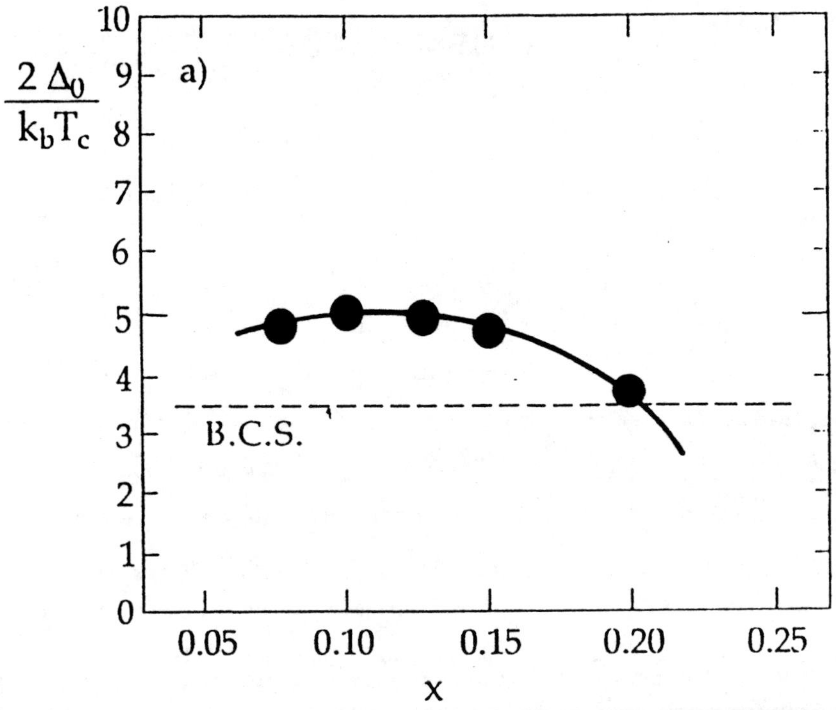

FIG. 9. Doping dependence of the ratio $2\Delta_0/k_BT_c$ using the results for Δ_0 and for T_c. Note, $\frac{2\Delta_0}{k_BT_c} \simeq 5$ for $x \lesssim 0.14$. The BCS value of the ratio is indicated.

For analytical calculations one may put the normal-state self-energy into the form [6,14]

$$\Sigma_R(\mathbf{k},\omega) = -\int \frac{d^n q}{(2\pi)^n} \int_{-\infty}^{\infty} \frac{d\omega'}{2\pi} \int_{-\infty}^{\infty} d\varepsilon Im V(\mathbf{q},\omega') Im G_R(\mathbf{q}+\mathbf{k},\varepsilon) \frac{(coth \frac{\omega'}{2T} + \tanh \frac{\varepsilon}{2T})}{\omega - \omega' + \varepsilon - i\delta}. \quad (9)$$

Then,

$$Im\Sigma_R(\mathbf{k},\omega) = \pi \int \frac{d^n q}{(2\pi)^n} \int_{-\infty}^{\infty} \frac{d\omega'}{2\pi} (coth \frac{\omega'}{2T} - tanh \frac{\omega' - \omega}{2T}) Im V(\mathbf{q},\omega') Im G_R(\mathbf{k}+\mathbf{q},\omega-\omega'). \quad (10)$$

The magnetic contributions result for $ImV \rightarrow Im\chi_s$, where the spin-susceptibility χ_s is of Ornstein-Zernike like form. Similarly, for approximate analytical calculations one may also use for the charge-fluctuations characterized by $\chi_c(\mathbf{q},\omega)$ the Ornstein-Zernike form. Since the in-plane frequency ω_c is fairly large ($\omega_c \sim eV$), the charge-fluctuations between neighboring CuO_2 planes characterized by $\omega_c'(\mathbf{q},x)$ might be most important [15]. If $\omega_s \simeq \omega_c'$, then the interplay between charge- and spin-fluctuations might be particularly interesting [16].

FLEX-like results for the density of states $\rho(\omega)$ and quasi-particle lifetimes are obtained from a momentum average of the spectral density, where the spectral density is given by ($\rho(\mathbf{k},\omega) = -\frac{1}{\pi} ImG(\mathbf{k},\omega+i\delta)$),

$$\rho(\mathbf{k},\omega) = -Im\Sigma(\mathbf{k},\omega)/[\omega - \varepsilon_k + \mu - Re\sigma(\mathbf{k},\omega))^2 + (Im\Sigma(\mathbf{k},\omega))^2]. \quad (11)$$

From results for $\rho(\mathbf{k},\omega)$ we estimate the characteristic temperature T^* at which pseudogaps appear in $\rho(\mathbf{k},\omega)$ and $\rho(\omega)$. [7] The doping dependence of the density of states at the Fermi-energy, $N(0) \equiv \rho(\omega = 0)$, and of $\rho(\mathbf{k},0)$ for $\mathbf{k} \simeq (\pi,0)$ is most important for the behaviour of the underdoped superconductors. The decrease of $N(0)$ as $x \rightarrow 0$ affects all quantities and reflects the appearance of anti-ferrogmagnetism. On general grounds one expects that $N(0)$ will be affected by spectral-weight transfer away from ε_F due to a.f. spin-excitations and by formation of local magnetic moments $\mu_s(x)$ and their short-ranged anti-ferromagnetic order.

The results shown in Fig. 7 for the scattering rate τ^{-1} of the quasi-particles were obtained from

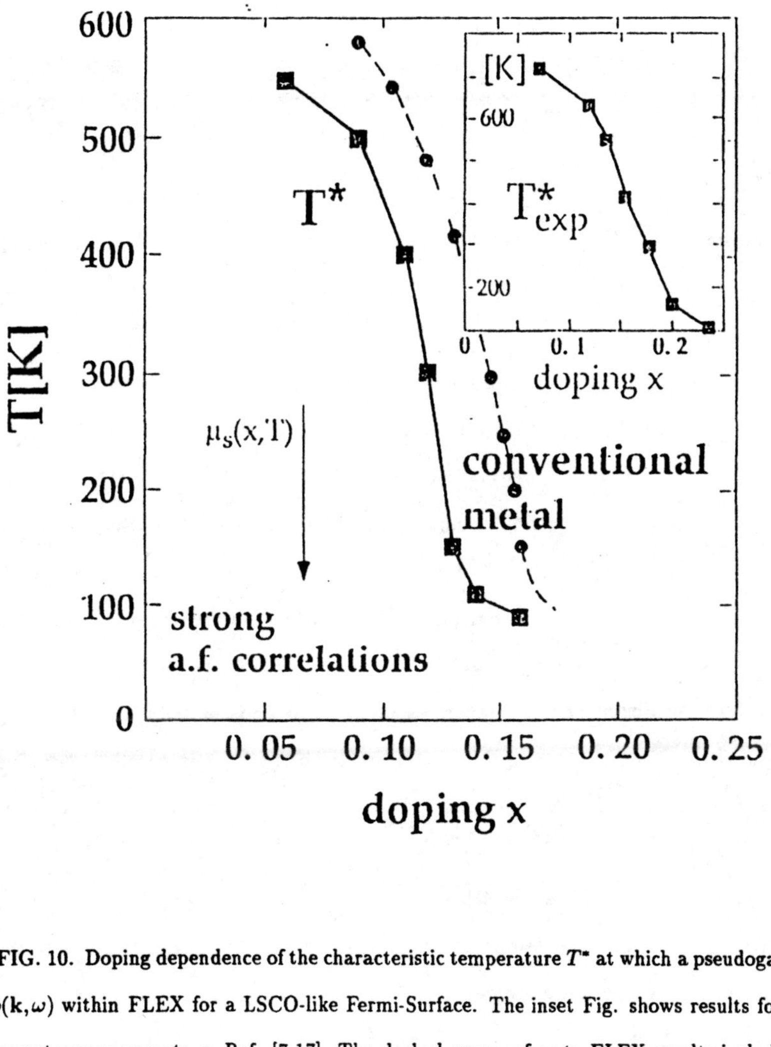

FIG. 10. Doping dependence of the characteristic temperature T^* at which a pseudogap appears in $\rho(\mathbf{k},\omega)$ within FLEX for a LSCO-like Fermi-Surface. The inset Fig. shows results for T^* from transport measurements, s. Ref. [7,17]. The dashed curve refers to FLEX results including CuO_2 interlayer coupling, for example. Above T^* the systems behave like conventional metals. Note, due to molecular fields acting on μ_s we expect for $x \to 0$ and $T \to 0$ another characteristic temperature below T^*, where the appearance of local magnetic moments can be marked by a temperature $T_\mu(x)$.

$$\tau_k^{-1}(\omega) = -Im \sum(\mathbf{k},\omega) + i\delta). \tag{12}$$

Notice the reduction of τ^{-1} due to the pseudogaps and the reduction of $N(0)$ as compared with previous FLEX results (open circles). Such behaviour is in particular expected for $\tau_k(x)$ at $\mathbf{k} \simeq (\pi, 0)$. The results shown follow from $\tau^{-1} \propto \rho(0)$ and assuming that $\rho(\mathbf{k}, 0)$ decreases linearly with x for $x \to 0$. Note, FLEX does not yield as expected around the Fermi-surface magnetic gaps of the order of $100 \div 200$ meV or somewhat smaller due to the dynamics of the magnetic activity [6,7].

In the following typical results characterising the elementary excitations in high-T_c-superconductors and obtained by FLEX-type calculations are shown. Generally, we find structure which is a fingerprint of spin-fluctuation effects.

In Fig. 10 we present results for the characteristic temperature T^* at which a gap appears in our FLEX results for the spectral density $\rho(\mathbf{k}, \omega)$. For comparison we show also experimental results deduced from transport measurements [17]. Interestingly we find within FLEX that CuO_2-interlayer coupling as in BSSCO and YBCO compounds enhances T^*, s. dashed curve [7]. Approximately, T^* saturates for $x \to 0$ and for large x and changes abruptly in-between. Note the remarkable agreement with the experimentally determined characteristic temperatures T^*, in particular due to the enhancement of T^* due to CuO_2 interlayer coupling [17].

Another characteristic temperature below T^* should signal the appearance of magnetic moments $\mu_s(x)$. Finally, at lower temperatures a characteristic temperature T_{sr} describes the occurence of short-range a.f. order as a function of x. Short-range a.f. order should affect $\chi_s(\mathbf{q}, \omega)$ and will be reflected in NMR measurements, for example, s. Baumgärtel et al. [8].

In Fig. 11 and Fig. 12 we present LSCO-FLEX results for the momentum averaged spectral density as a function of the temperature and doping. The occurence of magnetic moments $\mu_s(x, T)$ and short-range a.f. order will enhance the magnetic gap formation. The results for the magnetic pseudogap are summarized in Fig. 13. Note, the pseudogap in $\rho(\omega)$

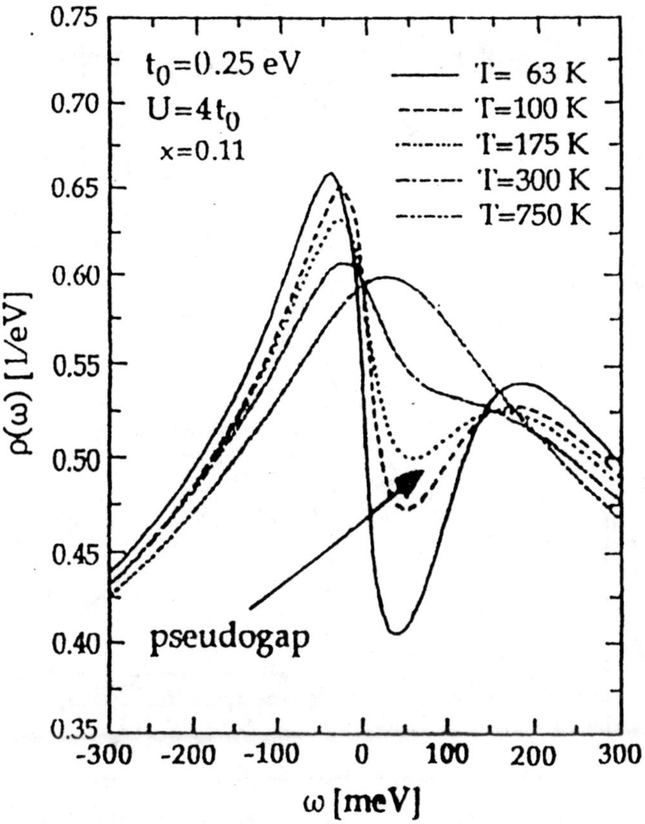

FIG. 11. LSCO-FLEX results for the temperature dependence of the density of states $\rho(\omega)$ obtained from the momentum averaged spectral density $\rho(\mathbf{k},\omega)$. The magnetic pseudogaps appear at T^* and increase as $T \rightarrow 0$. Magnetic moments μ_s and their short-range a.f. order will enhance the pseudogap and cause $\rho(0) \rightarrow 0$ as well as a gap for $\rho(\mathbf{k}_F, 0)$, in particular at $\mathbf{k} \simeq (\pi, 0)$.

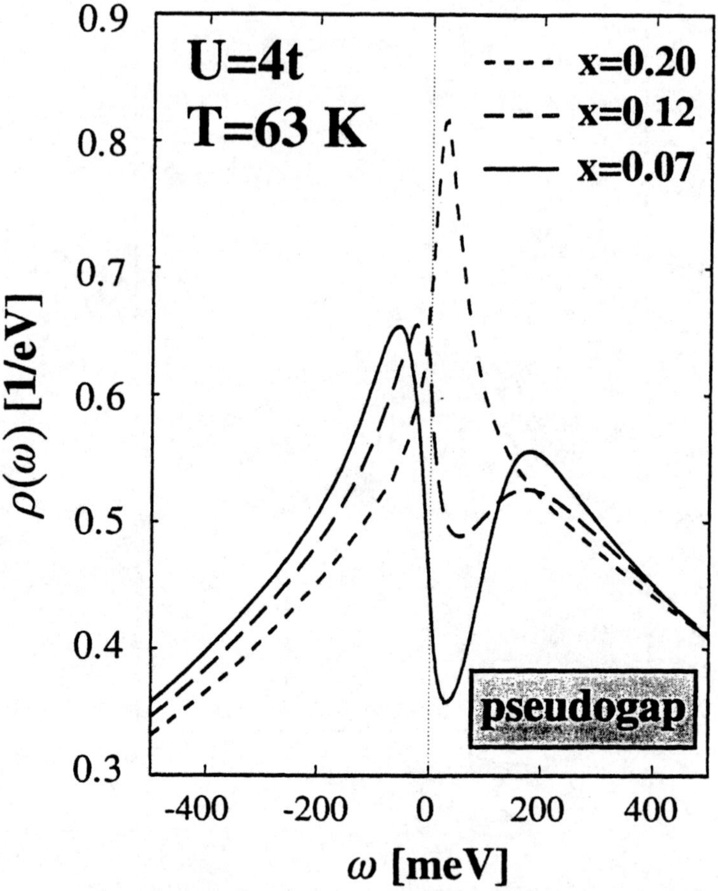

FIG. 12. Doping dependence of the density of states $\rho(\omega)$ using FLEX and a LSCO-like Fermi-surface. Note, $\rho(\omega = 0, x) \to 0$ as $x \to 0$. Decreasing doping x enhances the pseudogap which width δ is estimated from $\delta \sim U\mu_s \sim J$. Here, $J(x)$ is the effective n.n.a.f. exchange coupling. We find for $\rho(\omega)$ and $\rho(\mathbf{k}, \omega)$ a linewidth which is typically of the order of 0.2 to 0.3 eV as $x \to 0$. This corresponds to the quasi-particle bandwidth near the Fermi-surface and for $\mathbf{k}$ near $(\pi, 0)$, s. Ref. [6,7]. Magnetic moments $\mu_s(x)$ increasing for $x \to 0$ and short range magnetic order will further enhance the magnetic pseudogaps.

results mainly from $\rho(\mathbf{q},\omega)$ with $\mathbf{q} \simeq (\pi,0)$. Hence, we may assume that $\rho(\mathbf{q},0)$ behaves for $\mathbf{q} \simeq (\pi,0)$, approximately as $\rho(0)$. We expect that $\rho(0)$ decreases as $(U_{eff}\dot{\mu}_s(x))$ or J increases.

Note, in the vicinity of the Fermi-surface, for example for wave-vectors $\mathbf{k}+\mathbf{Q}$, $\mathbf{Q} = (\pi,\pi)$, the gap formation in $\rho(\mathbf{k},\omega)$ is weakest along the route $(0,0) \rightarrow (\pi,\pi)$ and strongest around $\mathbf{k} \simeq (\pi,0)$ in the Brillouin-zone (B.Z.). Interestingly, the normal-state simple FLEX-like calculations do not yield a gap in $\rho\mathbf{k},\omega \simeq 0)$ at $\mathbf{k} \simeq (\pi,0)$ on the F.S., the region which is most important for d-wave superconductivity.

In Fig. 14 and Fig. 15 results for BSSCO-like systems are shown for the $\mathbf{k}_F$-momentum dependence of the Gaussian convoluted spectral density $\rho_{conv} \equiv (\rho(\mathbf{k}_F,\omega)f_\omega)_{conv}$. Note, normal behaviour and no gap occurs for $\mathbf{k}_F \approx (\frac{\pi}{2},\frac{\pi}{2})$, while for $\mathbf{k}_F \approx (\pi,0)$ a gap appears. At $\mathbf{k}_F \approx (\pi,0)$ one finds that $\rho(\mathbf{k}_F,0)$ decreases further as $x \rightarrow 0$ and $T \rightarrow 0$, but there is still a reduced Fermi-surface crossing.

Note, extensions of Eqs. (9) and (10) should be used to analyze the possible occurence of a gap with $\rho(\mathbf{k}_F,0) \rightarrow 0$ at $\mathbf{k}_F \simeq (\pi,0)$. In general the magnetic pseudogap results from spectral weight transfer away from $\omega = 0$ to energies below ε_F as a result of transitions $\mathbf{k} \rightarrow \mathbf{k}+\mathbf{Q}$. This follows also from inspection of Eqs. (9) and (10). The different behaviour of $\rho(\mathbf{k},\omega)$ for $\mathbf{k}$ along $(0,0) \rightarrow (\pi,\pi)$ and $\mathbf{k}$ along $(0,0) \rightarrow (\pi,0)$ might indicate a change of the F.S. topology for $x \rightarrow 0$.

It is remarkable that we find already quantitatively the observed behaviour for $\rho(\mathbf{k},\omega)$. As seen in Fig. 16 the results for the pseudogap $\delta(T)$ in $\rho(\omega)$ seem in fair agreement with photoemission experiment [4]. For $x \simeq 0.17$ the gap closes at T_c, since the magnetic gap contribution is relatively small, and for $x = 0.08$ and $x \simeq 0.05$ only far above T_c. Also, along the route $0,0) \rightarrow (\pi,\pi)$ in the Brillouin zone no gaps occur. Further studies of $\delta(T)$ and its origin are necessary.

Note, that we presented results for the convoluted spectral density $\rho_{conv} \equiv (\rho(\mathbf{k},\omega)f_\omega)_{conv}$. To compare with experiments [1,4] we assumed a Gaussian broadening of the data and

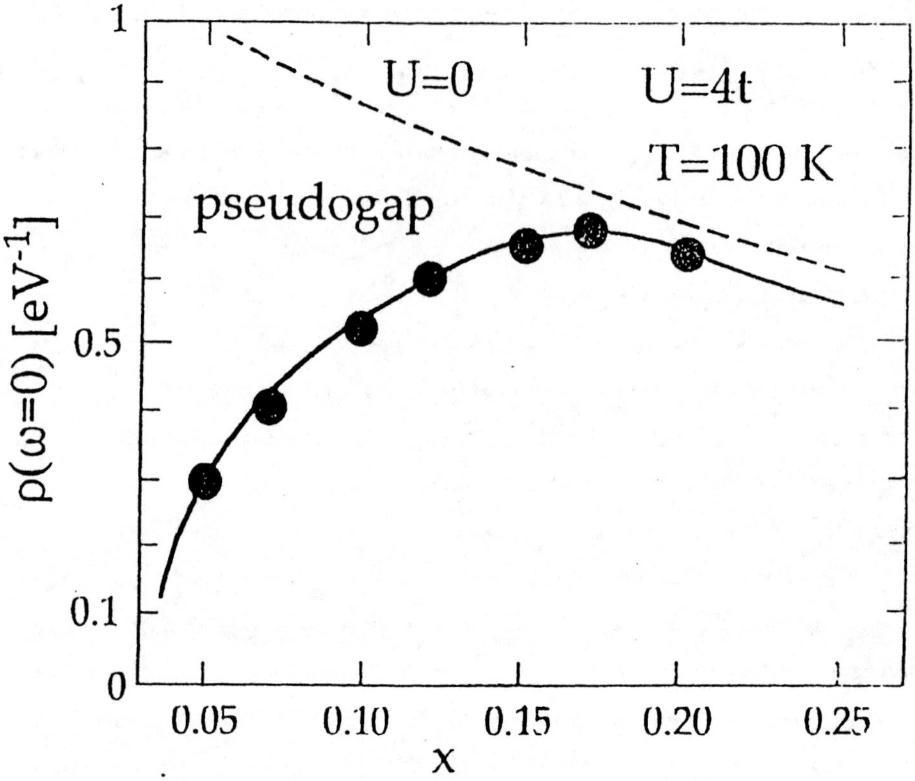

FIG. 13. Doping dependence of the density of states $\rho(0)$ which is most important for superconductivity and other properties. From $\rho(0) \rightarrow 0$ we estimate $T_c \simeq 0$ at $x \sim 0.05$. Note, formation of magnetic moments μ_s and short-range a.f. order affects the magnitude of the magnetic pseudogap, in particular for $x \rightarrow 0$.

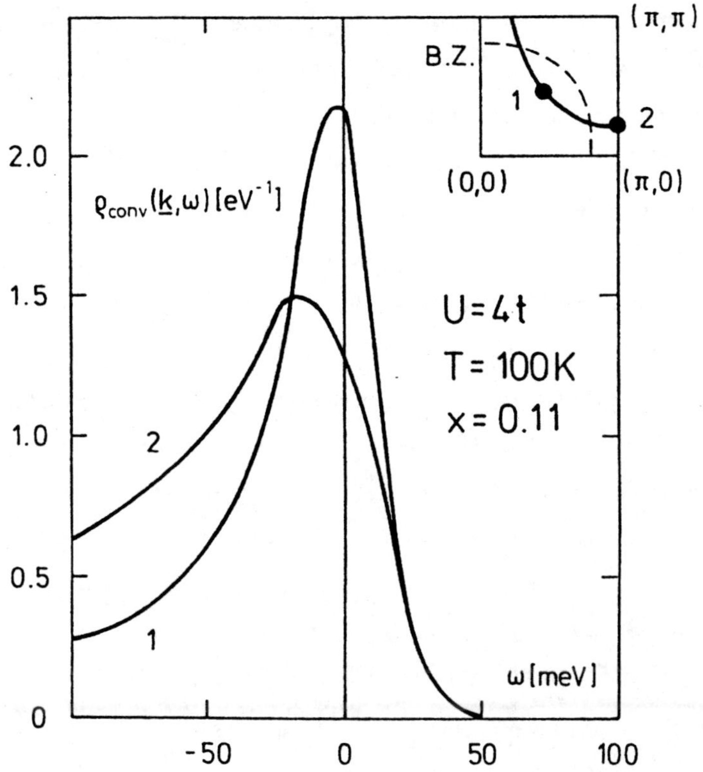

FIG. 14. Dependence on the Fermi-wave-vector $\mathbf{k}_F$ of the convoluted spectral density $[\rho(\mathbf{k}_F,\omega)f_\omega]$ for BSCCO-compounds. For $\mathbf{k}_F$ changing from $\mathbf{k}_F \simeq (\pi,0)$ towards $\mathbf{k}_F \simeq (\frac{\pi}{2},\frac{\pi}{2})$ on the F.S. one finds that the pseudogap is strongest at $(\pi,0)$ and then decreases continuously and disappears at $(\frac{\pi}{2},\frac{\pi}{2})$.

therefore perform a corresponding convolution of $(\rho(\mathbf{k},\omega)f_\omega)$ with a Gaussian distribution function of width σ. While we obtain qualitatively the observed behaviour of the pseudogaps $\delta(\mathbf{k},T)$, in particular the same $\mathbf{k}$-dependence as for $\phi(\mathbf{k},\omega)$, these FLEX-results may not properly account at temperatures such that $T > T_c$ for the gap in $\rho(\mathbf{k},\omega)$ at $\mathbf{k} \simeq (\pi,0)$. Note, phase disordered (precursor) Cooper-pairing above T_c might be reflected by a gap in $\rho(\mathbf{k},\omega)$ above T_c if measurements do not average over phases of the Cooper-pairs. However, we get already for the normal state that $\rho(\mathbf{k},0)$ decreases as $x \to 0$. A.F. correlations and short-range order will shift $\rho(\mathbf{k},\omega)$ and thus $\rho_{conv}(\mathbf{k},\omega)$ as indicated. This discussion of $\rho(\mathbf{k},\omega)$ demonstrates too that simple FLEX will fail somewhat for $x \to 0$ largely due to underestimating spin-excitations and their effect on the elementary excitations of the quasi-particles.

Note, recent tunneling experiments by Renner et al. [3] indicated a gap around ε_F far above T_c and which scales with the superconducting gap at $T < T_c$. In these experiments a momentum averaged $\rho(\mathbf{k},\omega)$ was observed. In agreement with these experimental findings we get a gap in $\rho(\omega)$ for both underdoped and overdoped superconductors for temperatures far above T_c, and even above T_c^*. Note, the gaps at $T > T_c$ still scale like at $T < T_c$ due to the common origin of the superconducting and magnetic gap in $\rho(\mathbf{k},\omega)$. Below T_c one has the superconducting gap of d-wave symmetry, above T_c one has a magnetic gap up to T^*. It is $\phi(\mathbf{k},\omega) > 0$ for $T_c^* > T$.

In general for the temperature range $T_c^* > T > T_c$ amplitude- and phase-fluctuations of the order parameter are expected. If the phase-fluctuations dominate then the resultant gap in $\rho(\omega)$ scales mostly like at $T < T_c$. Note, applying functional integral analysis to the theory outlined in Fig. 1 the same way as in Hubbard's treatment of ferromagnetism in Ni and Fe, one may derive an electronic theory for amplitude and phase-fluctuations of the superconducting order parameter [8].

To obtain a better physical understanding of the origin of the magnetic pseudogap contribution to $\delta(T,x)$ and of the behaviour of the density of states $N(0,x)$, we show for

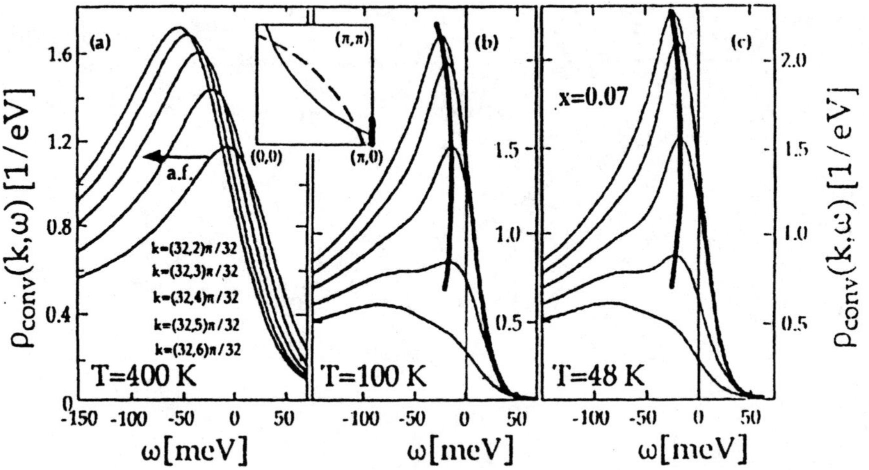

FIG. 15. For a BSCCO-system FLEX results for $(\rho(\mathbf{k},\omega)f_\omega)$ convoluted with a finite Gaussian broadening of width $\sigma = 15$ meV to compare with ARPES experiments. f_ω is the Fermi-function. (a) ρ_{conv} for $T > T^* \gg T_c$, where a regular Fermi-surface crossing is observed for $\rho(\mathbf{k},\omega)$; (b) ρ_{conv} for $T^* > T > T_c$, where indications occur for a pseudogap near $\mathbf{k} \approx (\pi, 0)$ and an anomalous Fermi-surface crossing; (c) ρ_{conv} for $T_c > T$. Note the similarity of the leading edge behaviour in Figs. (b) and (c).

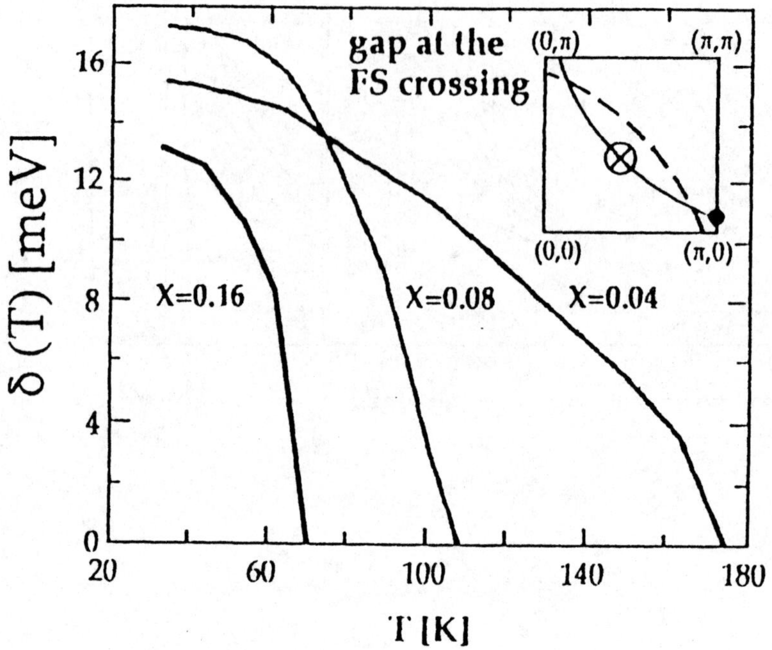

FIG. 16. Doping dependence of the gaps $\delta(T,x)$ derived from convoluting the spectral density $(\rho(\mathbf{k},\omega)f_\omega)$ with a Gaussian of width $\sigma = 15meV$. The gap disappears at temperature T_c for $x =$ 0.16, but above T_c for $x < 0.14$. No gaps appear for k along $(0,0) \rightarrow (\pi,\pi)$, for example at the k-point marked by the open circle. Including local magnetic moments $\mu_s(x,T)$ and their short-range order one expects in distinction to simple FLEX theory also a pseudogap at the Fermi-surface in $\rho(\mathbf{k}_F,0)$, in particular for $\mathbf{k} \simeq (\pi,0)$.

LSCO-systems in Fig. 17 results for the doping dependence of the particle dispersion ε_k with respect to the chemical potential $\mu(x)$ obtained by Langer et al. [6]. As doping x decreases the flat piece of $(\varepsilon_k - \mu)$ gets pushed down $(\varepsilon_k \rightarrow \mu)$ for $(\mathbf{k} \simeq (\pi, 0)$, becomes wider and more prominent. This flattening piece of the main band, which has a width of the order of $\sim 100 \div 200$ meV, and its pushing down towards μ causes a transfer of spectral weight. Thus, a decrease of $\rho(0)$ and a pseudogap occurs (the van Hove singularity at the point of inflection ω_{vH} shifts towards μ). Furthermore, Langer et al. [6] find that an increase of the Hubbard-U $(U \rightarrow 6t)$ enhances the flattening of the main band around $\mathbf{k} \simeq (\pi, 0)$. Note, including interlayer coupling affects the dispersions, mainly quantitatively, as was studied by Grabowski et al. [7].

In Fig. 17(c) we indicate changes of ε_k due to short-range spin-order of magnetic moments $(\mu_s \simeq 0.2$ for $x \leq 0.1$. These cause the appearance of a gap at the A.F. Brillouin zone and also $N(0, x) \rightarrow 0$ as $x \rightarrow 0$. Note, the increasing correlations (as U increases) cause for $x \rightarrow 0$ an increasing flat band at the chemical potential μ for $\mathbf{k}$ near $(\pi, 0)$, $\rho(0) \rightarrow 0$, and a satellite-band due to transitions $\mathbf{k} \rightarrow \mathbf{k} + \mathbf{Q}$ with increasing weight for $x \rightarrow 0$. Strong coupling is expected for states $\mathbf{k}'$ and $\mathbf{k}$ if $|\mathbf{k}' - \mathbf{k}| \leq \xi^{-1}$, where ξ denotes the a.f. spin-correlation length.

Fig. 18 illustrates why the satellite-band has a larger intensity around $\mathbf{k} \simeq (\pi, 0)$ with many states $\varepsilon_{k'} \sim \varepsilon_k$ available for the coupling $\mathbf{k} \leftrightarrow \mathbf{k} + \mathbf{Q}$ as compared with the region around $\mathbf{k} \simeq (\frac{\pi}{2}, \frac{\pi}{2})$ with no flat bands. The a.f. band gaps expected for long range a.f. order are indicated.

Fig. 19 shows dispersion curves for BSCCO-like compounds, including interlayer coupling $(t_\perp = 0.4t)$. [7]. Increasing correlations and short-range a.f. order (as $x \rightarrow 0$) will push down further the flat portion of the bands towards μ. (b = bonding, $a.b.$ = anti-bonding band.) Obviously, spectral weight transfer occurs away from ε_F towards the satellite bonding band which gets increasingly more weight as anti-ferromagnetism occurs. This spectral weight transfer, further enhanced by short-range a.f. order, causes $\rho(0, x) \rightarrow 0$. Of course, in view of the approximations used, these results are of qualitative significance.

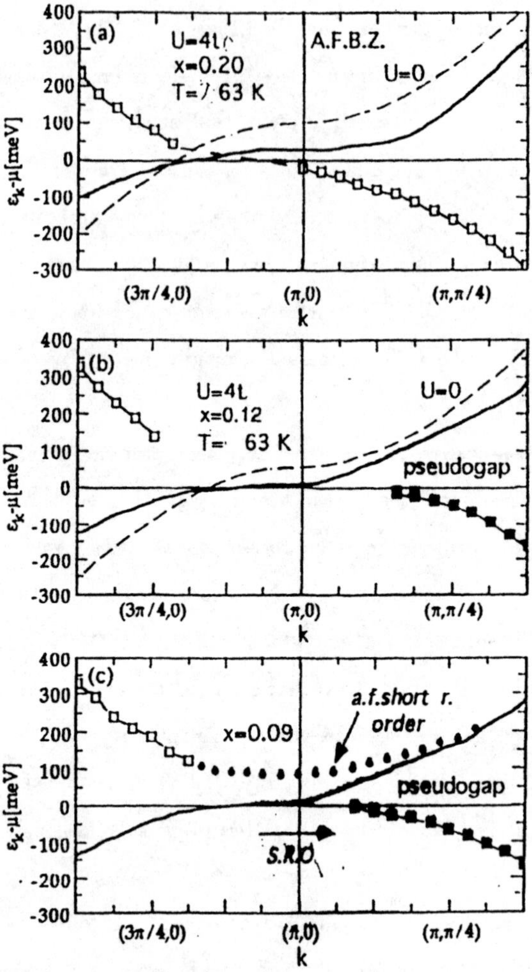

FIG. 17. Doping dependence of the particle dispersions ε_k in the vicinity of ε_F and of the a.f. Brillouin-zone (A.F.B.Z.) at $k \simeq (\pi, 0)$. FLEX results for the main- and satellite-band (open squares) are shown. As $x \to 0$ and U increases the flattening of the band transfers spectral weight towards the Fermi-energy μ and causes pseudogap formation. Thus, $\rho(0) \to 0$ as $x \to 0$. The approximate effects on ε_k due to short-range a.f. order (S.R.O.) are shown. Approximately we find for the width of the gap $\delta \simeq \alpha U_{eff} \mu_s$, $\alpha \lesssim 1$.

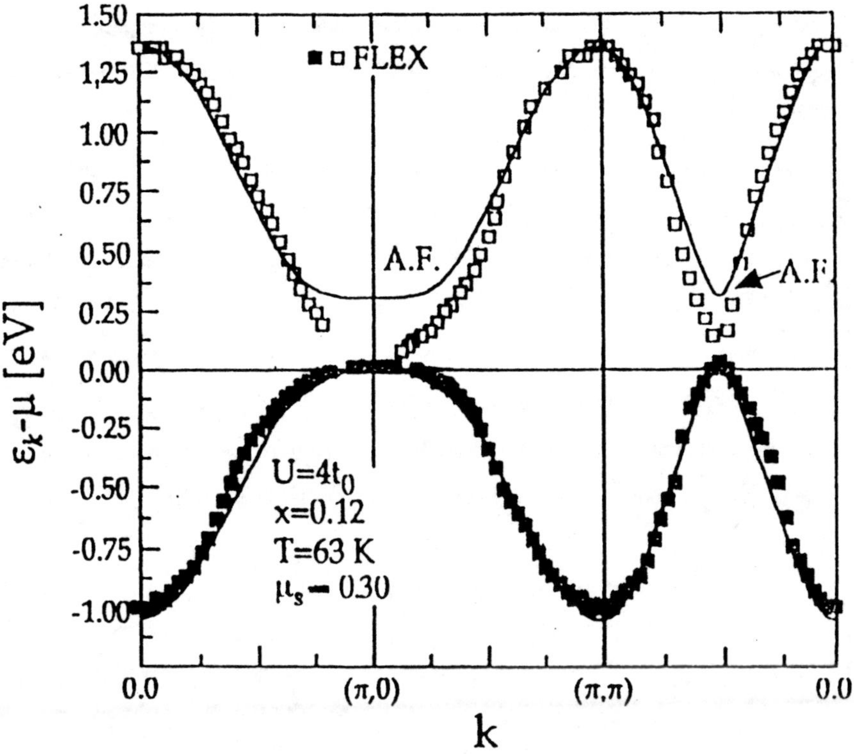

FIG. 18. FLEX results for ε_k are shown for a LSCO-like Fermi-surface. The expected bands assuming local magnetic moments ($\mu_s \equiv \langle m_s \rangle$) and long-range a.f. are indicated. Note, the largely dynamical magnetic effects at $x = 0.12$ and $T = 63$ K are within FLEX still not very pronounced, since $\omega \sim \omega_s$. Here, ω and ω_s refer to the typical elementary excitation and spin-excitation frequencies. The dispersions imply that magnetic pseudogap structure should be strongest around $\mathbf{k} \simeq (\pi, 0)$ and have weak intensity around $\mathbf{k} \simeq (\frac{\pi}{2}, \frac{\pi}{2})$.

In Fig. 20 the dependence of the dispersions on Fermi-surface topology is shown. The behaviour of the interlayer coupling, $t_\perp \rightarrow \tilde{t}_\perp$ due to the interplay of $t_\perp$-hopping with magnetic self-energy effets, is shown in Fig. 21. Note the interesting blocking behaviour $\tilde{t}_\perp \rightarrow 0$ for $T \rightarrow 0$ and $x \rightarrow 0$.

Note, the magnetic gaps at $\mathbf{k} \simeq \mathbf{k}_F$ are of the order of $50 \div 200$ meV. FLEX seems not to treat properly the formation of the gap at $\mathbf{k} \simeq (\pi, 0)$ arising from the arrangement of the main- and satellite bands to set up split bands. In general the overall behaviour of the dispersion (the increasing flattening for $x \rightarrow 0$ and increasing U, its $\mathbf{k}$-dependence, the indication of main- and satellite bands to form the split bands in the a.f. state, etc.) is in good agreement with experimental studies.

The interesting doping dependence of the lifetime of the quasi-particles characterising the elementary-excitations in the high-T_c-superconductors is obtained from the self-energy as [7].

$$\frac{1}{\tau_k(\omega)} = -Im\Sigma(\mathbf{k}, \omega). \tag{13}$$

For the underdopes superconductors we get [6,7,18]

$$\frac{1}{\tau_k(\omega)} = \alpha(\omega, x, T)\omega. \tag{14}$$

In Fig. 22 we present FLEX results [6] for LSCO-superconductors. These are typical for doping $0.15 > x \rightarrow 0$ and also for YBCO-superconductors. Note, the non-Fermi-liquid behaviour of $\Sigma(\mathbf{k}, \omega)$. For illustration see also the momentum averaged results for the inverse lifetime of the quasi-particles τ^{-1} presented in Fig. 23. Here, we used results obtained by Langer, Grabowski, Schmalian within the FLEX approximation for $\rho(\omega)$ and $\rho(k, \omega)$ [6,7]. Note, above a characteristic frequency $\omega_0 \propto T_0 \sim T^*$, the coefficient α in Eq. (14) is nearly independent of T and ω, but the slope of τ^{-1} vs. ω depends somewhat on x. Moreover, for $T < T_0$ the scattering rate τ^{-1} depends on ω and T due to the corresponding of the pseudogaps. Note, at $\hbar\omega < k_B T_0$ and for $T < T_0$ the increase of the lifetime $\tau_k(\omega)$ is due to the development of a gap in $\rho(0, x)$, since $\tau^{-1} \propto N(0)$ and the latter decreases for $x \rightarrow 0$

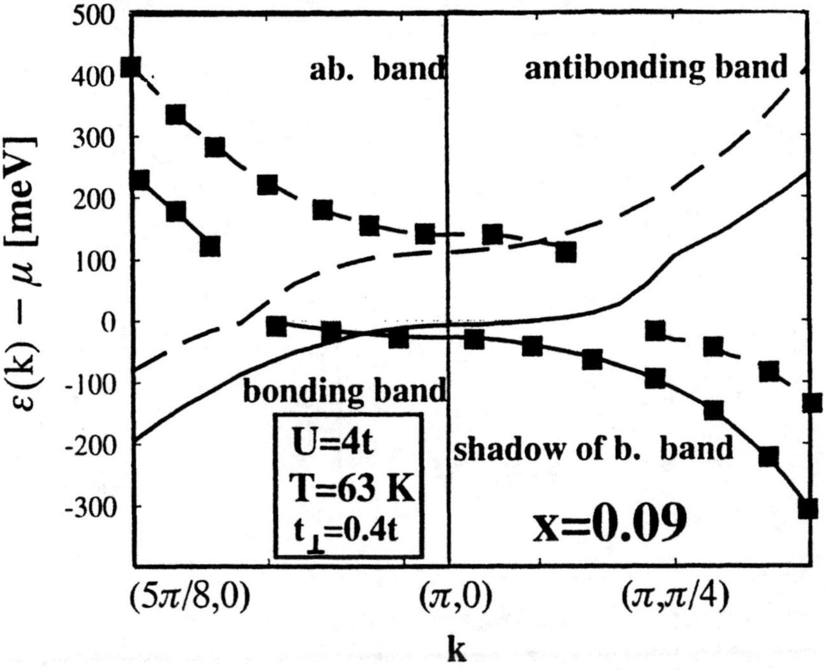

FIG. 19. Bands in bilayer-compounds with corresponding Fermi-surface (s. inset Fig. 15). The bonding band crosses the F.S. between $(\pi, 0)$ and (π, π). Increasing spectral weight transfer occurs for $x \to 0$ away from the Fermi-energy towards the satellite band (squares). $t_\perp$ is the interlayer hopping integral. Rearrangement of the bonding and corresponding satellite band should form split bands and a gap at $(\pi, 0)$.

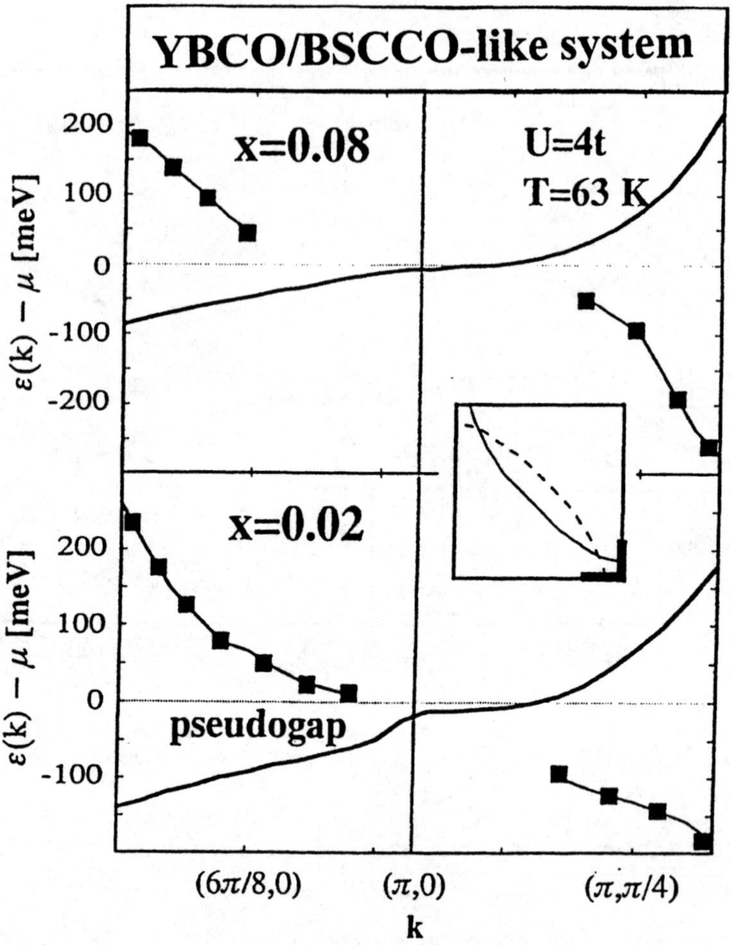

FIG. 20. Quasi-particle dispersions near k $\simeq (\pi, 0)$ which in agreement with ARPES studies are flatter than for LSCO-systems.

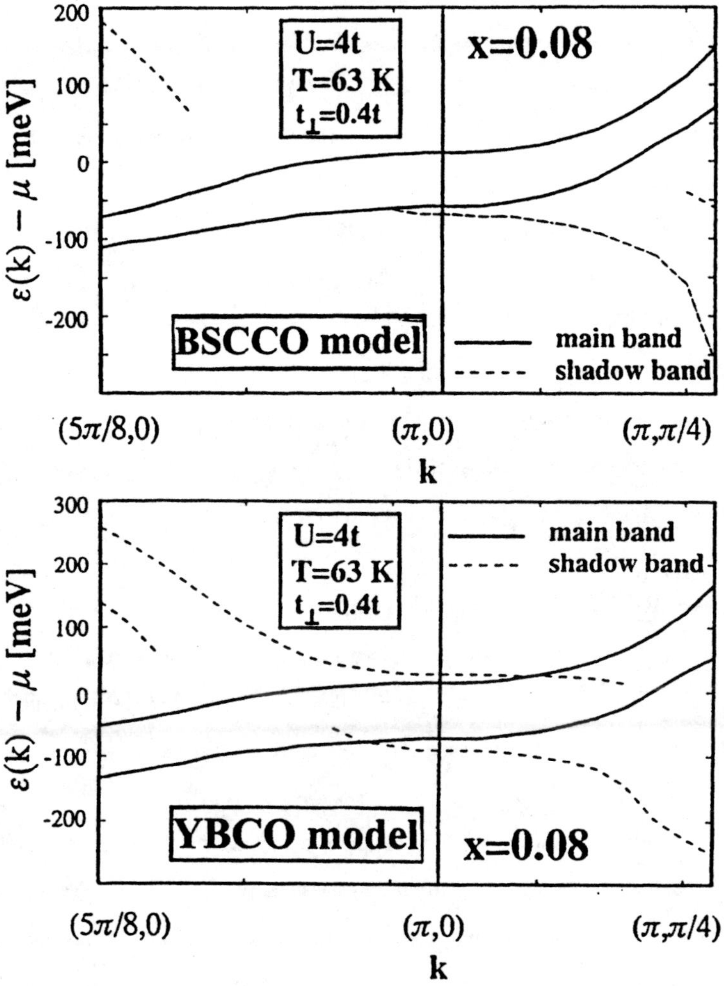

FIG. 21. Dependence of dispersions $\varepsilon(\mathbf{k})$ on F.S. topology. Note, the strong decrease of the bilayer splitting from 200 meV for $U = 0$ to 100 meV for YBCO and to 80 meV for BSCCO.

and increasing gap. This seems in fair qualitative agreement with experiment [5]. Eq. (14) is furthermore discussed in Appendix A. Note, ω_0 may be also related to the characteristic temperature T_{NMR} observed inNMR [4]. Clearly, $(T_1T)^{-1}$, where T_1 is the relaxation time, reflects a.f. spin correlations, magnetic moments and their short-range order, s. Baumgärtel et al. [8]. One expects approximately $\omega_0 \sim T^* \sim T^*_{NMR}$.

In Fig. 24 we present results for the temperature dependence of the electrical resistivity $\rho(T)$ of LSCO [6]. Again, $\rho \propto T$ is due to the anomalous dependence $\tau^{-1} \propto \omega$ of the self-energy $Im\Sigma(\mathbf{k},\omega)$. Fairly satisfactory agreement with experiments is also obtained for the sensitive Hall-coefficients R_H [6]. We find $R_H(T)$ is only weakly temperature-dependent. This gets weaker for increasing x and saturates for $T > 500K$.

In the following we present results for the spin-susceptibility $\chi_s(\mathbf{q},\omega)$ and its doping- and temperature dependence. Note, χ_s is responsible for the magnetic activity in general, for structure in $\rho(\mathbf{k},\omega)$ and for Cooper-pairing.

FLEX-theory yields a spin susceptibility $\chi_s(\mathbf{q},\omega)$ which is of Ornstein-Zernike form. This is illustrated in Fig. 25 where results are shown for $Im\chi_s(\mathbf{q},\omega)$ and $\mathbf{q} \simeq (\pi,\pi)$. Note, for $\mathbf{q}$ away from the route $(0,0) \to (\pi,\pi)$ in the Brillouin zone one finds no pronounced peak structure [6]. We find also that $Im\chi_s(\mathbf{q},\omega)$ peaks more strongly as $x \to 0$ and that then $\omega_s \to 0$.

In Fig. 26 results are shown demonstrating the incommensurable peak structure of $\chi_s(\mathbf{q},\omega)$. Dependent on doping x the minimum of the spin-excitation energy $\omega_{\mathbf{q}}$ at which $Im\chi_s(\mathbf{q},\omega)$ peaks is shifted away from $\mathbf{q} = \mathbf{Q} = (\pi,\pi)$. Note, we get the tendency $\omega_q \to 0$ as $x \to 0$. Of course, as a.f. order occurs the results change and also the Ornstein-Zernike expression changes to $\chi_s^{-1} \sim (1+\xi^2(q-Q)^2 - i\frac{\omega}{\omega_s} - \frac{\omega^2}{\Delta_{af}^2})$. That pronounced magnetic effects occur in $\rho(\mathbf{k},\omega)$, $\phi(\mathbf{k},\omega)$, etc. at $\mathbf{k} \simeq (\pi,0)$ is due to the dynamical interplay of magnetic excitations ($\sim \omega_s$) and elementary excitations ($\sim \omega \sim T$) as has been mentioned already.

In Fig. 27 we present results showing how superconductivity affects $\chi_s(\mathbf{q},\omega)$ and the frequency ω_s at the peak. Note, the interesting behaviour of $Im\chi_s(\mathbf{q},\omega)$ in the superconducting

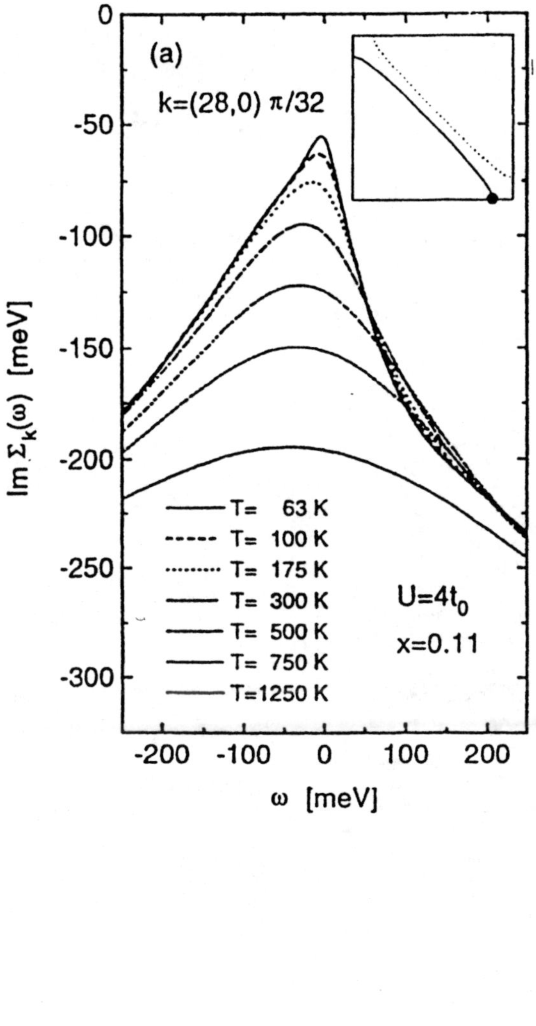

FIG. 22. Results for $(-Im\Sigma(\mathbf{k},\omega)$ for a LSCO-model. The results demonstrate marginal Fermi-liquid behaviour (M.F.L.) and approximately $Im\Sigma(\mathbf{k},\omega)\alpha(-\omega)$.

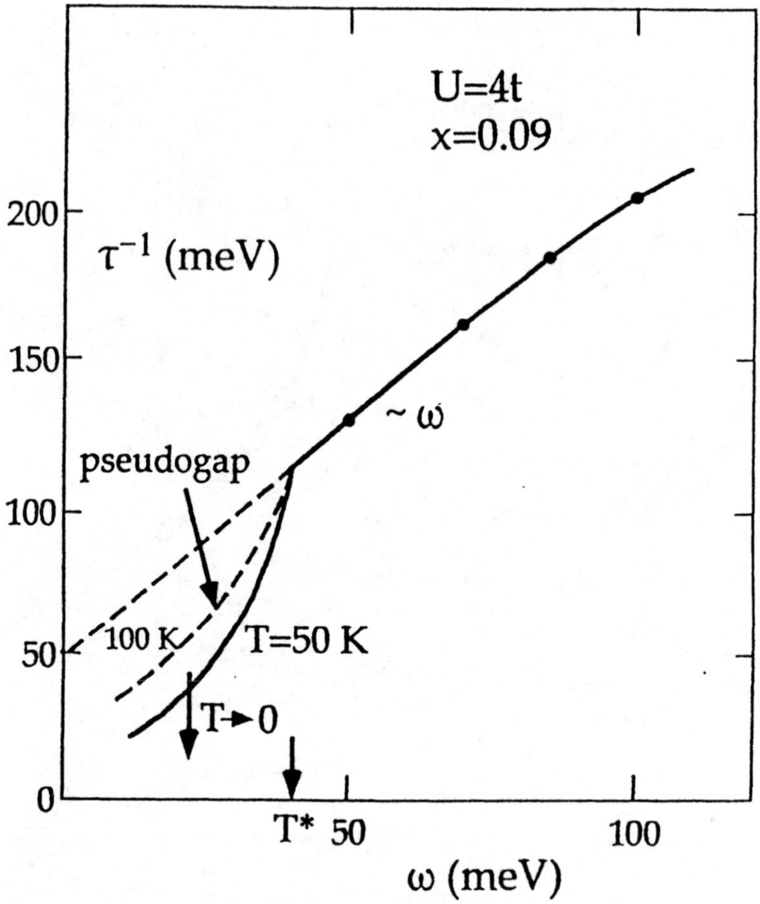

FIG. 23. FLEX results for the quasi-particle lifetimes $\tau(\omega, T)$ of a LSCO-model. Using results for the density of states $\rho(\omega, T)$ we estimate the effect of pseudogaps on $\tau^{-1}(\omega)$ to appear at $\hbar\omega < k_B T^*$. $N(0, x) \to 0$ and short-range a.f. order will enhance the increase of the lifetimes as $x \to 0$.

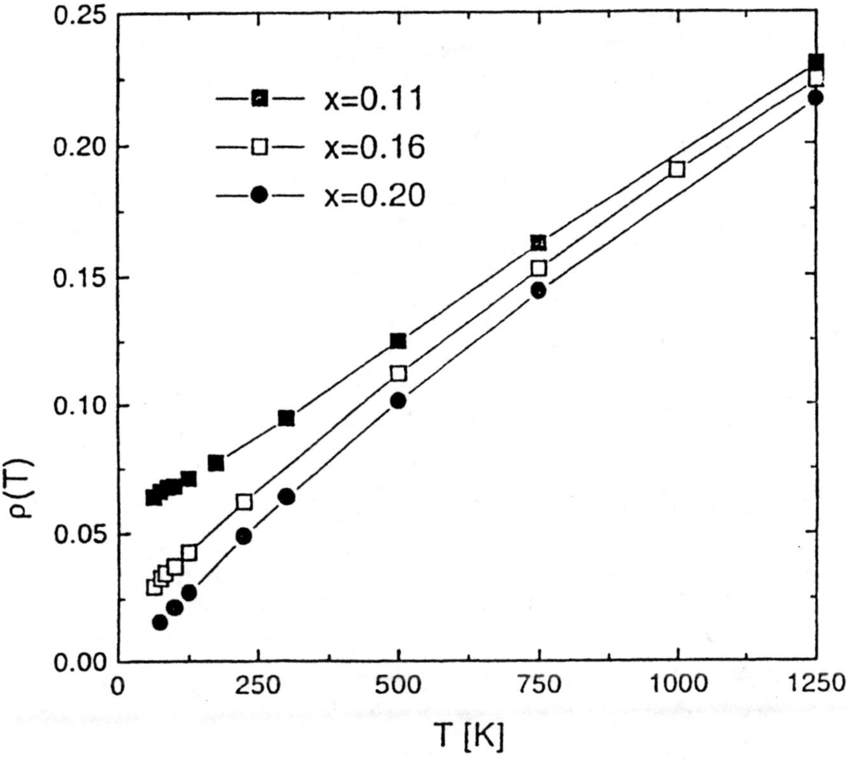

FIG. 24. Doping dependence of the electrical resistivity using the FLEX results for $\rho(\mathbf{k},\omega)$ and a LSCO-model F.S.

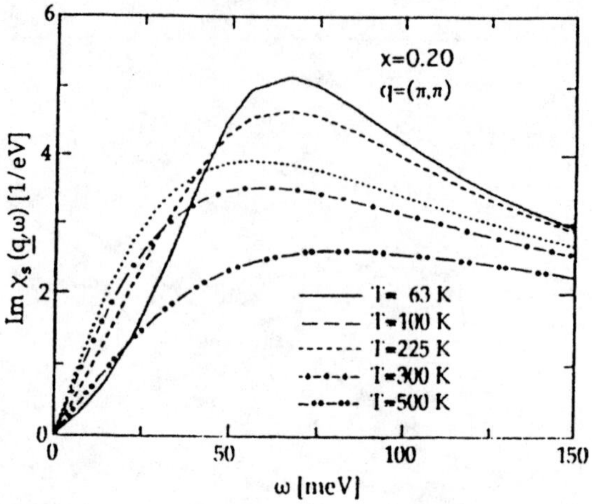

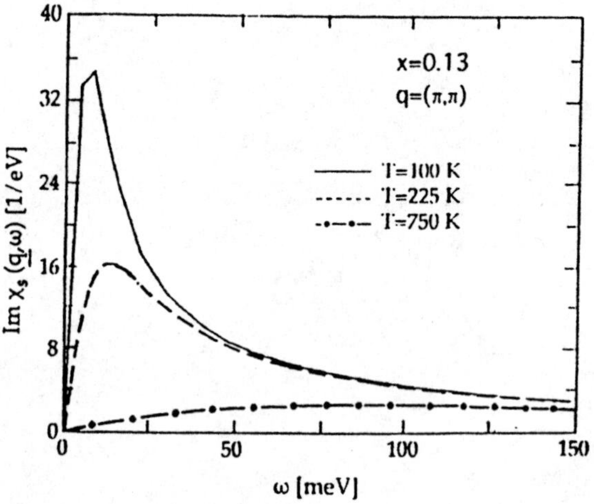

FIG. 25. Typical FLEX results for the spin-susceptibility $\chi_s(\mathbf{q},\omega)$ using a LSCO-Fermi-surface. $Im\chi_s$ peaks at ω_s and resembles for $\mathbf{q} \to \mathbf{Q}$ and $x \to 0, T \to 0$ the Ornstein-Zernike function. As $x \to 0$, $Im\chi_s$ peaks more sharply and $\omega_s \to 0$. Away from $\mathbf{q} \simeq (\pi,\pi)$ the function $Im\chi_s$ has a less pronounced structure. Local magnetic moments μ_s and their a.f. order will of course affect $\chi_s(\mathbf{q},\omega)$ somewhat.

state. As temperature decreases the peak in $\chi_s(\mathbf{q} \simeq \mathbf{Q}, \omega)$ shifts to larger frequencies and at $\omega \simeq 0$ spectral weight is suppressed. Also note, the peak position is always such that $\omega_\mathbf{q}$ is below the value 2Δ. Of course, an interdependence is expected, since the same electrons (holes) cause Cooper-pairing and spin-excitations. Clearly these results will change if short-range a.f. order of magnetic moments occur.

In the following some typical results for spin-fluctuation induced superconductivity and obtained within FLEX-type theory are shown. The FLEX-theory yields that the spin-fluctuation induced superconductivity is for all doping concentrations x of d-wave symmetry. Interlayer coupling affects superconductivity and shifts $T_c(x)$ [7]. Electron-phonon coupling affects the spin-fluctuation induced superconductivity. According to our FLEX-like calculations possibly strongest for optimal doping. One expects tunneling spectra to reveal characteristically strong coupling effects due to the intimate interplay of spin-excitations and Cooper-pair formation.

In Fig. 28 we present results for the superconducting gap function $\phi(\mathbf{k}, \omega)$ and its doping dependence obtained within Eliashberg theory using FLEX [7]. We get d-wave symmetry superconductivity for all doping concentrations. Moreover, note the overall **k**-dependence of the superconducting order parameter $\phi(\mathbf{k}, \omega = 0)$ is the same as of the magnetic pseudogaps. We find $\phi(\mathbf{k}, \omega = 0) \simeq \phi_0 \cdot (cosk_x - \cos k_y)$ for $x \gtrsim 0.1$ and for underdoped superconductors. However, as $x \to 0$ the appearance of higher harmonics in ϕ is interesting. It reflects the momentum dependence of the pairing interaction below T_c.

Note, that we obtain from the gap function $\phi(\mathbf{k}, \omega)$ a superconducting gap $\Delta(\mathbf{k}, \omega) = \phi(\mathbf{k}, \omega)/Z(\mathbf{k}, \omega)$ which is largest when T_c is maximal. For $x \to 0.05$ we get that $\Delta(x)$ decreases again, in accordance with $\Delta(x) \sim \lambda_L^{-1}$. This decrease may get weaker as one corrects in FLEX the density of states $\rho(0, x)$ and then the lifetime of the quasi-particles, s. Eq. 6. Recent experiments claim that $\Delta(x)$ continues to increase for $x \lesssim 0.14$ for decreasing x in contrast to physical intuition [3]. Further studies are needed to resolve this discrepancy.

In Fig. 29 results are shown for the Cooper-pairing potential $V(\mathbf{k}, \omega)$ above and below T_c.

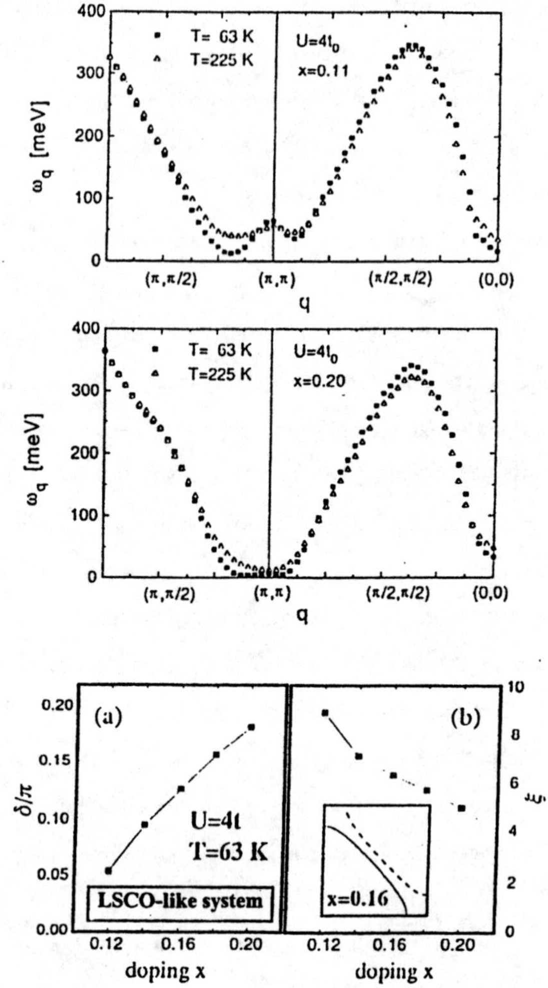

FIG. 26. Results for the frequency ω_q for which $Im\chi_s(\mathbf{q},\omega)$ peaks along the route $(\pi,0) \to (\pi,\pi)$ and $(\pi,\pi) \to (0,0)$ in the B.Z. Note, the incommensurability $\mathbf{Q}^* < \mathbf{Q} = (\pi,\pi)$ for larger doping x. The peak in $Im\chi_s(\mathbf{q},\omega)$ occurs at $\mathbf{Q}^*$. $\mathbf{Q}^* \to \mathbf{Q}$ as $x \to 0$. Also the doping dependence of the incommensurability δ and the spin correlation length ξ of $\chi_s(\mathbf{q},0)$ are shown.

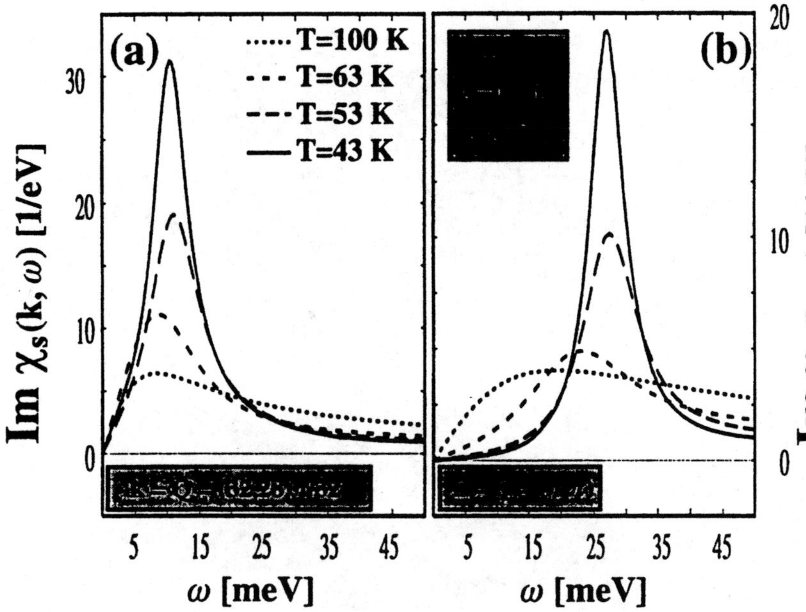

FIG. 27. Temperature dependence of the effective interaction and approximate susceptibility $\chi_s(\mathbf{k},\omega)$ for $\mathbf{k} = \mathbf{Q}^* = (\pi, \frac{28}{32}\pi)$ and for $\mathbf{k} = \mathbf{Q} = (\pi,\pi)$, where $\chi_s(\mathbf{k},\omega)$ is maximal. Note, the changes due to superconductivity for $T < T_c$; the peak gets sharper and shifts to larger frequencies as $T \to 0$.

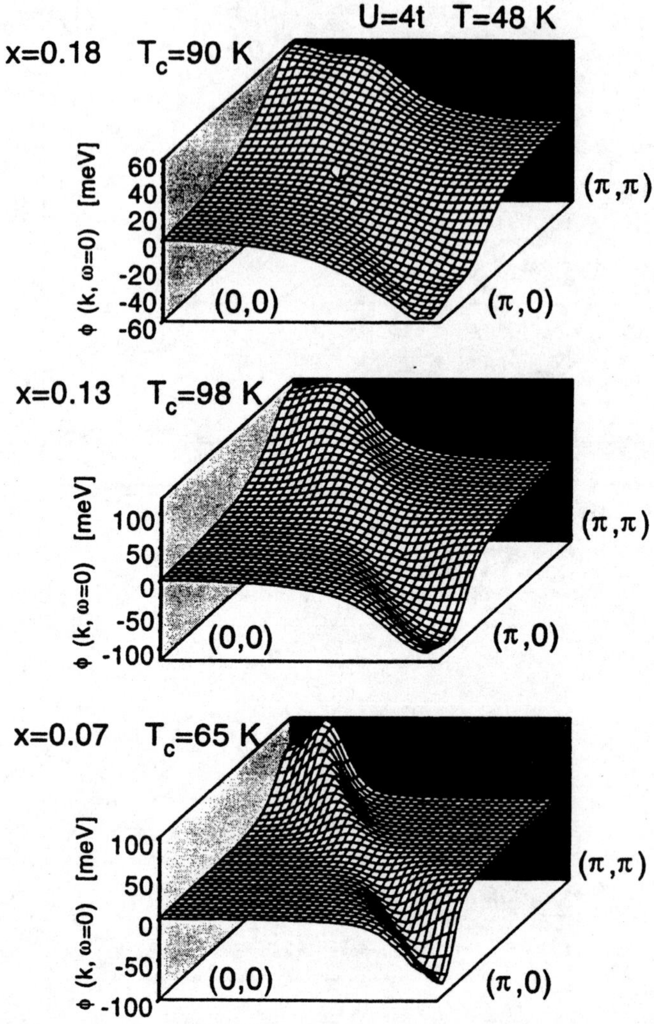

FIG. 28. Illustration of the doping dependence and d-wave symmetry of the superconducting order parameter $\phi(\mathbf{k}, \omega = 0)$ for a LSCO-model F.S. and T_c values obtained from $\Delta_k = Re\Delta(\mathbf{k}, \Delta_k) = 0$. Within FLEX clearly $\rho(\mathbf{k}, \omega)$ or the pseudogaps and $\phi(\mathbf{k}, \omega)$ exhibit the same **k**-dependence.

One notices the interesting interplay of superconductivity and a.-f. spin-fluctuations. Note, in the normal-state the pairing potential for $\mathbf{q} \simeq (\pi, \pi)$, where it is strongest, continues to increase as $x \rightarrow 0.05$, but for $T < T_c$ the ratio $V_s(\mathbf{k}, \omega = 0; \phi)/V_N(\mathbf{k}, \omega = 0; \phi = 0)$ decreases for $x \rightarrow 0.05$. Of course, this is expected since the particles engaged in the Cooper-pairs are somewhat lost as particles building up $\chi_s(\mathbf{q}, \omega)$. This behaviour expresses that for a certain range of x the gain of energy due to Cooper-pairing is larger than the gain in energy due to a.f. spin-correlations. Clearly, as the spin-correlation length ξ_s gets larger than the coherence length ξ, $\xi_s > \xi$, for $x \rightarrow 0$ the gain in a.f. spin correlation-energy wins this energetic competition. Note, (V_s/V_N) is maximal when T_c is maximal.

In Fig. 30 results are presented for the pairing potential in real space. These are particularly interesting for estimating the effect of short-range a.f. order on Cooper-pairing. $V(1, 0, \omega)$ describing the nearest neighbor pairing interaction reflects again the intimate interplay of superconductivity and spin-excitations. Note, $V(1, 0, \omega)$ gets larger (more attractive) below T_c for decreasing T before its maximum shifts to finite frequencies due to the feedback caused by the Cooper-pair formation. The opening of the superconducting gap shifts quasi-particle states to larger energies (s. effects $\rho(0, x) \rightarrow 0$ in the density of states), thus the scattering rate τ^{-1} decreases below T_c and this stabilizes the pairing. Interesting is also the doping dependence of the pairing potential $V(i, 0; \omega = 0)$, where i refers to sites neighboring the site 0. This reflects the increase in the coherence-length ξ as $x \rightarrow 0$.

However, it is not sufficient to study only the behaviour of $V(i, 0; \omega)$. Remember that the lifetime of the quasi-particles reduces the superconducting gap below $x \simeq 0.14$. As a consequence the nearest neighbor pairing amplitude $\Delta(1, 0, \omega)$ obtained from a spectral analysis of $\Delta(\mathbf{k}, \omega)$ reveals better the occurence of superconductivity in real space. For illustration see the results presented in Fig. 31. This suggests that the increasing stiffness of n.n. spin-correlations reduces the spin-polarizability necessary for Cooper-pair formation and the freezing out of n.n. sites for Cooper-pairing.

In Fig. 32 we show that interplay of spin correlation and pairing may cause an effective

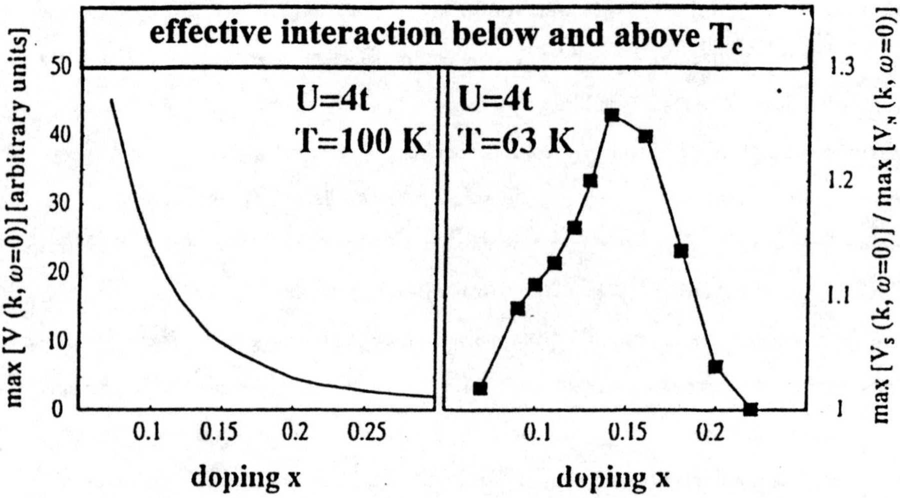

FIG. 29. Effective pairing interaction $V(\mathbf{k},\omega)$ below (T = 63 K) and above $T_c(T$ = 100 K). In the normal state V_N is maximal for $\mathbf{k} \simeq \mathbf{Q}$ and continues to increase for doping $x \to 0$. Note, the maximal enhancement of $(V_s(\mathbf{k},0)/V_N(\mathbf{k},0))$ ocurs for $x \simeq 0.14$. V_N results from $V(\mathbf{k},\omega)$ for $\phi \equiv 0$. Clearly, the ratio V_s/V_N reflects the origin of the doping dependence of T_c and of T_c^{max}.

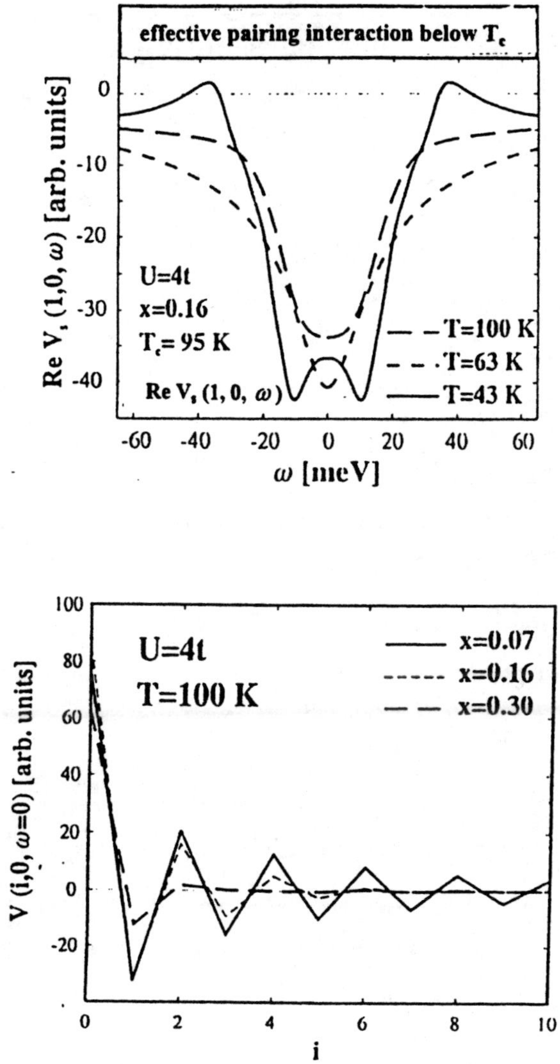

FIG. 30. Effective Cooper-pairing potential $V(1,0;\omega)$ between nearest neighbor sites 1 and 0. Also results are shown for the doping dependence of $V(i,0;\omega 00)$, where i refers to sites neighboring the site 0. These results demonstrate the interplay of a.f. spin-dynamics and superconductivity.

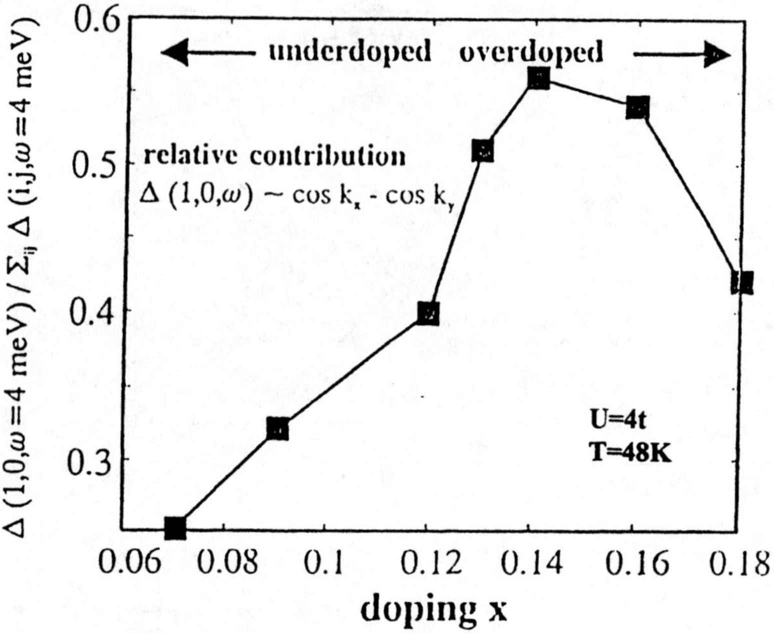

FIG. 31. The nearest neighbor pairing amplitude $\Delta(1,0;\omega)$ obtained by spectral analysis from $\Delta(\mathbf{k},\omega)$. The decrease of $\Delta(1,0;\omega)$ for $x \to 0.05$ is due to the increasing stiffness of the n.n. spin-correlation. $\rho(0,x) \to 0$ weakens the decrease for $x < 0.14$.

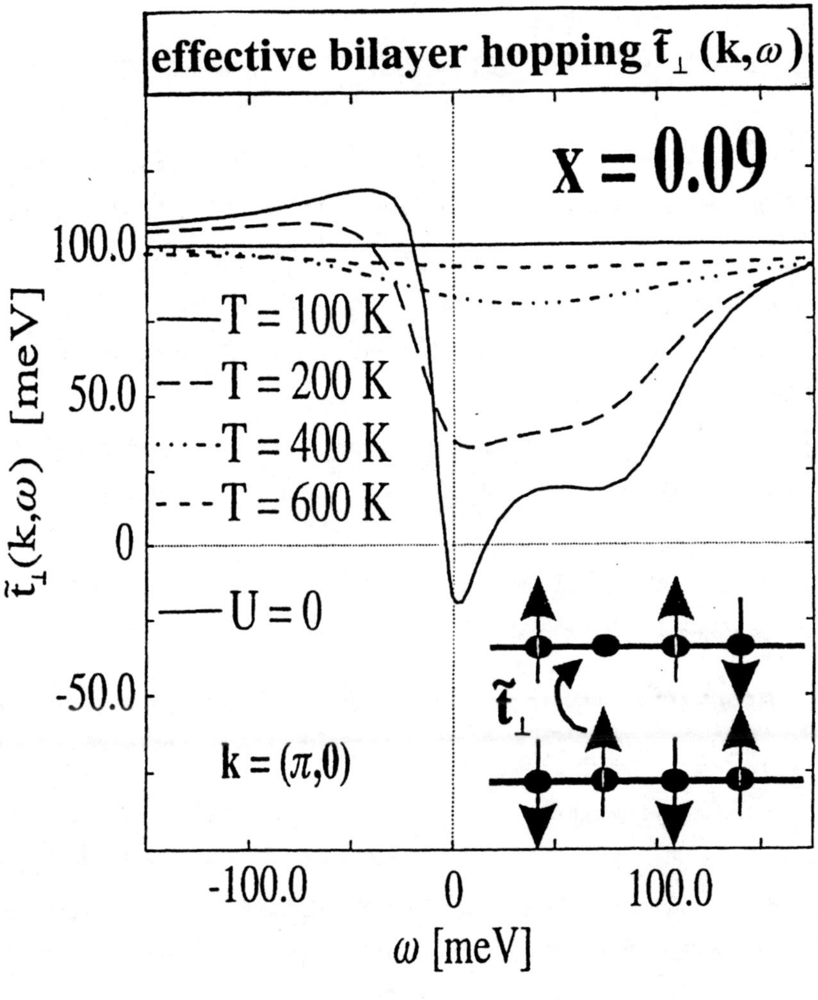

FIG. 32. Effective interlayer hopping $\tilde{t}_\perp(\mathbf{k},\omega)$ compared with the interaction-free case ($U = 0$) and $t_\perp = 0.4\ t$. Inset: $\tilde{t}_\perp(\mathbf{k},\omega)$ is reduced, since a quasi-particle with an up (down) spin that hops to an empty site in the other plane also hops in the opposite antiferromagnetic environment due to the interlayer coupling. This causes the unfavourable parallel alignment of neighboring spins and a corresponding energy loss.

interlayer coupling $\tilde{t}_\perp$ and blocking $\tilde{t}_\perp \to 0$ for $x \to 0$, $T \to 0$.

In Figs. 33 and 34 we show results for the effect of interlayer coupling on $\phi(\mathbf{k},\omega)$ and $T_c(x)$.

The effect of magnetic correlations on $\phi(\mathbf{k},\omega)$ near $\mathbf{k}_F \simeq (\pi,0)$ could also be estimated analytically by using $\omega_s \simeq 0$ in the spin susceptibility $\chi_s(\mathbf{q},\omega)$ and in calculating the self-energy matrix $\Sigma(\mathbf{k},\omega)$ [6]. Generally, stiffening a.f. correlations for $x \to 0$ will reduce $\phi(\mathbf{k},\omega)$ around $\mathbf{k} \simeq (\pi,0)$. Thus, we expect that short-range order of the moments μ_s reduces $\phi(\mathbf{k},\omega)$. The k-dependence of $\Delta(\mathbf{k},\omega)$ and of the gaps $\delta_\mathbf{k}(x,T)$ reflects the interplay of ω_s and $(\varepsilon_{k+Q} - \varepsilon_k)$ or ω, respectively.

Clearly, tunneling spectra are also expected to exhibit a sensitive fingerprint of the interplay of spin-excitations and Cooper-pair formation and thus of the mechanism for high-T_c-superconductivity.

In Fig. 35 FLEX results are presented for SIS and NIS tunneling within a LSCO-model for the Fermi-surface using the expression

$$I(eV) \simeq 8\pi e^2 N^2 |T|^2 \int_{-\infty}^{\infty} \frac{d\varepsilon}{2\pi} \rho_R(\varepsilon)\rho_L(\varepsilon + eV)[f(\varepsilon) - f(\varepsilon + eV)], \tag{15}$$

where T is the tunneling matrix element, R and L refer to the right and left side of the junction, f is the Fermi-function and eV the bias voltage. The dips reflect structure in $\rho(\omega)$ at $\omega \simeq 2\Delta$, s. Fig. 36. In SIS spectra the dips appear at $\omega = \pm 3\Delta$. Note the asymmetric dip structure for NIS-tunneling. We find a stronger dip at $eV = -2\Delta$, but also one at positive bias voltage $eV = 2\Delta$. Note, we get that this dip is larger for BSCCO. At T_c the dips disappear. This is very important. These results are in fair agreement with recent experiments [3,4]. It is remarkable that FLEX-theory yields such a good agreement with fine structure in tunneling spectroscopy. Of course, the theoretical results depend on the Fermi-surface topology. The dips get more pronounced, increase going from LSCO- to BSCCO-superconductors.

In summary, using an effective one-band model Hubbard-hamiltonian, the FLEX approximation and combination of FLEX and short-range magnetic order (quasi-static approxima-

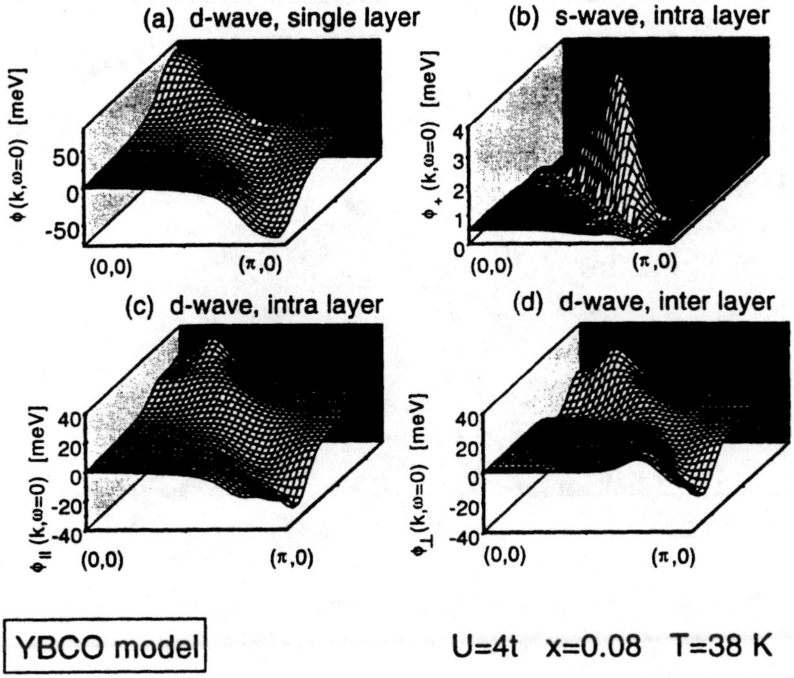

FIG. 33. Superconducting order parameter for the YBCO-model. (a) Monolayer with $t_\perp = 0$. (b) Bilayer with $t_\perp = 0.4\ t$ for the metastable $s^{\pm}$-wave state. (c) Bilayer with $t_\perp = 0.4\ t$ for the d-wave state in the layer representation. $\phi_{\|}$ refers to in-plane pairing and $\phi_\perp$ interplane one. ($T_c^{YBCO} = 95$K versus $T_c^{LSCO} = 37$K).

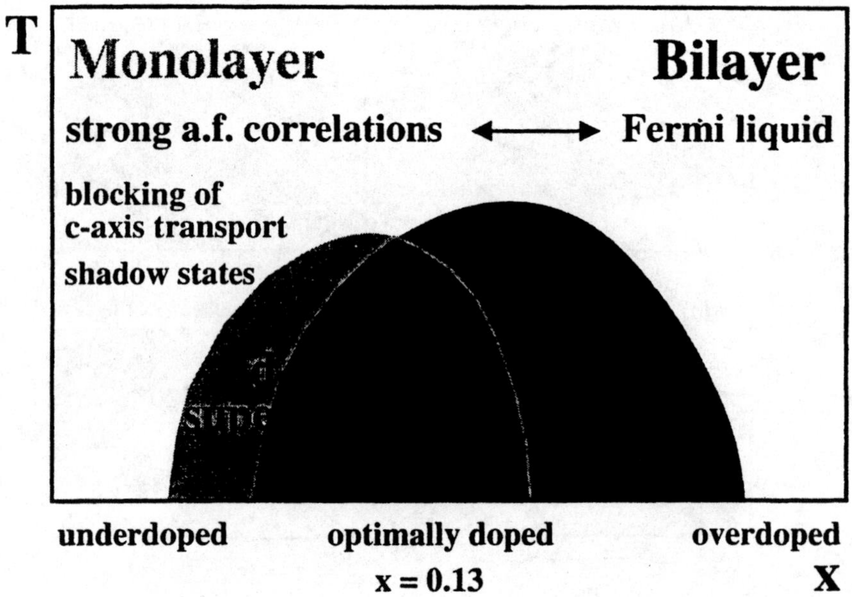

FIG. 34. Phase diagram of mono- and bilayer high-T_c-superconductors within FLEX-theory. Note, T_c shifts as a function of x. For $x \to 0$ blocking of c-axis carrier hopping occurs.

tion, etc.) we are able to describe in fair agreement with experiments characteristic properties and their doping dependence of overdoped and of the underdoped high-T_c-superconductors. As $x \rightarrow 0$ anti-ferromagnetic spin correlations become more prominent and cause magnetic pseudogaps in the spectral density and a decrease in the density of states $N(0)$. This reduction of $N(0)$, also for $\rho(\mathbf{k}, 0)$ at $\mathbf{k} \simeq (\pi, 0)$, reduces T_c, the quasi-particle lifetimes τ^{-1} and this in turn enhances Δ_0 and most remarkably $2\Delta_0/k_B T_c$. The origin of the doping dependence of T_c is the interplay of Cooper-pair formation and spin-dynamics, or the interplay of quasi-particle and Cooper-pair lifetimes.

The resultant effects of a.f. correlations for $x \rightarrow 0$ on the various properties are expected to be even stronger if we include the formation of local magnetic moments μ_s and within a Bethe-Peierls approximation, for example, their short range anti-ferromagnetic order [8]. The results shown for the pseudogaps in BSCCO illustrates the need for such an extension, since simple FLEX without μ_s and short-range a.f. order yields not the observed magnitude of the pseudogap at the F.S. around $\mathbf{k} \simeq (\pi, 0)$ and particularly still a Fermi-surface crossing, $\rho(\mathbf{k}_F, 0) > 0$, $\mathbf{k}_F \simeq (\pi, 0)$ as $x \rightarrow 0$. Of course, if precursor superconductivity occurs, one gets dependent on the averaging over the Cooper-pair phases and on time $\rho(\mathbf{k}_F, \omega) \rightarrow 0$ at $T > T_c$. Note, however, already FLEX and the quasi-static approximation gives the correct k-dependence and origin of the superconducting gap and of the magnetic pseudogaps. Due to short-range a.f. order we estimate for the width of the magnetic pseudogap at $\mathbf{k}_F$ and $\mathbf{k} \simeq (\pi, o)$ as $x \rightarrow 0$ a value $\delta \sim \eta U \mu_s$, where $\eta \lesssim 1$. Itinerancy and magnetic dynamics may reduce δ to $10 \div 50$ (meV), to something of that order.

Note, the results for the BSCCO systems are similar to the ones using the LSCO-model Fermi-surface. Quantitatively the FLEX-type theory needs to be improved to describe better interlayer coupling effects, the magnitude of the structure in the spectral density and the doping dependence and width of the pseudogaps. Again, μ_s and their short-range magnetic order should be included in the analysis.

Of course, a more critical assessment of the use of an effective one-band model Hubbard-

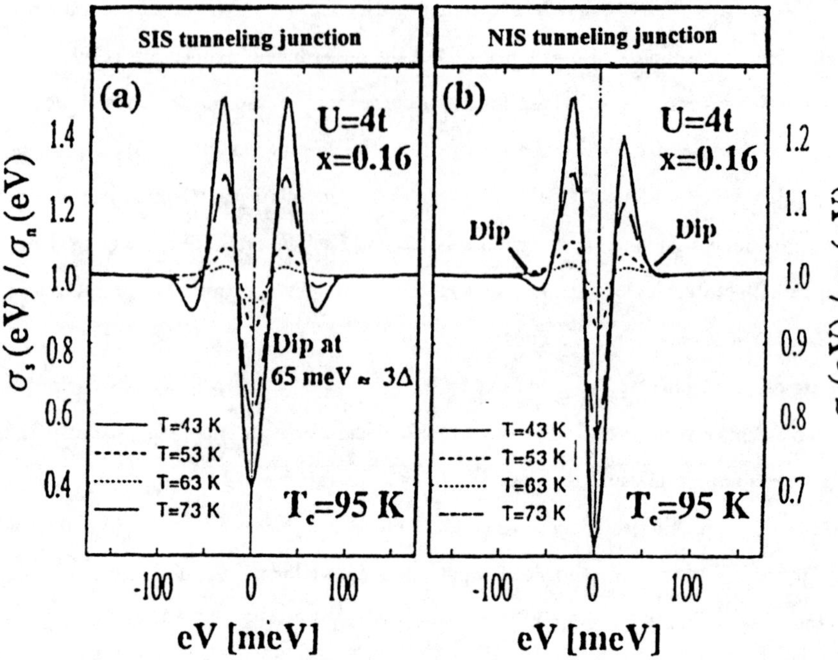

FIG. 35. FLEX results for tunneling spectra (conductance) using a LSCO-model for the F.S. Note, the dip structure at about 3Δ in the SIS spectra and at 2Δ for SIN tunneling. V is the bias voltage. For NIS tunneling the dip at negative voltage is more pronounced than the one at $eV = 2\Delta$. The dips disappear at T_c. For a BSCCO-system we get that the dips are deeper.

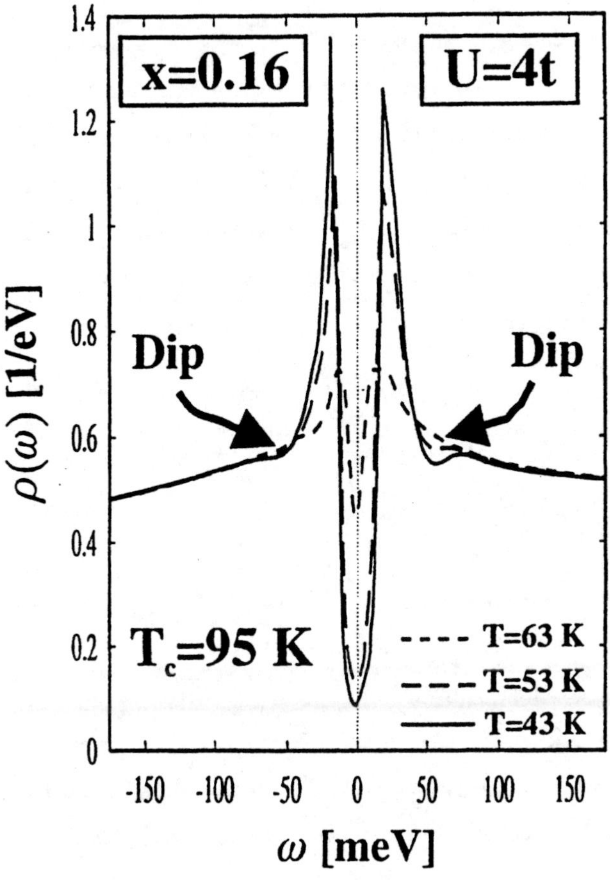

FIG. 36. Temperature dependence of D.O.S. $\rho(\omega, T)$ for $T < T_c$. Dips disappear at T_c.

hamiltonian, its model parameters, and a perturbative like treatment of the electronic structure is necessary. It is very remarkable that the model treatment of high-T_c-superconductors used here yields so many results in fair agreement with experiments. It is important that this is achieved within the context of one ansatz, since obviously one needs an unified theory.

Clearly, a 3-band Hubbard-hamiltonian is required to describe specific behaviour at oxygen- and Cu-sites, singulett formation, etc. It is of interest to find out whether similar results as presented here and d-wave superconductivity is also obtained within FLEX using a 3-band model Hubbard-hamiltonian [19]. Therefore, we also calculated some properties by using the 3-band model hamiltonian

$$\begin{aligned} H = & \sum_{i,\sigma}(\varepsilon_d - \mu) d^+_{i\sigma} d_{i\sigma} + \sum_{j\alpha\sigma}(\varepsilon_p - \mu) p^+_{j\alpha\sigma} p_{j\alpha\sigma} \\ & + \sum_{i,j,\sigma_\alpha} t_{pd} p^+_{j\alpha\sigma} d_{i\sigma} + h.c. + \sum U d^+_{j\uparrow} d_{j\uparrow} d^+_{j\downarrow} d_{j\downarrow} \\ & + \cdots \end{aligned} \tag{16}$$

The usual notation is used [19]. p- and d refer to p-oxygen and d-Cu-like states. Here, we neglect for simplicity Coulomb interactions U in p-states at oxygen sites. We apply FLEX- and Eliashberg-type theory to Eq.(16) to determine the matrix Green's function $G_{pd}(\mathbf{k},\omega)$ and then the gap function $\phi(\mathbf{k},\omega)$, the quasi-particle lifetimes $\tau_k(\omega)$, etc. As parameters we use for the d-states $U_d = 1.2t_{pd}$, $\varepsilon_d - \varepsilon_p = 4eV$ for the separation of p- and d-states and $t_{pd} \simeq 1eV$ for the hopping integral between Cu- and O-sites. These values correspond to the parameters $U = 4t$, $t = 0.25eV$, and $U/W \approx 1/2$ used for the one band Hubbard calculations (W = band-width, $t \sim t_{pd}^2/(\varepsilon_d - \varepsilon_p)$). Note, using larger values for U_d we get scattering rates τ^{-1} in strong disagreement with experiments. It is also interesting that $\phi(\mathbf{k},\omega) > 0$ for a large range of U-values (U up to 6 eV), while a superconducting gap in the D.O.S. $\rho(\omega)$ is obtained only for smaller U-values [20].

We find that spin-fluctuations generate also within the 3 band-Hubbard model Cooper-pairing and a spin-fluctuation induced $d_{x^2-y^2}$-symmetry superconducting state. Again, the Cooper-pairing is reduced by the inelastic scattering of the quasi-particles. The various properties are affected by the Fermi-surface topology and U and $\chi_s(\mathbf{q},\omega)$, respectively.

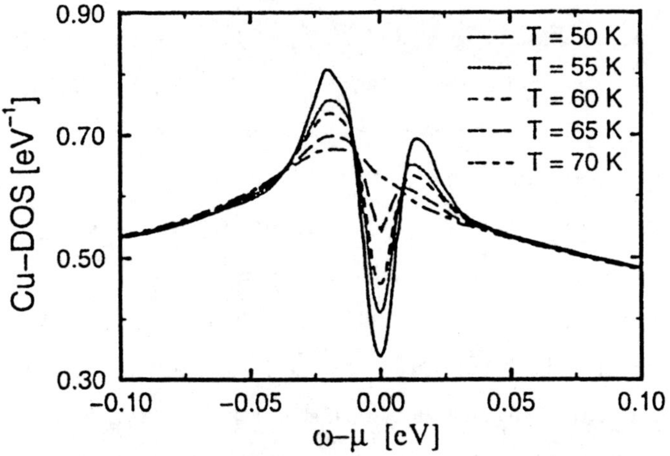

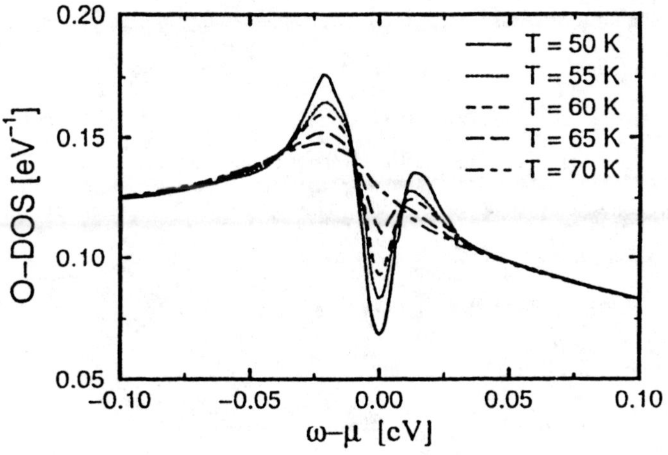

FIG. 37. Results for the temperature dependence of the density of states $\rho(\omega)$ for $x = 0.18$ and $T_c \simeq 70K$ at both copper- and oxygen sites.

In Fig. 37 we show typical results for the density of states at oxygen- and copper-sites. Remarkable is the simultaneous opening of a superconducting gap at both atomic sites. Hence, both O- and Cu-sites feel superconductivity. We calculate $T_c \lesssim 70K$ and at higher temperatures $\Delta \simeq 23meV$ for a doping $x \simeq 0.18$. Furthermore, we get $2\Delta/k_B T_c = 7.6$ and $m^*/m \simeq 4$ for the effective mass ratio.

In Fig. 38 results are shown for the gap function $\phi(\mathbf{k},\omega)$ clearly exhibiting d-wave symmetry superconductivity for the 3-band Hubbard-hamiltonian.

Of course, further analysis is needed to judge critically these results obtained for the 3-band Hubbard-model of high-T_c-superconductors. In view of the strong correlations one expects effects due to vortex corrections, (somewhat absorbed in $U \rightarrow U_{eff}$) magnetic moments and their short-range order, in particular as $x \rightarrow 0$. Presently it remains unclear how the model used here incorporates all the essential physical behaviour of high-T_c-superconductors. However, note there is no discouraging discrepancy with experiments.

Finally, we discuss briefly the interplay of spin-fluctuation induced superconductivity and electron-phonon coupling. Upon adding the electron-phonon interaction H_{eph} to the hamiltonian we apply Eliashberg type theory within the one-band Hubbard model-hamiltonian. The spin-fluctuation pairing potential is given by [21]

$$V_s(\mathbf{q},\omega) = g_s^2 \chi(\mathbf{q},\omega) \tag{17}$$

and the pairing potential due to phonons by

$$V_{ep}(\mathbf{q},\omega) = \frac{1}{N_Z} \sum_{q_Z,\lambda} g_\lambda^2(\mathbf{q},q_Z) \frac{2\omega_{q,q_z\lambda}}{(\omega)^2 - \omega^2_{q,q_z,\lambda}}. \tag{18}$$

Here, $\mathbf{q}$ lies in the CuO_2 planes, q_z is $\perp$ to the planes, $\omega_{q,q_z,\lambda}$ are phonon frequencies, $\lambda =$ polarization and g_λ is the coupling constant.

In Fig. 39 results are given for the gap in the D.O.S. $\rho(\omega)$ showing that the electron-phonon coupling reduces the spin-fluctuation induced superconductivity. This results from the unfavourable enhancement of the quasi-particle scattering by the phonons [21].

Yet we find that $d_{x^2-y^2}$ symmetry superconductivity persists in the presence of electron-phonon coupling. From a detailed analysis we find that all phonon modes (of a YBCO

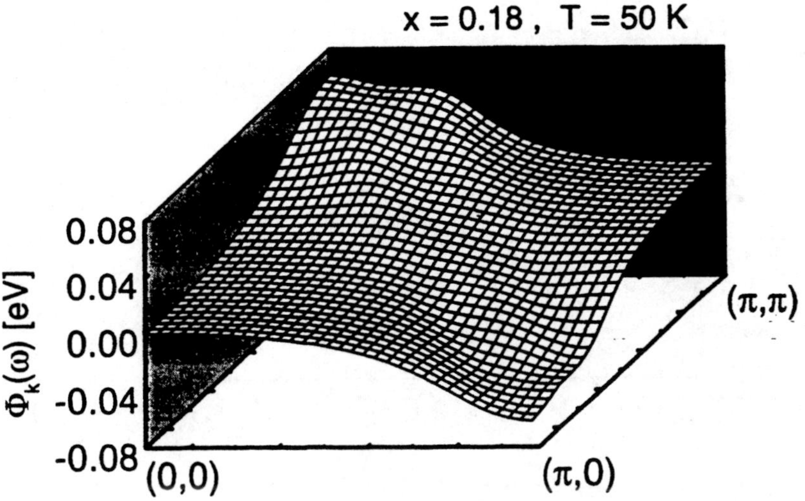

FIG. 38. $d_{x^2-y^2}$-symmetry of the gap function $\phi(\mathbf{k},\omega)$ below $T_c \simeq 70K$ for the 3-band Hubbard-hamiltonian. $\phi(\mathbf{k},0)$ vanishes along the B.Z. diagonal and changes sign for $k_x \leftrightarrow k_y$.

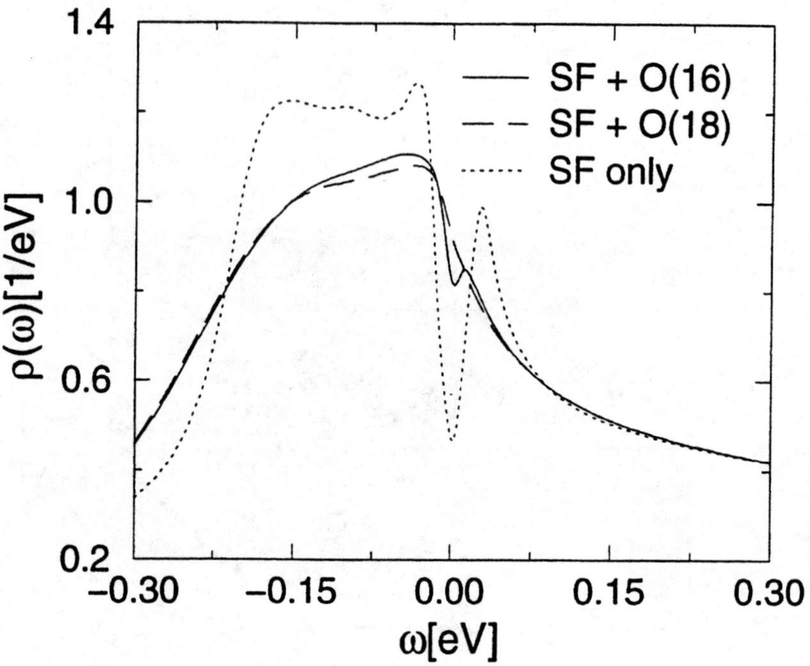

FIG. 39. Effect of electron-phonon coupling on the spin-fluctuation induced gap function. $\rho(\omega)$ is the momentum averaged density of states at $T = 77K$ ($T_c \simeq 82K$) for YBCO-like superconductor with oxygen isotopes O(16) and O(18). S.F. only denotes the behaviour without electron-phonon coupling and exhibits the largest gap.

system) contribute to an attractive pairing potential $V(1,0;\omega)$ for n.n. sites, thus stabilizing d-wave symmetry superconductivity. However, the on-site interaction $V(0,0;\omega)$ due to phonons causes an enhancement of the quasi-particle scattering rates. As a result then the gap function $\phi(\mathbf{k},\omega)$ is decreased due to phonons. The oxygen atoms in the CuO_2-planes couple strongly to the quasi-particles. For the out of plane buckling mode of these O-atoms one has $g_{ep}(\mathbf{q}) \sim (\cos q_x + \cos q_y)$ and for the breathing mode $g_{ep}(\mathbf{q}) \sim (\sin q_x + \sin q_y)$. Obviously, the latter reduces spin-fluctuation induced superconductivity, while the stronger coupling buckling mode supports this.

One expects that the isotope effect depends on whether the potential $V(1,0;\omega)$ outweights the effects due to $V(0,0;\omega)$. We find ($\lambda_{ep} \simeq 0.4$) that the isotope exponent

$$\alpha = -\frac{\partial \ell n T_c}{\partial \ell n m} \approx -\frac{\Delta T_c}{T_c}\frac{m}{\Delta m} \tag{19}$$

is given by $\alpha \approx 0.2$ for optimally doped YBCO with $T_c \simeq 80K$ and for the oxygen isotopes O(16) and O(18). This is observed. As a function of the spin-fluctuation pairing potential or λ_s, respectively, one gets a small α, $\alpha \gtrsim 0$, and that α increases as λ_s decreases, s. Fig. 40. It needs further analysis to see that this explains the increase of α observed away from optimal doping for both over- and underdoped superconductors [21].

III. SUMMARY

The properties of highly correlated high-T_c-superconductors have been analyzed using for an unifying treatment the one-band Hubbard-hamiltonian as a model. In fair agreement with experiments the normal- and superconducting state properties of the low-energy elementary-excitations have been derived. In particular the doping dependence of characteristic temperatures like T^*, T_c^* and T_c has been determined. For large doping x one gets conventional Fermi-liquid behaviour, while for lower doping marginal- and non Fermi-liquid behaviour occurs. In the temperature range T such that $T_c < T < T_c^*$ a superconducting state consisting of phase-disordered Cooper-pairs exists. One gets $\Delta(\mathbf{k},\omega) > 0$ for $\mathbf{k} \simeq (\pi, 0)$

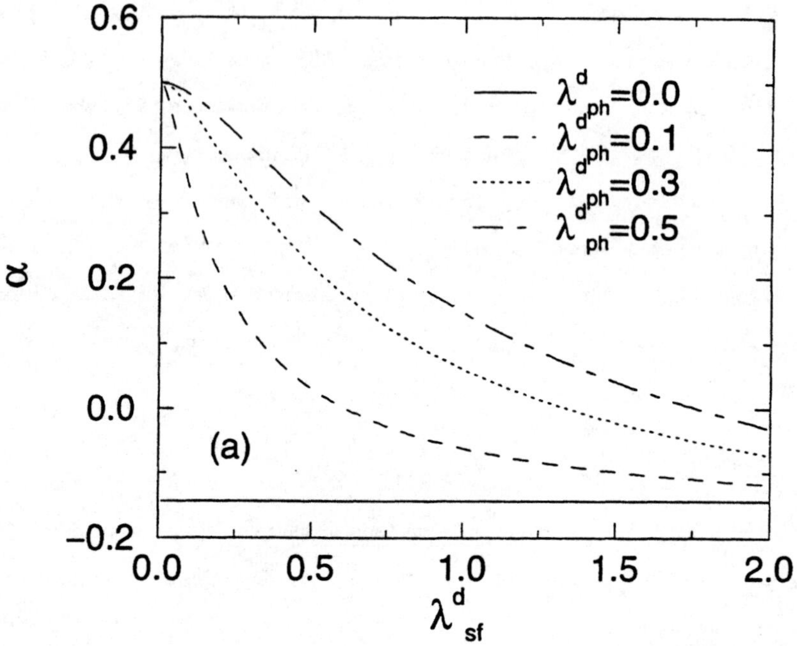

FIG. 40. Dependence of the isotope coefficient α on the spin-fluctuation coupling strength λ_{sf} for different electron-phonon coupling strength λ_{ph}.

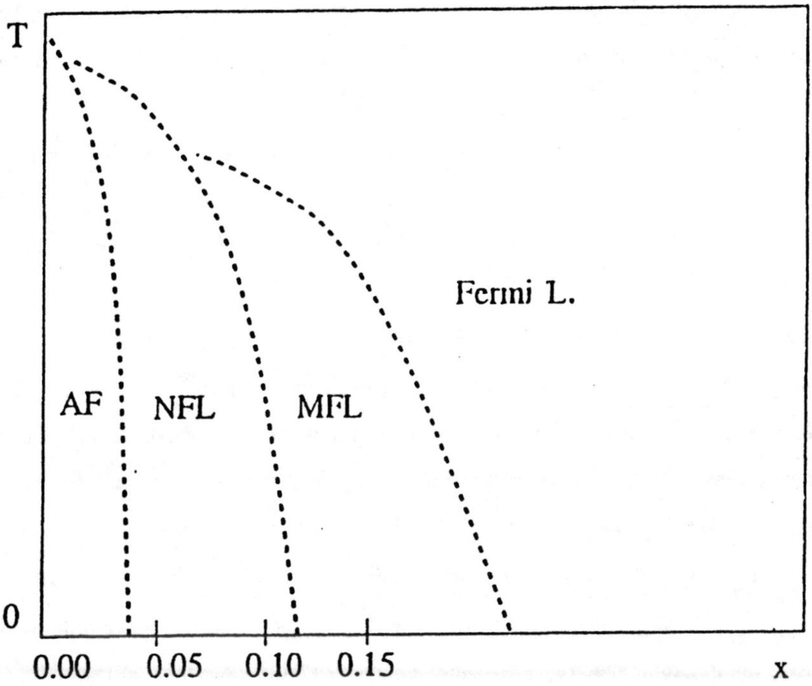

FIG. 41. Illustration of Fermi-liquid (F.L.), marginal (M.F.L.) and non-Fermi-liquid (NFL) behaviour within FLEX-type theory as a function of T and x.

and $\omega > 0$ due to the dynamics of the Cooper-pairs. Further analysis is needed to see this reflected in the spectral density. A theory is necessary treating on the same footing both amplitude and phase-fluctuations of the Cooper-pairs as has been done for ferromagnetism in transition-metals by Hubbard, Hasegawa et al. [25].

The theory presented here needs to be extended to include the formation of local magnetic moments, their short-range order and to treat better the oncoming anti-ferromagnetism for doping $x \to 0$. Also the analysis must be extended to the 3 band Hubbard hamiltionian to describe better the electronic structure , the specific behaviour of the elementary excitations at oxygen- and copper-sites, spin-singulett behaviour, Knight-shift, T_1, etc. results. For $x \to 0$, in particular charge-fluctuations at O-sites might be important.

Presently, the theory has model character and one must better understand how realistic the model is. Nevertheless, it is particularly remarkable that spin-fluctuation induced $d_{x^2-y^2}$-symmetry superconductivity is derived for the high-T_c-superconductors, an optimal superconducting transition temperature T_c due to the interplay of quasi-particle and Cooper-pair dynamics, different behaviour for overdoped and underdoped superconductors and generally structure in the electronic spectral density in fair agreement with experiments. In view of the Fermi-surface topology and frequent transitions $\mathbf{k} \leftrightarrow \mathbf{k} + \mathbf{Q}$ it is natural to include pairing contributions $\langle c^+_{k+Q} c^+_{-k} \rangle$ etc. in the analysis. This corresponds to superconductivity in the presence of a current with Cooper-pair amplitudes $\langle c^+_{-k} c^+_{k'} \rangle$, etc.

Finally, in Fig. 41 we characterize illustratively in the (T, x)-plane the Fermi-liquid (F.L.), marginal (MFL) and non-Fermi-liquid (NFL) behaviour of the high-T_c-superconductors.

In summary, using an effective FLEX-like theory we have obtained many properties of the high-T_c-superconductors in fair agreement with experiment, at least qualitatively. The origin of the pseudogaps above T_c and the role played here by spin-density- and charge-density waves remain unclear. The theory does not properly account for the occurence of gaps at the Fermi-surface. The calculated superconducting gaps are dependent on x of the order of 20 - 60 meV and the magnetic gaps are of the order of 60 - 200 meV (as suggested by the dispersons, for example). Extensions of FLEX and the quasi-static approximation ($T \gg \omega_{sf}$) are necessary to determine $\omega_{sf}(T,x)$ and $\Delta(\mathbf{k},\omega)$, in particular in the range $T_c^* > T > T_c$, the quasi-particle dispersions (at $\mathbf{k} \simeq \mathbf{k}_F$), and the role played by magnetic moments μ_s and their short-range order for $T \to 0$ and $x \to 0$. The latter, for example, could strongly affect ω_{sf} for $T \to 0$.

To understand more reliably the differences between LSCO, YBCO and BSSCO etc. compounds the different dispersions and Fermi-surface topologies have to be included more carefully.

We are grateful for many discussions and for providing us with results to M. Langer and S. Grabowski. M. Avignon and B.K. Chakraverty helped us to get a better understanding of the significance of magnetic effects and phase-fluctuations of the order parameter, respectively, in underdoped high-T_c superconductors.

APPENDIX A: THE SPECTRAL DENSITY AND THE QUASI-STATIC APPROXIMATION

To determine the electronic structure in the underdoped high-T_c-superconductors one must include as correctly as possible the spin-excitations and the building up of the a.f. gap in the spectral density $\rho(\mathbf{k},\omega)$ and in the density of states $N(0)$. As $T \to 0$ and $x \to 0$ local magnetic moments $\mu_s(x,T)$ form and short range a.f. order builds up. This affects in particular $\rho(\mathbf{k}_F,\omega)$ at $\mathbf{k}_F \simeq (\pi,0)$, $N(0)$, the quasi-particle lifetime $\tau^{-1} = -Im\sum(\mathbf{k},\omega)$, etc. The spin-fluctuation energy $\hbar\omega_s$ at which $Im\chi_s(\mathbf{q},\omega)$ peaks and which is expected to behave as $\omega_s \to 0$ for $x \to 0$ acts like a molecular field on the quasi-particles if $\omega_s \ll \omega \sim T$. This reduces then $N(0)$ and tends to form a pseudogap at the Fermi-surface.

First, we analyze FLEX. According to Fig. 1 the Green's function for the quasi-particles in the effective one-band Hubbard-hamiltonian [6,7] are given by

$$G(i\omega_n) = G^0(i\omega_n) + G^0(i\omega_n)\Sigma(i\omega_n)G(i\omega_n), \tag{A1}$$

with

$$G^0(\mathbf{k}, i\omega_n) = (i\omega_n - \varepsilon_k + \mu)^{-1}. \tag{A2}$$

The self-energy is given by

$$\Sigma(i\omega_n) = \frac{T}{N}\sum_m V(\omega_n - \omega_m)G(i\omega_m). \tag{A3}$$

Here,

$$V = \frac{1}{2}UU_{eff}(\chi_c + 3\chi_S - 2\chi) + \cdots, \tag{A4}$$

where χ_c is the charge density-susceptibility and χ_s the spin-susceptibility. Further, it is $\chi = \frac{T}{N}\sum_M G(\omega_n+\omega_m)G(\omega_m)$. U_{eff} approximates vertex corrections [22].In RPA like theory one gets $\chi_c = \chi/(1+U\chi)$ and $\chi_s = \chi/(1-U\chi)$. We find for overdoped superconductors ($x \gtrsim 0,12$) that χ_c is less important than χ_s, but gets increasingly more important as doping

$x \to 0$. V should also include particle-particle scattering. As $x \to 0$, interlayer coupling of the CuO_2-planes has to be included. G and the self-energy Σ are self-consistently determined (with regards to $\Sigma(\omega)$) on the real frequency axis using $i\omega_n \to \omega + i\delta$. [6,7,13] Thus, after Fourier-transformation one gets

$$G(\mathbf{k},\omega) = (\omega - \varepsilon_k + \mu - (\Sigma\mathbf{k},\omega))^{-1} \tag{A5}$$

and

$$\Sigma(\mathbf{k},\omega_n) = \frac{T}{N}\sum_{\mathbf{k}',m} V(\mathbf{k}',\omega_m)G(\mathbf{k}-\mathbf{k}', i\omega_n - i\omega_m). \tag{A6}$$

This can be evaluated using Schmalian et al. procedure [6,7,13] or by usual contour integration [14]. In the latter case one has

$$\Sigma(\mathbf{k},\omega+i\delta) = -\frac{1}{\pi}\int\frac{d^nk'}{(2\pi)^n}\int_{-\infty}^{\infty}\frac{d\omega'}{2\pi}\int_{-\infty}^{\infty}d\varepsilon(\tanh\frac{\varepsilon}{2T}+\coth\frac{\omega'}{2T})\cdot$$
$$\cdot\frac{ImG_R(\mathbf{k}',\varepsilon)ImV(\mathbf{k}-\mathbf{k}',\omega')}{\omega'+\varepsilon-\omega-i\delta}. \tag{A7}$$

Here, $n = 2$ if the a.f. correlation-length $\xi(T,x)$ is smaller than the CuO_2 interlayer distance, otherwise $n = 3$. Since the spectral density is given by $\rho(\mathbf{k},\varepsilon) = (-1/\pi)ImG_R(\mathbf{k},\varepsilon)$ one may write

$$\Sigma(\mathbf{k},\omega+i\delta) = \int\frac{d^nk'}{(2\pi)^n}\int\frac{d\omega'}{2\pi}\int d\varepsilon(\tanh\frac{\varepsilon}{2T}+\coth\frac{\omega'}{2T})$$
$$\cdot\frac{\rho(\mathbf{k}',\varepsilon)ImV(\mathbf{k}-\mathbf{k}',\omega')}{\omega'-\omega+\varepsilon-i\delta}. \tag{A8}$$

Regarding now the contribution due to χ_s, we note that $Im\chi_s$ peaks at $\omega_s \simeq 0$ for $x \to 0$. Then,

$$\Sigma(\mathbf{k},\omega+i\delta) \simeq UU_{eff}\int\frac{d^nk'}{(2\pi)^n}\int\frac{d\omega'}{2\pi}\int d\varepsilon(\tanh\frac{\varepsilon}{2T}+\coth\frac{\omega'}{2T})$$
$$\cdot\frac{\rho(\mathbf{k}',\varepsilon)Im\chi_s(\mathbf{k}-\mathbf{k}',\omega')}{\varepsilon-\omega-i\delta}+\cdots \tag{A9}$$

which is called the quasi-static approximation [6,14]. Furthermore, for an analytical evaluation one may approximate $\chi_s(\mathbf{q},\omega)$ by the Ornstein-Zernike like expression, s. Pines et al. [1] and Vilk et al. [6], for example. Then, one has for the spin-susceptibility

$$\chi_s(\mathbf{q},\omega) \simeq \frac{\chi_0(\mathbf{q},0)}{1+(\mathbf{q}-\mathbf{Q})^2\xi^2 - i\frac{\omega}{\omega_s}}, \qquad \text{(A10)}$$

which peaks at $\mathbf{q} \simeq \mathbf{q} = (\pi,\pi)$ and for $\omega \simeq \omega_s$, ($\omega_s \propto \xi^{-2}$ and $\chi_0(Q,0) \sim \xi^2$, s. Pines et al.) Note, the results shown in Fig. 20 of our self-consistent calculation for $Im\chi_s(\mathbf{q},\omega)$ are in fair accordance with the Ornstein-Zernike form. However, without including spin correlations, μ_s and their short-range a.f. order in our calculation one gets not the correct behaviour of ω_s as $x \to 0$. Hence, within simple FLEX yielding not the essential contribution to $\Sigma(\omega)$ for $\omega' < \omega$ one gets that $\rho(\mathbf{k},\omega)$ does not open up a gap for $\mathbf{k} \simeq (\pi,0)$ at the F.S., for example. To get this, one may model χ_s such that a self-consistent solution of Eq. (A10) yields the observed $\rho(\mathbf{k},\varepsilon)$. Thus, the occurence of molecular fields is guaranteed.

Using then the Ornstein-Zernike approximation for $\chi_s(\mathbf{q},\omega)$ one may evaluate the self-energy $\Sigma(\mathbf{k},\omega)$ analytically [6,14]. With $\mathbf{k}-\mathbf{k}' = \mathbf{q}$ we have for the quasi-particles

$$\Sigma(\mathbf{k},\omega+i\delta) \simeq UU_{eff}\int\frac{d^nq}{(2\pi)^n}\int_{-\infty}^{\infty}\frac{d\omega'}{2\pi}\int_{-\infty}^{\infty}d\varepsilon(\tanh\frac{\varepsilon}{2T}+\coth\frac{\omega'}{2T}) \cdot \frac{\rho(\mathbf{k}+\mathbf{q},\varepsilon)Im\chi_s(\mathbf{q},\omega')}{\varepsilon-\omega-i\delta}+\cdots. \qquad \text{(A11)}$$

Using Eq. (A10) the lifetimes of the elementary excitations are given by

$$Im\Sigma(\mathbf{k},\omega) \simeq UU_{eff}\int\frac{d^nq}{(2\pi)^n}\int_{-\infty}^{\infty}\frac{d\omega'}{2\pi}(\coth\frac{\omega'}{2T}-\tanh\frac{\omega'-\omega}{2T})Im\chi_s(\mathbf{q},\omega')\rho(\mathbf{k}+\mathbf{q},\omega-\omega'). \qquad \text{(A12)}$$

This is straightforwardly evaluated using for $\chi_s(q,\omega)$ the Ornstein-Zernike expression and $\omega' \sim \omega_s$ and $\mathbf{q} \approx \mathbf{q}$. The quasi-static approximation uses $\rho(\mathbf{k}+\mathbf{q},\omega-\omega') \simeq \rho(\mathbf{k}+\mathbf{q},\omega)$. From Eq. (A13) follows using known analysis $\tau^{-1} \propto \omega$ as well as the Fermi-liquid result $\tau^{-1} \propto (\omega^2+\pi^2T^2)$. [14,23] It follows approximately for $\omega \geq T$ that

$$\tau^{-1} \sim \int_0^{\omega} d\omega' Im\chi_s(\mathbf{Q},\omega')\rho(\mathbf{k}+\mathbf{q},0) \sim \omega. \qquad \text{(A13)}$$

For nesting one may use $\varepsilon_{k+Q} \approx -\varepsilon_k$. Then, however, one will not get the observed interesting k-dependence of the pseudogaps.

Also, for $\omega' \sim \omega_s \ll T$ one has $\coth \frac{\omega'}{2T} \simeq 2T/\omega' + \cdots$ and then $\int d\omega' Im\chi_s(\mathbf{q},\omega)/\omega' \rightarrow \chi(q,0)$, which is the static susceptibility ($\chi(\mathbf{q},0) \sim T/(\xi^{-2} + (\mathbf{q}-\mathbf{Q})^2)$), s. Vilk et al. [6]. Thus, within the quasi-static approximation FLEX yields a magnetic pseudogap. This has important consequences for $\rho(\mathbf{k},\omega)$, $N(0,x)$, $\tau^{-1}(x)$, etc. The approximation might underestimate dynamics and thus overestimate the gap which turns out to be of the order of $100 \div 200$ meV. Note, the spectral density follows from

$$\rho(\mathbf{k},\omega) = -Im\Sigma(\mathbf{k},\omega)/([\omega - \epsilon_k + \mu - Re\Sigma]^2 + [Im\Sigma]^2). \tag{A14}$$

The above analysis can be extended to include particle-particle scattering in V and local magnetic moments. Then,

$$\Sigma'_\sigma(\omega) \simeq \frac{U}{2}n - \frac{U}{2}\sigma\mu_s + \Sigma(\omega), \tag{A15}$$

where Σ is the dynamical contribution analyzed above. μ_s is the magnitude of the magnetic moment. [24] The term $\frac{U}{2}n$ can be absorbed as usually in μ. As short-range a.f. order increases one gets in the density of states a gap at the a.f. Brillouin-zone of the order of

$$\delta \sim \alpha U \mu_s. \tag{A16}$$

Here, $\alpha < 1$ due to dynamical effects and $\alpha \rightarrow 1$ as ξ increases. Clearly, $\rho(\mathbf{k},\omega)$ and $\chi_s(\mathbf{q},\omega)$ are affected by the occurence of magnetic moments and short-range a.f. order, s. also previous discussion by Baumgärtel et al. [8] and by Langer [6].

Note, the contribution to the self-energy Σ due to $\chi_c(q,\omega)$ can be determined similarly by using also for χ_c an Ornstein-Zernike expression with a characteristic energy ω_c for the charge-fluctuations. Since the CuO_2-in-plane ω_c is much larger than the interplane ω'_c, the latter one is more important for the interplay of χ_s and χ_c as $x \rightarrow 0$.

Finally, it is important to note that the above analysis may be extended by using the Eliashberg-type theory to treat superconductivity [7,14] .

APPENDIX B: FORMATION OF LOCAL MAGNETIC MOMENTS AND SHORT-RANGE ANTI-FERROMAGNETIC ORDER

The dynamical molecular field theory is suited amongst other methods to describe the formation of magnetic moments [24]. As illustrated in Fig. 1(b) one has for a lattice site i, using the the one-band Hubbard-hamiltonian for simplicity,

$$G_{ii\sigma}(\omega) = (\omega - \sum_j t_{ij}^2 G_{jj,\sigma} - \Sigma'_{i,\sigma}(\omega))^{-1}, \tag{B1}$$

where t_{ij} denotes the nearest neighbor hopping integral and the self-energy is given by [8]

$$\Sigma'_{i,\sigma}(\omega) = \frac{U}{2}n - \frac{U}{2}\sigma\mu_s + U^2\chi^0_{-\sigma}n_\sigma + \Sigma_\sigma(\omega), \tag{B2}$$

and

$$\Sigma'_\sigma(\omega) = UU_{eff}\sum_{\omega'} G_{ii,\sigma}(\omega - \omega')\chi_{-\sigma}(\omega). \tag{B3}$$

For $G_{jj,\sigma}$ one may use an average Green's function or one determined by using the coherent potential approximation (CPA). A self-consistent calculation yields then the magnetic moment

$$\mu_s(x,T) = \int_{-\infty}^{\infty} \frac{d\omega}{\pi} f_\omega Im(G_{ii\uparrow}(\omega) - G_{ii\downarrow}(\omega)). \tag{B4}$$

Here, like the self-energy in FLEX-theory μ_s can be determined as a self-consistent solution of Eq. (B1) - (B4). [24]

For further analysis, one may rewrite $G_{ii,\sigma}$ as

$$G_{ii,\sigma} = (\omega - \varepsilon_{i\sigma} - \sum_j t_{ij}^2 G_{jj,\sigma} - \Sigma_\sigma(\omega))^{-1}, \tag{B5}$$

with

$$\varepsilon_{i\sigma} = \frac{n - \sigma\mu_s}{2}U. \tag{B6}$$

Then, the average Green's function for the paramagnetic state is

$$< G_{ii,\sigma} >= p_A G^A_{ii,\sigma} + p_B G^B_{ii,\sigma}, \tag{B7}$$

where p_A is the probability to find on site i a magnetic moment pointing upward. p_B refers to sites with a magnetic moment pointing downward. Furthermore, for the Green's function of sites of type A, B one has $G^A_{ii,\sigma} = G^B_{ii,-\sigma}$.

To take into account short-range a.f. order, we take

$$G^A_{ii,\sigma} = (\omega - \varepsilon_{A\sigma} - \sum_{j,\alpha} t^2_{ij} G^\alpha_{jj,\sigma})^{-1}, \tag{B8}$$

with

$$\sum_{j,\alpha} t^2_{ij} G^\alpha_{jj,\sigma} = zt^2 (p_{AA} G^A_{ii,\sigma} + p_{AB} G^B_{ii,\sigma}). \tag{B9}$$

Here, z denotes the number of nearest neighbors and p_{AA} is the probability to find a n.n. site of type A when the central site (i) is of type A. Short-range a.f. order can be implemented now by putting $p_{AA} = 0$ and $p_{AB} = 1$. [25].

Note, $G(\mathbf{k}, \omega)$ is related to the Wannier type Green's functions by

$$G_{ii,\sigma}(\omega) = \sum_{\mathbf{k}} G(\mathbf{k}, \omega). \tag{B10}$$

REFERENCES

[1] Z.X. Shen and D.S. Dessau, Phys. Rep. **253**, 1 (1995); E. Dagotto, Rev. Mod. Phys. **66**, 763 (1994); B. Brandow, Phys. Rep., **296**, 1 (1998); A.V. Puchkov, P. Fournier, T. Timusk, and N.N. Kolesnikov, Phys. Rev. Lett.**77**, 1853 (1997); P.A. Lee and Xiao-Gang Wen, Phys. Rev. Lett. **78**, 4111 (1997); R.Nemetschek et al., Phys. Rev. Lett. **78**, 4873 (1997); D. Pines, progress report (University of Illinois, 1997), and Z.f. Physik **103**, 129 (1997); M.R. Norman et al., Nature **392**, 157 (1998).

[2] J. Schmalian, S. Grabowski, and K.H. Bennemann, Phys. Rev. B **56**, 1 (1997).

[3] M. Takigawa et al., Phys. Rev. B **43**, 247 (1991); J. Tranquada et al., Phys. Rev. B **46**, 5561 (1992);

[4] Y. De Wilde et al., Phys. Rev. Lett. **80**, 153 (1998); A.G. Loeser et al., Science **273**, 325 (1996); H. Ding et al., Nature (London) **382**, 51 (1996).

[5] A.V. Puchkov et al., J. Physics: Condensed Matter **8**, 10049 (1996)

[6] M. Langer, thesis FU Berlin (1996); Y.M. Vilk and A.M.S. Tremblay, J. Physics I France **7**, 1309 (1997); Y.M. Vilk and A.M.S. Tremblay, Europhys. Lett. **33**, 159 (1996).

[7] S. Grabowski, thesis FU Berlin (1997); P. Monthoux and D.J. Scalapino, Phys. Rev. Lett. **72**, 1874 (1994); N.E. Bickers, D.J. Scalapino, and S.R. White, Phys. Rev. Lett. **62**, 961 (1989); N.E. Bickers and D.J. Scalapino, Annals of Physics, **193**, 206 (1989); D.J. Scalapino, Phys. Rep. **250**, 329 (1995); T. Dahm and L. Tewordt, Phys. Rev. Lett. **74**, 793 (1995).

[8] M. Avignon and K.H. Bennemann, to be published; s. also G. Baumgärtel, thesis FU Berlin (1993). For observation of a.f. correlations s. P. Dai et al., Phys. Rev. Lett. **77**, 5425 (1996); and S. Petit et al.,to be published.

[9] In view of the small values for n_s one expects phase-fluctuations of the order parameter,

since the distance d between the Cooper-pairs may become larger than their size of the order of the coherence-length ξ. Note, $d^{-3} \sim \rho(0)\Delta/2$. Presently the state above T_c has not been identified experimentally. Note, the role of phase-fluctuations were previously discussed by B.K. Chakraverty, A. Taraphder, and M. Avignon, Physics C **235 - 240**, 2323 (1994); V.J. Emery and S.A. Kivelson, Nature (London) **374**, 434 (1995); and also by S. Grabowski et al., s. Ref. [7].

[10] Y. Uemura et al., Phys. Rev. Lett. **62**, 2317 (1989); Phys. Rev. Lett. **66**, 2665 (1991); Ch. Niedermayer et al., Phys. Rev. Lett. **71**, 1764 (1993)

[11] S. Grabowski et al., Europhys. Lett. **34**, 219 (1996); J. Schmalian et al., Physica B **230** 922 (1997).

[12] Note, presumably simple FLEX overestimates the doping dependence of τ^{-1} as $x \rightarrow 0$, since without correct reduction of $\rho(0)$, the lifetime τ is not decreasing strongly enough, in particular $\rho(\mathbf{k}, \omega = 0)$ for $\mathbf{k} \approx (\pi, 0)$.

[13] Here, we use for $i\omega_n \rightarrow \omega$ the treatment discussed by Schmalian et al., Comp. Phys. Comm. **93**, 141 (1996), s. also M. Langer, thesis FU Berlin (1996).

[14] A.A. Abrikosov, L.P. Gorkov, I.E. Dzyaloshinskii, Quantum Field Theory in Statistical Physics, Prentice Hall, (1963).

[15] Approximately, the dynamics of n.n. CuO_2-planes in the YBCO and BSCCO compounds is characterized by $\omega_c' \gtrsim 0$ and decreasing ω_c' for $x \rightarrow 0$.

[16] The charge-fluctuations might weaken the a.f. coupling between the neighboring CuO_2-planes.

[17] H.Y. Hwang et al., Phys. Rev. Lett. **72**, 2636 (1994); B. Batlogg et al., Physica C **235 - 240**, 130 (1994).

[18] Of course, this result can be derived analytically by using for $\chi_s(\mathbf{q}, \omega)$ the Ornstein-

Zernike like expression $\chi_s(\mathbf{q},\omega) = \chi_s(Q,0)/[1+(\mathbf{q}-\mathbf{Q})^2\xi^2 - i\omega/\omega_s]$, where ξ is the a.f. correlation length. Note, our expression for χ_s using Flex is of similar form. Eq. (13) for τ^{-1} follows also, for example, if the quasi-static approximation is used, see Y.M. Vilk and A.M.S. Tremblay, cond.-mat. 9702188 (20.02.1997); B.P. Stojkovic and D. Pines, Phys. Rev. B **55**, 8576 (1996).

[19] J. Schmalian, F. Schäfer and K.H. Bennemann, Phys. Rev. B (1998); F. Schäfer, Diploma-thesis, FU Berlin (1997).

[20] N.E. Bickers et al., Phys. Rev. Lett. **62**, 961 (1989); J. Luo and N.E. Bickers, Phys. Rev. B **47**, 12153 (1993).

[21] T. Nunner, J. Schmalian and K.H. Bennemann, to be published (1998); T. Nunner, Diploma-thesis, FU (1997).

[22] Note, $\chi_s(\mathbf{q},\omega)$ must fullfill the conditions $\chi_s(\mathbf{q},\omega \neq 0) \rightarrow 0$, as $q \rightarrow 0$, and $(T/N)\sum_{\mathbf{q}} \chi_s(\mathbf{q}) = n - 2 < n_\uparrow, n_\downarrow >$, s. Vilk et al., in Ref. [6]. An elegant way to implement these as well as other sum rules may be the use of a Lagrange formalism with corresponding Lagrange multipliers like in Slave-Boson type theories.

[23] A. Virosztek and J. Ruvalds, Phys. Rev. B **42**, 4064 (1990).

[24] P. Lombardo, M. Avignon, J. Schmalian and K.H. Bennemann, Phys. Rev. B **54**, 5317 (1996).

[25] J.L. Morán-López, M. Avignon and K.H. Bennemann, Phys. Rev. B **23**, 5978 (1981).

Studies of High Temperature
Superconductors
Volume 27

ISBN 1-56072-684-9

DOPING DEPENDENCE OF THE PSEUDOGAP IN HIGH TEMPERATURE SUPERCONDUCTORS: A RAMAN STUDY

J. C. IRWIN, J. G. NAEINI AND X. K. CHEN

Physics Department
Simon Fraser University
Burnaby, British Columbia, Canada V5A 1S6

1. INTRODUCTION

Since the discovery [1] of superconductivity in Barium doped Lantanum cuprate in 1986 an intense research effort has been expended in an attempt to identify the mechanism responsible for superconductivity in High Temperature Superconductors (HTS). Much of this research involved experiments designed to identify the symmetry of the order parameter since it was thought that this knowledge would provide important and informative constraints for possible theoretical models. However, the pairing mechanism remains controversial, despite the fact that it is now generally accepted [2] that the order parameter has d-wave type symmetry in those materials whose critical temperatures are near their maximum or optimum value. In part, this is because the physical properties of the hole-doped cuprates are strongly dependent on the doping level or hole concentration in the CuO_2 planes. In contrast to the situation for optimally doped compounds, an experimental consensus is completely lacking in overdoped and underdoped compounds. To clarify this situation, a great deal of recent work has involved studies of the doping dependence of the physical properties of HTS in both the normal and superconducting states. However rather than clarifying the situation these experiments have produced additional disagreements and revealed strong deviations from normal Fermi liquid behaviour. It now appears [3-5] that the electronic properties of the underdoped state are heavily influenced by the presence of a pseudogap that opens at temperatures well above the superconducting critical temperature T_c in these materials. The origin of this pseudogap is unclear, with opinion divided between those who associate it with precursor pairing and others who believe that it arises from a competing mechanism, such as short range antiferromagnetic correlations. It is, however, generally agreed that an understanding of the normal state properties will provide important clues that will assist, and may even be essential, in reaching a complete understanding of the superconducting state.

In this article we will give a cursory review of some of the experimental work that has led to the realization that a pseudogap state plays an important role in determining the electronic properties of underdoped cuprates. We will also list a few of the theoretical models that have been proposed in an attempt to explain the physical origin of the pseudogap. The primary aim of this paper is, however, to present a discussion of the Raman scattering technique and its relevance to investigations of the normal state electronic properties of the cuprates. We will thus first outline the basic capabilities of the Raman technique with an emphasis on those aspects that make it a powerful tool for studies of the high-T_c cuprates. We will then review the results of experiments we have carried out in an attempt to gain insight into the electronic excitations of the cuprates in both the normal and superconducting states. Most of our experiments have been carried out on $YBa_2Cu_3O_y$ (YBCO) and $La_{2-x}Sr_xCuO_4$ (LSCO) in the overdoped, optimally doped and underdoped regimes. The Raman technique allows one to obtain spectra from selected regions of the Brillouin zone and thus obtain direct information on the symmetry of the superconducting gap and its dependence on doping. Similarily the influence of the pseudogap on different parts of the Fermi surface can be studied as a function of both doping and temperature. These studies have led to a detailed picture of the influence of doping on the electronic Raman spectra of the cuprates. In spectra obtained from underdoped materials the pseudogap appears to manifest itself primarily by a depletion of spectral weight from regions of the Fermi surface located near the axes in reciprocal space. Our results and interpretation will be compared to the very different results and interpretations obtained by other groups and by other techniques. We will attempt to reconcile these different points of view and, although we are not able to provide a consensus summary, we will point out those areas in which some common ground has been achieved experimentally.

2. THE PSEUDOGAP

2.1. Experimental Evidence

It has been recognized for some time that the normal state electronic properties of the HTS are very different from those of a conventional Fermi liquid. For example in optimally doped compounds the unusual nature of these properties is manifested in transport measurements [6,7] by a resistivity that varies linearly with temperature over a large temperature region. Also Raman spectra obtained from the cuprates [8-10] are characterized by a relatively featureless continuum that extends to large energies (> 1 eV). The existence of this electronic continuum appears to violate selection rules based on the conservation of crystal momentum and energy, which restrict the electronic scattering in normal metals to much lower energies ($\omega \leq qv_F \approx 50cm^{-1}$). More recent studies [11-47] of the normal state, have revealed even more striking deviations from normal Fermi liquid behavior. Much of this behavior appears to be associated with the presence of a pseudogap [3], a term that is generally used to mean a suppression of low energy spectral weight. Many experiments on underdoped compounds have provided evidence for a strong quasiparticle renormalization, or spectral weight depletion that appears at relatively high temperatures ($T^* > T_c$). For example anomalies in the temperature dependence of scattering rates have been observed in NMR [11-18], Infrared reflectivity (IR) [19-21], and transport experiments [22-24] on underdoped and even slightly overdoped compounds. A strong quasiparticle renormalization at $T^* > T_c$ was suggested by all these experiments. More direct evidence of a depletion of spectral weight in underdoped compounds was obtained from normal state specific heat measurements [25-28] on YBCO, LSCO and more recently Ca doped YBCO.

In our electronic Raman scattering experiments on underdoped YBCO and LSCO we have found [29-31] that decreasing the hole concentration below optimum leads to a significant depletion of low energy spectral weight in the B_{1g} channel. This means that in underdoped compounds, spectral weight is missing from regions of the Fermi surface located near the axes in k-space. In LSCO, the scattered intensity at low energies decreases [31] by about a factor of fifteen as the hole concentration is decreased from $p_{opt} \sim 0.16$ to $p \sim 0.10$. This dramatic change in the measured intensities implies a significant depletion of the Fermi surface (FS) in underdoped compounds. This loss of spectral weight from regions of the Fermi surface located near $(\pi,0)$, which is also observed using other techniques [3], is associated with the presence of a pseudogap (PG). The low energy portions ($\omega < 500cm^{-1}$) of the B_{1g} spectra are approximately independent of temperature in both LSCO and YBCO [29-31]. This is in direct contrast to the strong renormalization of the B_{1g} spectrum that occurs at T_c in optimally doped compounds. The invariance of the of B_{1g} spectrum in passing through the superconducting state constitutes further evidence of the existence of a normal state gap in underdoped compounds.

In Raman experiments carried out on underdoped $Bi_2Sr_2CaCu_2O_{8+\delta}$ (BSCCO) and YBCO [32,33], Nemetschek et al. have also found that the B_{1g} spectra are essentially independent of temperature (T < 300K) and focussed their attention on the B_{2g} channel. In underdoped samples they found that, as the temperature was reduced below T = 250K, a loss of spectral weight occurred in the B_{2g} spectra [32,33] for energies $\omega \leq 750cm^{-1}$. In this case the loss of spectral weight is from regions of the Fermi surface located near $(\pi,\pi)/2$. The loss is also relatively small in that the integrated depletion at low temperatures is about 10% of the total spectral weight. The observed redistribution of spectral weight has been attributed to a pseudogap and the authors have thus concluded that the energy scales of the superconducting gap ($\Delta_m \approx 250cm^{-1}$) and pseudogap ($E_g \approx 750cm^{-1}$) are different. They also found that the dependence of B_{2g} intensity on frequency at low energies, and for $T > T_c$, was incompatible with the presence of nodes near $(\pi,\pi)/2$. On this basis, they concluded that the pseudogap cannot have d-wave symmetry.

In other Raman experiments carried out on underdoped BSCCO the normal state B_{1g} continuum was observed to weaken gradually with temperature [34-37]. It has been suggested [36] that the relatively small loss of low energy intensity with decreasing temperature is associated with a deepening of the PG. Blumberg et al. [34,35] used long-wavelength excitation to discriminate against phonons and found a peak in the B_{1g} spectrum of BSCCO at about 75meV. They concluded that this peak is associated with a quasiparticle bound state. That is, they believe that this peak constitutes evidence of precursor pairing of the doped holes. However, in experiments carried out on cation substituted BSCCO, Kendziora [37] was unable to detect a mode at $600cm^{-1}$. He also noted, in agreement with other experiments [29,31,32], that a pair-breaking, or 2Δ, peak was not formed in B_{1g} spectra obtained from underdoped compounds.

The most detailed characterization of the pseudogap appear to be provided by Angle Resolved Photoemission Spectroscopy (ARPES). In these experiments [38-47] the leading edge shift of the signal, relative to the Fermi energy is associated with the energy of the gap. It is found to have a maximum value in directions parallel to the axes in reciprocal space, that is in regions of the Brillouin zone (BZ) located near $(\pm\pi,0)$ and $(0,\pm\pi)$. The leading edge shift has been found [40] to decrease to zero as one moves toward the diagonal directions in k-space in a manner that is consistent with d-wave type symmetry. Along the (1,0) directions the pseudogap is found [43] to open at a temperature $T^* > T_c$ and increase in magnitude as the temperature is reduced. It reaches a value E_g that is approximately equal to $\Delta(\mathbf{k})$; the magnitude of the superconducting gap. Recently Norman et al. [44] have suggested that the angular extent of the pseudogap also grows with decreasing temperature such that when $T < T_c$ the Fermi contour is reduced to a point , or gapless node in k-space.

In ARPES results obtained from the $(\pi,0)$ regions of underdoped BSCCO the leading edge shift remains unchanged [39,42,43] as the sample is warmed through T_c, which suggests that the superconducting gap evolves smoothly into the pseudogap. Harris et al. [40] also found that the energy of the gap increased slightly as the doping level is decreased. Similar results have been obtained from tunneling measurements [48,49] on BSCCO. In summary ARPES experiments on BSCCO find that the pseudogap has d-wave symmetry and the same energy as the superconducting gap, thus suggesting that the pseudogap arises from precursor pairing.

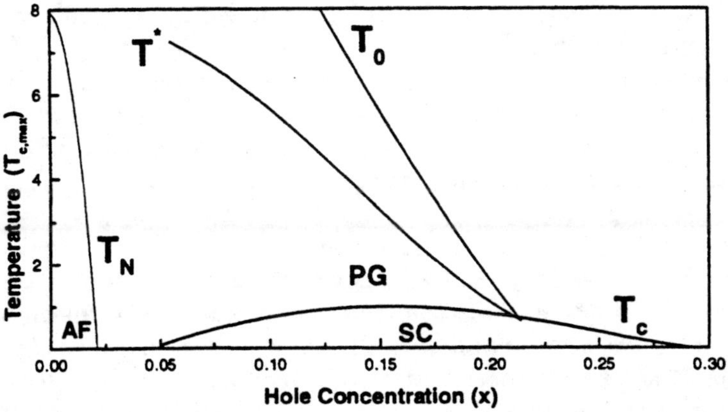

Figure 1. A schematic phase diagram indicating the phase boundaries and crossover temperatures that have been proposed [3].

The results of some of the above experiments have been summarized [3] in the form of a phase diagram (Fig. 1) in which the pseudogap onset temperature T^* decreases with increasing doping and becomes equal to T_c for optimally or slightly overdoped compounds. In addition (as indicated in Fig. 1) some experiments [3] have provided evidence of a crossover temperature at which the temperature dependence of the nuclear relaxation rates or Knight shift undergoes a change in slope. Not all compounds appear to exhibit this type of behaviour, however, and the origin of such crossovers is not well understood.

2.2. Theoretical Models

Despite the extensive experimental effort that has been expended the physical origin of the pseudogap remains controversial. Many models have been proposed in an attempt to identify the nature of the physical mechanisms that will provide an appropriate description of the pseudogap. The different approaches can be roughly separated into two categories as outlined by Maly et al. [50]. In the first group there are several models [50] based on the idea of preformed pairs, that is models in which the pseudogap develops as a precursor to superconductivity and thus the pseudogap should evolve continuously into the superconducting gap $\Delta(\mathbf{k})$. In this category Emery and Kivelson [51,52] have proposed that a microscopic phase separation into hole rich stripes separated by hole-deficient antiferromagnetically ordered regions occurs at a crossover temperature T_0. Incoherent pairing correlations are established at a lower crossover temperature T^* (pseudogap onset) in association with a spin gap in the antiferromagnetic stripes. As the temperature is lowered further to T_c Josephson coupling between the metallic stripes becomes large enough to produce global coherence and superconductivity.

Randeria et al. [4,53], in a somewhat more direct approach, have used the attractive Hubbard model to demonstrate that pairing can take place at $T^* \sim U$, where U is the Hubbard potential, with phase coherence occuring at a lower temperature T_c that depends on the hopping parameter t and U.

The second group [50] of theories involve magnetic-pairing scenarios in which the properties of the PG are not related to those of the superconducting gap. Pines and coworkers [54-60] have developed a nearly antiferromagnetic Fermi liquid (NAFL) model in which a tendency to order antiferromagnetically competes for the available quasiparticles with a spin fluctuation mediated pairing mechanism. The NAFL is characterized by a very anisotropic scattering rate since regions of the Fermi surface connected by the antiferromagnetic (AFM) ordering vector $\mathbf{Q} \approx (\pi,\pi)$ can be very strongly affected. This condition is approximately satisfied (Fig. 2) for regions of the Fermi surface located near the axes in k-space [which we will designate as $(\pi,0)$] and quasiparticles on these regions are termed "hot". In comparison quasiparticles on regions of the Fermi surface centered near the diagonal directions (π,π) are weakly scattered and are termed "cold". From comparisons with NMR and transport measurements Pines and coworkers [54-60] have developed a phase diagram in terms of the variation of the AFM correlation length ξ with temperature and doping. They define a crossover temperature T_{cr}, at which $\xi = 2a$, that separates a mean-field region ($T > T_{cr}$) from an interval ($T_c > T > T^*$) in which magnetic pseudoscaling prevails and ξ increases rapidly with decreasing temperature. At $T^* > T_c$ they predict another crossover to the pseudogap regime in which ξ is approximately constant. Their model leads to a phase diagram similar to that shown in Fig. 1 with $T_o \equiv T_{cr}$. In a similar vein Chubukov et al. [61] have examined the evolution of the FS as a function of the coupling strength between a two dimensional Fermi liquid and low energy spin fluctuations. For large coupling, or small doping levels, they find that the Fermi surface reduces to small pockets centered at $(\pi,\pi)/2$ with the spectral weight concentrated on pieces of the pockets that face the origin of the BZ.

Other theories in this second category involve "spin-charge separation" into charge neutral spinons, and charged, spinless holons [62]. Onset of the PG is associated with the formation of spinons at T^* and superconductivity with the condensation of holons at T_c. Finally it has been suggested [63] that interlayer coupling is responsible for the pseudogap in bilayer materials and that the crossover temperature T^* in LSCO should be approximately equal to T_c [64]. The results presented in this paper can be used to assess this prediction. Although experiment has yet to fully determine the relative merits of the various models that now exist, we believe that our results clearly suggest that the superconducting and pseudogap mechanisms are different.

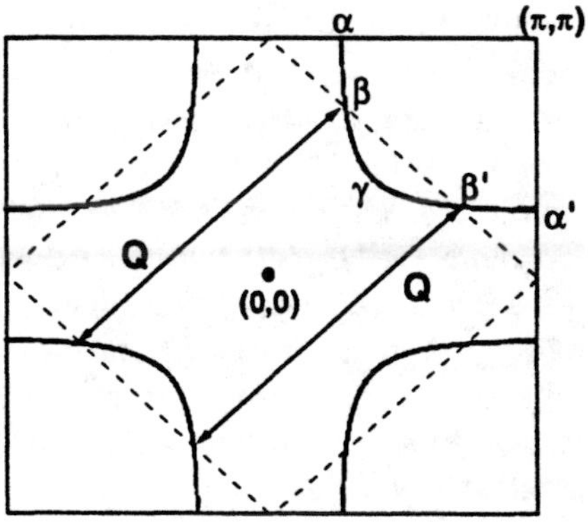

Figure 2. A schematic diagram illustrating the formation of hot spots on the Fermi surface of the cuprates [55].

3. THEORY OF RAMAN SCATTERING

3.1. Raman Cross-Section

The cross-section for the intensity of scattered light is given by [65]

$$\frac{\partial^2\sigma}{\partial\omega\partial\Omega} = r_o^2\, \omega_S/\omega_L\, S(\vec{q},\omega)\,, \tag{1}$$

where r_0 is the Thomson radius, $\omega_L(\omega_S)$ is the frequency of the incident(scattered) light and $S(\bar{q},\omega)$ is the dynamical structure factor. q and ω, are respectively, the momentum and energy transferred in the scattering process. Using the fluctuation-dissipation theorem the structure factor $S(\bar{q},\omega)$ is related to the response function by

$$S(\bar{q},\omega) = [1+n(\omega,T)]\,\chi''(\bar{q},\omega)\,, \tag{2}$$

where $1+n(\omega,T)=\{1-\exp(-\hbar\omega/k_BT)\}^{-1}$ is the Bose Einstein factor and $\chi''(\bar{q},\omega)$ is the imaginary part of the response function.

The normal state electronic Raman spectra of the cuprates are characterised by the presence of a flat, featureless continuum [8-10] that extends from $\omega \approx 0$ to at least $\omega \approx 2$eV. The extension of the electronic continuum to such high energies is very surprising. In good metals the electronic Raman spectrum is normally due to intraband transitions, that is the excitations of quasiparticles with energies near the Fermi energy. Both energy and crystal momentum must be conserved in the scattering process and because of the relatively small wavevector of the incident light ($q < 10^5$ cm^{-1}) the spectrum is limited to energies less than $\omega \sim qv_F \sim 50$ cm^{-1}. In this context the nature of the cuprate continuum is very puzzling and many different explanations have been proposed [9]. Recently, Devereaux and Kampf [66,67] have found that the electronic continuum can be reproduced within the NAFL model. In this approach momentum conservation is provided by spin fluctuations and hence scattering at large energies becomes allowed. However the scattering cross-section cannot be expressed in an analytical form and hence cannot be used to illustrate basic principles. For this purpose we can use an expression derived by Zawadowski and Cardona [68], who studied scattering from an impure metal in the collision limited regime. For scattering in channel L they found

$$\frac{\partial^2\sigma}{\partial\omega\partial\Omega} = \{1+n(\omega,T)\}[\gamma_L(\bar{k})]^2\frac{\omega\Gamma_L}{\omega^2+\Gamma_L^2}\,, \tag{3}$$

where $\gamma(\bar{k})$ is the Raman vertex or tensor and Γ is the scattering rate. Equation 3 provides a good description of the spectrum if one assumes a frequency and temperature dependent scattering rate of the form $\Gamma^2 = \omega^2 + \beta T^2$. Viroztek and Ruvalds [69] derived a very similar expression to (3) using a nested Fermi Liquid model and obtained reasonable agreement with experiment with a frequency and temperature dependent scattering rate.

The first theoretical studies [70] of Raman scattering from superconductors, which were based on the Bardeen-Cooper-Schrieffer (BCS) model, were carried out in the limit of large wavevector (q) transfer. In a metal q

$\approx \delta^{-1}$, where δ is the optical penetration depth and large q means that $\delta < \xi_0$ where ξ_0 is the coherence length. This theory was generalized by Klein and Dierker [65] to deal with the case $\delta > \xi_0$, which is the limit that pertains to HTS. Their calculations were also based on the BCS theory with quasiparticle energies given by $E_k = \{(\varepsilon_k)^2 + \Delta^2\}^{1/2}$. In the limit $q \to 0$ and for T = 0 the unscreened response is given by [65]

$$\chi''(\bar{q},\omega) = S(\bar{q},\omega) \propto \left\langle \frac{(\gamma(\bar{k}))^2(\Delta(\bar{k}))^2}{\omega\sqrt{\omega^2 - 4(\Delta(\bar{k}))^2}} \right\rangle, \tag{4}$$

where $\Delta(\bar{k})$ is the superconducting gap and the triangular brackets imply an average that is carried out over the Fermi surface for k-vectors such that $\omega > 2|\Delta(k)|$. In general the Raman tensor $\gamma(\bar{k})$ is a complex function [65] of the energy levels and eigenstates of the metal and cannot be calculated directly. If however the incident (ω_L) and scattered (ω_S) frequencies are far from resonance with the energy levels in the solid the (SL) component of $\gamma(\bar{k})$ is given approximately by

$$\gamma_{SL}(\bar{k}) = \hat{\varepsilon}_S \bullet \bar{\mu}^{-1} \bullet \hat{\varepsilon}_L = \frac{m}{\hbar^2}\frac{\partial^2 E}{\partial k_S \partial k_L}, \tag{5}$$

where $\bar{\mu}^{-1}$ is the reciprocal of the generalised effective mass tensor and $\hat{\varepsilon}_S$ ($\hat{\varepsilon}_L$) is the polarization of the incident (scattered) light. In the high-T_c cuprates the non-resonance condition is not particularly well obeyed and hence (5) cannot be used to obtain quantitative results. The effective mass approximation can however be used to good effect for the purposes of illustration and is useful in obtaining a qualitative picture.

In underdoped compounds, in the presence of the PG, Loram et al. [28] have suggested that the quasiparticle energies should be written as $E(k)^2 = \varepsilon(k)^2 + \Delta'(k)^2$ where $\Delta'(\bar{k})$ is the total spectral gap in the superconducting state and is given by

$$\Delta'(\bar{k})^2 = \Delta(\bar{k})^2 + E_g(\bar{k})^2. \tag{6}$$

$E_g(k)$ is the normal state gap and, in accord with ARPES experiments [41,42], it is assumed to have the same d-wave symmetry as the superconducting gap (or order parameter) Δ. If we also assume that $E_g(k)$ results from a pairing mechanism, then following Klein and Dierker [65], the unscreened Raman response (4) at T = 0 will be given by

$$\chi''_{SL}(\bar{q},\omega) \propto \left\langle \frac{(\gamma_{SL}(\bar{k}))^2(\Delta(\bar{k})^2 + E_g(\bar{k})^2)}{\omega\sqrt{\omega^2 - 4\{\Delta(\bar{k})^2 + E_g(\bar{k})^2\}}} \right\rangle. \tag{7}$$

In the remainder of this paper we will refer to the above relations (3-7) in the course of interpreting our experimental results. In doing so, we hope to gain some insight into the interactions responsible for the observed phenomena.

3.2. Symmetry Properties of the Raman Tensor

As pointed out above a calculation of the Raman tensor, and hence the Raman spectrum, requires a much more detailed knowledge of the material properties than is generally available. In the absence of such knowledge one can, however, use constraints imposed by symmetry. For example, the symmetry properties of a particular excitation in the crystal can be described by a tensor that transforms as one of the irreducible representations of the crystal point group. In other words the Raman tensor for channel L must have symmetry properties that are dictated by the symmetry of the crystal structure, irrespective of the exact nature of the vertex. A knowledge of the conditions placed on $\gamma_{SL}(\bar{k})$ by the applicable point group symmetry enables one to obtain [71-73] a great deal of useful information from the spectra. To demonstrate this we must first define an appropriate coordinate system. The experiments described in this paper were carried out with the k-vectors of the incident and scattered light travelling parallel to the c-axis (z) of the crystal. The Raman spectra are then acquired in the $z(xx)\bar{z}$, $z(xy)\bar{z}$, $z(x'x')\bar{z}$ and $z(x'y')\bar{z}$ scattering geometries where the letters outside (inside) the brackets indicate the directions of propagation (polarization) of the incident and scattered light. Here the x and y axes are taken parallel to the Cu-O bonds and another set, x′ and y′, are rotated by 45 degrees with respect to (x,y). The orthorhombic distortion in the cuprates is small and thus we will assume that the symmetry properties of the spectra are determined by the underlying tetragonal symmetry (D_{4h} point group) of the crystal.

The Raman tensors, γ^L must then transform as one or more of the irreducible representations of the D_{4h} point group. In this case there is a Raman tensor $\gamma(B_{1g})$ that transforms as the B_{1g} irreducible representation, or as the basis function $(k_x^2 - k_y^2)$. Also there is a $\gamma(B_{2g})$ tensor that transforms as the B_{2g} irreducible representation or as the basis function $k_x k_y$. The individual elements of these tensors can be selected by suitable choices of the polarization and in some cases the elements involved are present in a single tensor. For example (xy) elements are present only in $\gamma(B_{2g})$ and thus the scattering geometry designated by γ_{xy} selects only the B_{2g} tensor which transforms as the basis function $k_x k_y$. γ_{xy} must vanish along the k_x and k_y axes and for most band structures [71] will have maxima along the diagonal directions. Also the $\gamma_{x'y'}$

scattering geometry selects only elements of $\gamma(B_{1g})$ and must transform as $(k_x^2 - k_y^2)$. Thus $\gamma_{x'y'}$, or $\gamma(B_{1g})$, must be zero along the diagonal (±1, ±1) directions in k-space and for most band structures $\gamma(B_{1g})$ will have maxima along the k_x and k_y axes. These two scattering geometries thus allow us to probe complementary regions of the Brillouin zone. The diagonal geometries are not as useful in this respect in that the tensor is too symmetric and γ_{xx} and $\gamma_{x'x'}$, cannot be used to isolate a single channel. In these cases, $\gamma_{x'x'}$ selects elements common to both $\gamma(A_{1g})$ and $\gamma(B_{2g})$ and thus transforms as $(A_{1g} + B_{2g})$. Similarily γ_{xx} reflects contributions from $(A_{1g} + B_{1g})$.

To schematically illustrate these statements we can use a tight binding model for the band structure and hence calculate the spectra. Thus we assume that [71,72]

$$E(\vec{k}) = -2t[\cos(k_x a) + \cos(k_y a)] - 4t'[\cos(k_x a)\cos(k_y a)] - \mu \qquad (8)$$

where μ is the chemical potential. Choosing parameters ($\mu/2t = 0.58$, $2t'/t = 0.60$) to give a Fermi surface similar to that used by other workers ([72] and Fig. 3), the (xy) and (x'y') components of the Raman tensor are calculated using (5). The results are shown in Fig. 3 in the form of polar plots. From these plots one can see that the (x'y') or B_{1g} spectra will be dominated by contributions from regions of the Fermi surface located near the $k_x(\pm1,0)$ and $k_y(0,\pm1)$ axes while the (xy) or B_{2g} geometry will probe regions of the Fermi surface located near the diagonal directions. Referring to Fig. 2 it is clear that properties of the hot quasiparticles will be reflected in the B_{1g} spectra while the B_{2g} spectra will be dominated by scattering from the cold quasiparticles.

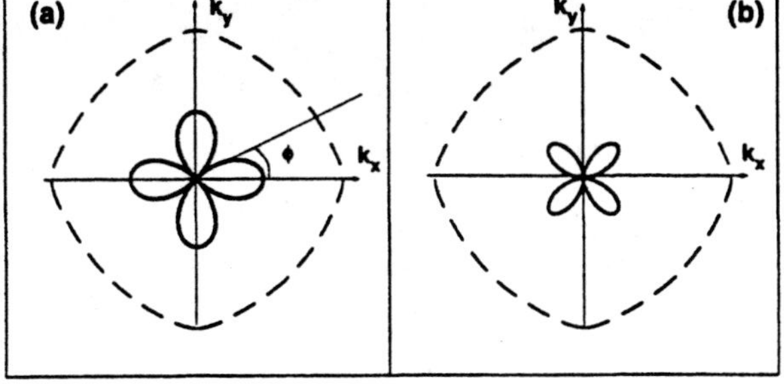

Figure 3. Calculated Fermi surface (dashed line) and polar plots of the (a) B_{1g} and (b) B_{2g} components of the Raman tensor.

4. EXPERIMENTAL RESULTS

4.1. Raman Spectra of $YBa_2Cu_3O_y$ (YBCO)

YBCO has been the most widely studied of all the high temperature superconductors, partly because of its relatively high critical temperature but more importantly because it can be obtained in the form of very high quality single crystals [74]. Results obtained from YBCO can thus be analyzed in a framework developed from the results of many other experiments carried out on similar samples. Spectra obtained in the B_{1g} scattering geometry from an underdoped single crystal of YBCO with $y \approx 6.5$ ($T_c = 60K$) are shown in Fig. 4. The scattered intensity shown in Fig. 4(a) is quite interesting in that it appears that a low energy gap ($\omega < 300cm^{-1}$) opens as the temperature is reduced below about 200K. As can be seen from Fig. 4(b), however, these effects are thermal in origin in that the low energy portion of the response function is independent of temperature for $T < 200K$. It is also evident that the response function does not undergo a superconductivity induced renormalization at T_c and there is no indication of a 2Δ peak in the 35K ($T < T_c$) B_{1g} spectrum (Fig. 4b).

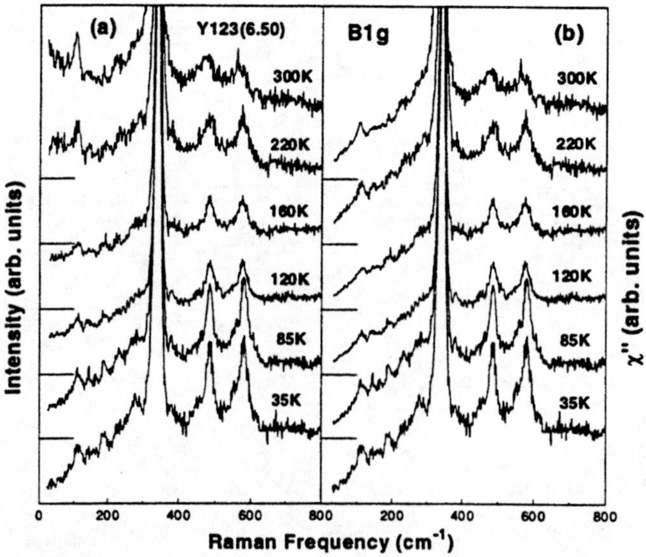

Figure 4. $B_{1g}(x'y')$ Raman spectra of YBCO (y=6.5) at several different temperatures. (a) The scattered intensity is shown on the left (a) and the response function on the right (b).

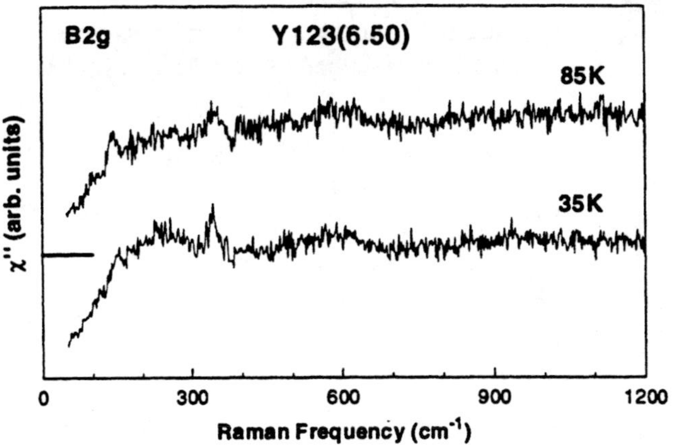

Figure 5. B_{2g}(xy) response function of YBCO(y=6.50) above and below T_c.

Spectra obtained in the B_{2g} geometry are shown in Fig. 5 and in this geometry there is a clear renormalization as the sample is cooled below T_c and a broad peak centered at about 230cm^{-1} is visible in the 35K spectrum. The spectra shown in Figs. 4 and 5 differ in several respects from those obtained from optimally doped compounds. Spectra obtained from optimally doped crystals with y = 6.95 (T_c = 93.5K) at low temperatures display a strong 2Δ peak at about 500cm^{-1} in the B_{1g} channel (Fig. 6) and a broad peak forms at about 250cm^{-1} in the B_{2g} spectra when the sample is cooled through T_c. Another feature that is not obvious from Figs. 4 and 5 concerns the relative scattered intensities in the two channels. This is demonstrated in Fig. 6 where the low temperature spectra are compared and it is clear that the B_{1g} spectrum obtained from the underdoped compound is much weaker than that obtained from the optimally doped sample. To be more quantitative we measured the ratio

$$R = \int d\omega[\chi''(B_{1g})] / \int d\omega[\chi''(B_{2g})] \tag{9}$$

in both the optimally doped and underdoped samples. Here the spectra were integrated up to 600cm^{-1} (with the phonons subtracted) to give $R = 3$ for optimal doping and $R = 1$ for the underdoped samples. From Fig. 6 it is clear that $\chi''(B_{1g})$ decreases significantly as the doping level is decreased while $\chi''(B_{2g})$ is almost unaffected by the change in doping. We thus conclude that spectral weight is lost from regions of the Fermi surface located near the (π,0) points as the doping level is decreased while regions of the Fermi surface located near (±π,±π)/2 are essentially unaffected. In other words in underdoped crystals the quasiparticle scattering rate depends strongly on direction in k-space. To investigate the universality of these observations among the cuprates we have carried out similar measurements on LSCO as described in the following section.

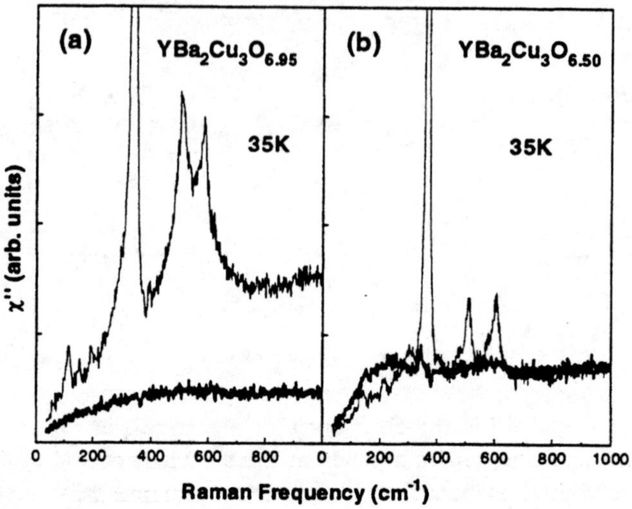

Figure 6. The low temperature B_{1g} and B_{2g} spectra of YBCO plotted on the same scale for (a) an optimally doped and (b) an underdoped crystal.

4.2. Raman Spectra of $La_{2-x}Sr_xCuO_4$ (LSCO)

In many ways LSCO represents a very attractive system in which to study the influence of doping on the physical properties of HTS. As the Sr content is varied from x = 0 to about x = 0.16 the material changes [75] from an antiferromagnetic insulator to a superconductor with a critical temperature of about 38K. As the Sr content is further increased the critical temperature decreases and becomes very small when x ≈ 0.27. LSCO can thus be tuned through the complete phase diagram (Fig. 1) without introducing major changes in the nature of the material. This means that good quality single crystals, with a prescribed doping level, can be obtained for all Sr concentrations [75,76] in the superconducting range. In addition the unit cell of LSCO contains a single CuO_2 plane and thus the results obtained are unaffected by any possible effects due to interplane interactions. Or, from another point of view, by comparing the results obtained from LSCO with those from double layer materials such as YBCO one can obtain an estimate of the relative importance of interplane coupling.

Despite the fact that LSCO represents a very attractive system for HTS studies, it has been the subject of relatively few Raman investigations. Chen et al. [72,73] found that the superconducting gap in optimally doped LSCO is anisotropic with maxima near the axes in reciprocal space and nodes along the diagonal directions. These features are consistent with d-wave symmetry and appear to be common to all the hole doped cuprates. The gap has a maximum value $2\Delta_m \approx 8k_BT_c$, a value that is also similar to that found [73] in other HTS. In overdoped crystals, however, the gap appears to "collapse" [77,78] and the symmetry cannot be clearly identified from the spectra (see section 5.3.1 and [78]). In underdoped crystals the 2Δ peak in the B_{1g} spectrum is absent and evidence for the superconducting transition is found only in the B_{2g} channel.

To obtain systematic information on the influence of doping we have carried out Raman measurements on LSCO samples with x = 0.10, 0.13, 0.17, 0.19, and 0.22. The optimum critical temperature of LSCO is about 38K for $x_{opt} \approx$ 0.16 and hence the x = 0.17 sample (T_c = 37K) is likely to be slightly overdoped. However, given that its' critical temperature T_c lies near the apex of the x-T_c curve [79], we will assume that results obtained from the x = 0.17 sample are representative of the optimally doped state and will refer to it as optimally doped. Spectra obtained from the x = 0.17 sample are shown in Fig. 7 for both the B_{1g} and B_{2g} channels illustrating the changes that occur as the sample is cooled below T_c. As is evident a renormalization occurs in both channels and broad pairbreaking peaks appear in the spectra obtained at 15K.

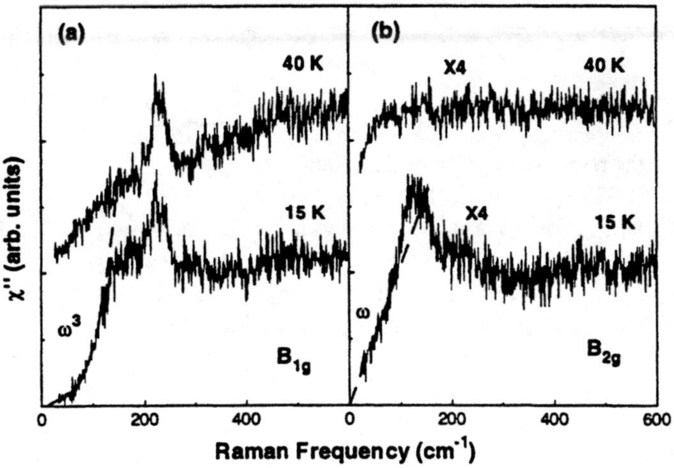

Figure 7. (a) The B_{1g} Raman Spectrum of optimally doped LSCO (x=.17) above (40K) and below (15K) T_c. (b)The B_{2g} Raman Spectra of the x=.17 crystals above and below T_c. The dashed lines represent power law fits to the low energy portions of the spectra.

The highest energy peak ($\approx$ 200cm^{-1}) occurs in the B_{1g} channel, which samples regions of the Fermi surface located near the k_x and k_y axes, and the peak in the B_{2g} spectrum occurs at about 130cm^{-1}. These results are consistent with an anisotropic gap having a maximum value of $2\Delta_m \approx 200\text{cm}^{-1} \approx 8k_BT_c$. As shown in Fig. 7 the low energy B_{1g} response increases as ω^3, while the B_{2g} response increases linearly in the region $\omega < \Delta_m$. These results are consistent [80] with a superconducting gap having nodes along the $k_x = k_y$ directions.

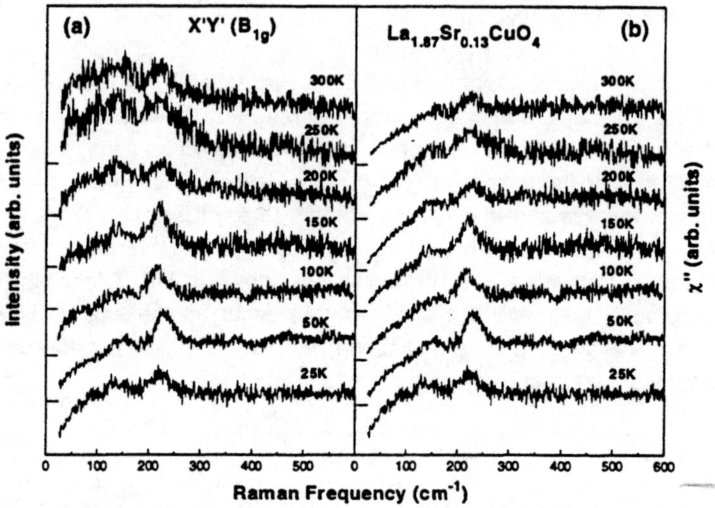

Figure 8. The B_{1g} Raman spectra of underdoped LSCO(0.13) at several different temperatures. (a). The scattered intensity is shown on the left and (b). the response function on the right.

As an illustration of spectra obtained from underdoped LSCO the B_{1g} spectra obtained from the x = 0.13 sample are shown in Fig. 8 for several different temperatures. Now we see that as the sample is cooled below T_c no superconductivity induced renormalization, or 2Δ peak can be detected in the B_{1g} spectra. Furthermore, in the $I(B_{1g})$ spectra (Fig. 8a), it appears that a gap opens up at low energy as the sample is cooled down below about 250K. However the response function, $\chi''(B_{1g})$, is again, as it is in underdoped YBCO, almost independent of temperature at low energies (Fig. 8b). The B_{2g} spectra obtained from the x = 0.13 sample are shown in Fig. 9 for several different temperatures. There is very little variation with temperature as the sample is cooled from 300K to about 40K but there is a superconductivity induced renormalization as the sample is cooled through T_c.

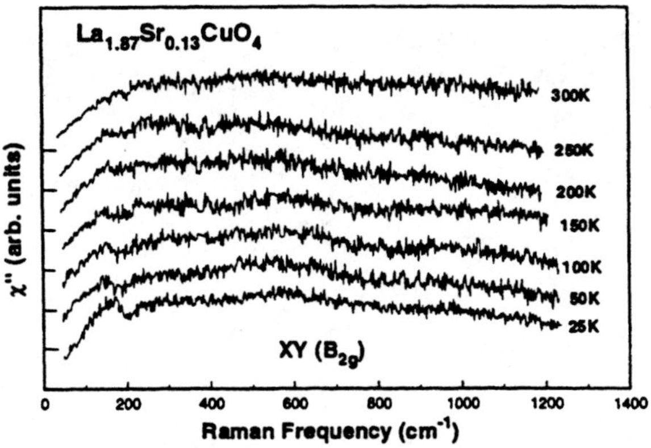

Figure 9. The B_{2g} response function of underdoped LSCO (0.13) at several different temperatures.

To summarize, the B_{1g} spectra obtained from underdoped compounds are unaffected by the transition into the superconducting state, but a superconductivity induced renormalization is observed (Fig. 10) in the B_{1g} spectra obtained from optimally and overdoped samples. In contrast the B_{2g} spectra undergo a renormalization at T_c for all doping levels studied here.

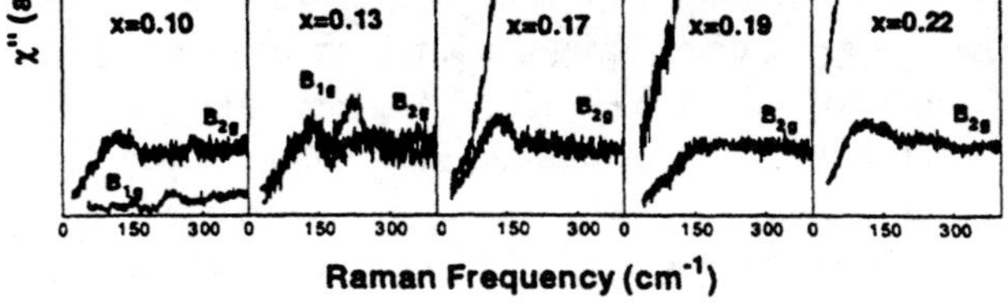

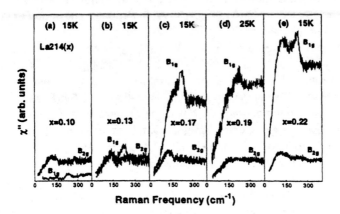

Figure 10. The B_{1g} and B_{2g} Raman response functions of five LSCO samples with: (a) x=0.10, (b) x=0.13, (c) x=0.17, (d) x=0.19, and (e) x=0.22. All the spectra were obtained at low temperatures ($T< T_c$) and all are plotted on the same scale. The relative intensities of all the different spectra can thus be compared directly.

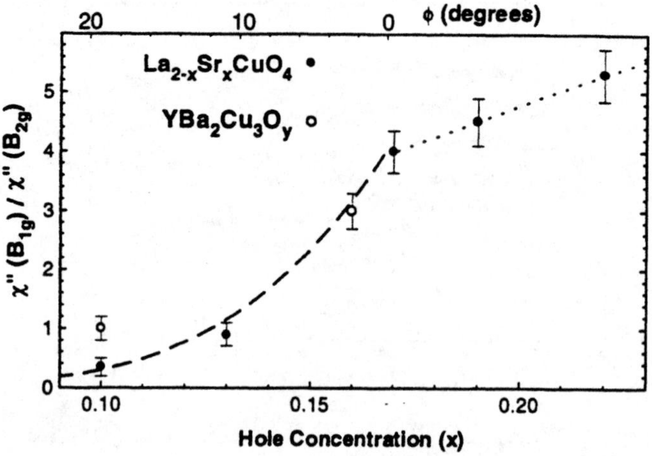

Figure 11. The ratio $R = \int d\omega[\chi''(B_{1g})] / \int d\omega[\chi''(B_{2g})]$ for several different hole concentrations for both LSCO and YBCO. The ratio was determined for $0 < \omega < 600\ cm^{-1}$ in all cases. The dashed line represents the calculated R using Eq. (4) for different values of ϕ (Fig. 3) and is superimposed using the top scale. The dotted line ($x > 0.16$) serves only as a guide to the eye.

The low temperature ($T < T_c$) B_{1g} and B_{2g} response functions obtained from each sample are compared in Fig. 10. All the spectra shown in Fig. 10 are plotted on the same scale and thus their relative magnitudes can be compared. As is evident from the figure the strength of $\chi''(B_{2g})$ is relatively insensitive to doping while $\chi''(B_{1g})$ decreases rapidly when the doping is reduced below optimum. The ratio R has been determined for all five samples and the results are plotted in Fig. 11. From Figs. 10 and 11 it is evident that R decreases rapidly as the doping level is decreased below optimum. R decreases primarily because of the loss of low energy spectral weight from regions of the Fermi surface probed in the B_{1g} geometry. Again, as in YBCO, the loss of spectral weight in the B_{1g} channel suggests that underdoping leads to a loss of spectral weight from regions of the Fermi surface located near $(\pi,0)$ and hence to the effective existence of a pseudogap in this region. In fact, as is evident from Fig. 10(a), the low energy B_{1g} spectrum of the $x = 0.10$ sample is very weak, implying that the quasiparticles located near $(\pi,0)$ are almost completely gapped at this hole concentration. The values of R obtained from YBCO [29,30] are also shown in Fig. 11 and as is evident they are quite consistent with the LSCO results. This suggests that the spectral weight depletion that is reflected in the B_{1g} spectra of underdoped LSCO and YBCO is common to all underdoped cuprates. This result is reinforced both by ARPES measurements [38] and Raman observations in BSCCO [81]. The spectral weight depletion reflected in the B_{1g} spectra can be attributed to an anisotropic scattering mechanism that strongly scatters quasiparticles on regions of the Fermi surface near (π,0), but leaves those located near (π,π)/2 unaffected.

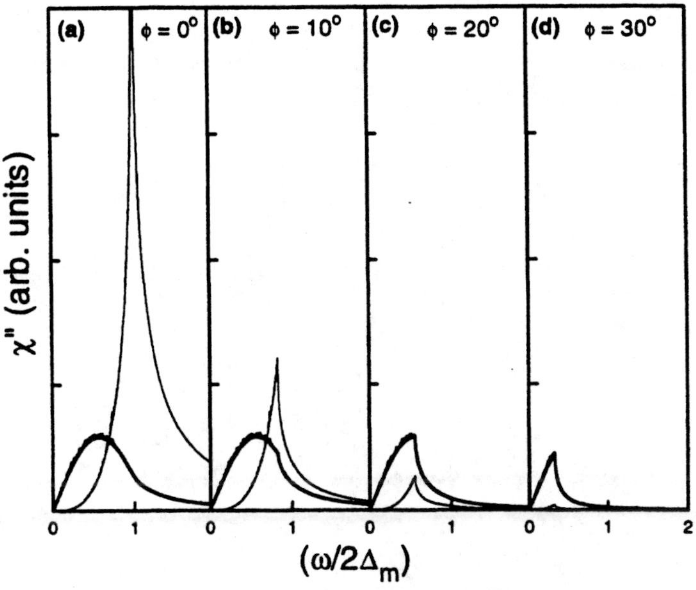

Figure 12. Spectra calculated (a) using the full Fermi surface and (b-d) by integrating only over the arcs lying between ϕ and 90 - ϕ in each quadrant. Heavy lines ≡ B_{2g} ; Light lines ≡ B_{1g}.

To illustrate the effect of loss of spectral weight from regions of the Fermi surface near (π,0), we can calculate the spectra assuming that there is no contribution from portions located near the k_x and k_y axes. That is, using equations 4, 5 and 8, we have first calculated the spectra by integrating over the complete Fermi surface. The resulting spectra are shown in Fig. 12(a). The spectra were then calculated by integrating only over those segments located near the diagonal directions. That is the parts of the contour lying near the axes and defined by the angle ϕ (Fig. 3) were excluded from the integration, and the resulting spectra are shown in Figs. 12(b-d) for different values of ϕ.

We have also calculated the ratio *R* of the integrated response functions as a function of the angle ϕ and the results (dashed line) are superimposed on the data points in Fig. 11. For the purpose of this comparison both the measured and calculated response functions were integrated from $\omega = 0$ to 600 cm^{-1}. From our observations it is plausible to assume that the observed spectra could result from the loss of spectral weight from regions of the Fermi surface located near $(\pi,0)$. Finally we should note that the effective gapping of segments located near $(\pi,0)$ is completely consistent with the absence of a superconductivity induced renormalization in the B_{1g} spectra of the underdoped compounds. The Raman *spectra thus allow us to characterize the presence of the pseudogap by both a loss of spectral weight in the B_{1g} spectra, and the absence of a superconductivity induced renormalization in the same channel.*

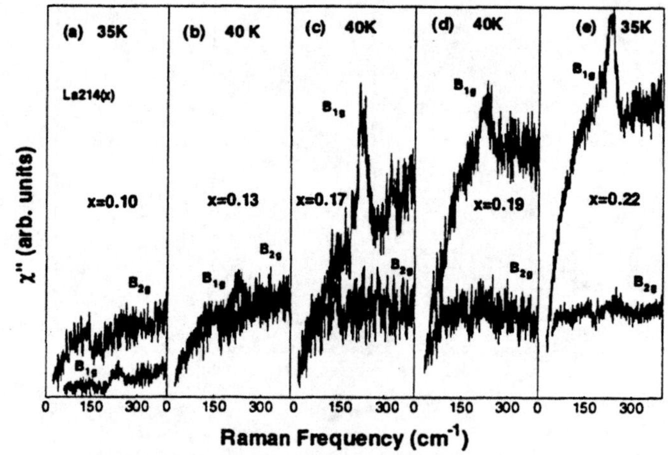

Figure 13. The B_{1g} and B_{2g} Raman response functions for five LSCO samples with: x=0.10, (b) x=0.13, (c) x=0.17, (d) x=0.19, (e) x=0.22. All the spectra were obtained in the normal state ($T > T_c$) and all are plotted on the same scale.

Thus far our discussion of relative intensities has involved a consideration of the low temperature ($T < T_c$) spectra only. We would like to point out however that the same conclusions are reached if we consider the normal state spectra. Analytically (Eq. 3), the normal state spectra are also proportional to $(\gamma)^2$ and will have the same symmetry at all temperatures. This is perhaps evident from an inspection of Figures 8 and 9 where one can see that the low energy portions of the response functions are essentially independent of temperature. To illustrate this more clearly we have plotted the normal state spectra in Fig. 13 for the different doping levels. Consideration of the spectra in Fig. 13 yield the same values of R as those shown in Fig. 11 (to within the indicated error bars). Consideration of the normal state spectra thus leads to the same conclusions reached using the low temperature spectra. The normal state dependence of the relative scattering intensity on doping was first noted by Katsufuji et al. [82].

To conclude this section we would like to address the apparent discontinuity, at $p = p_{opt}$, in the doping dependence of R (Fig. 11). Given that a renormalization is observed in the B_{1g} channel in optimally doped and overdoped compounds we can conclude that the quasiparticles located near $(\pi,0)$ are not gapped above T_C. That is, the pseudogap is not present in the overdoped state. We thus expect the pseudogap to be "filled" at optimum doping and this can be interpreted to be consistent with the discontinuity at p_{opt}. However one might ask why R continues to increase with doping, albeit at a reduced rate, as the doping level is increased beyond optimum. Although more data will be required to answer this question definitively one can speculate that the approximately linear variation of R with doping is due to a corresponding increase in the quasi-particle concentration on regions of the Fermi surface located near the $(\pi,0)$ points. One can speculate [83] that overdoping moves the van Hove singularity closer to the Fermi surface [46,47] giving rise to an increase in spectral weight near $(\pi,0)$.

5. IMPLICATIONS FOR THE PSEUDOGAP

5.1. Symmetry Considerations

From Figure 12 one can see that $\chi''(B_{1g})$ is strongly attenuated by removing a relatively small part of the Fermi surface ($\varphi \sim 10°$) from the integral and that a much larger segment ($\varphi \sim 30°$) must be removed to obtain a noticeable reduction of $\chi''(B_{2g})$. Given that $\chi''(B_{1g})$ is very sensitive to hole concentration, particularly when $p \approx p_{opt}$, while $\chi''(B_{2g})$ is essentially unaffected by doping we conclude that the depletion of spectral weight is confined to a region defined by $\varphi < 30°$. This is consistent with a previous result, where we have considered [30] depletion of the Fermi surface by a d-wave weighted distribution, rather than a sharp cutoff at the angle ϕ. In this case $\chi''(B_{1g})$ is still attenuated in a manner similar to that shown in Fig.12, but in the d-wave case $\chi''(B_{2g})$ is also significantly attenuated by the opening of the pseudogap. This is in direct contrast to the experimental observations. Furthermore a d-wave pseudogap would have nodes near $(\pi,\pi)/2$ and thus $\chi''(B_{2g})$ should increase linearly [80] at low frequencies in both the superconducting and normal states. This in turn means there should be very little change as the sample is warmed through T_C. Experimentally, however, the B_{2g} spectra undergo (Figs. 4,9,10) a clear

renormalization at T_c. Nemetschek et al. [32] have also pointed out that when underdoped BSCCO is warmed through T_c the low frequency ($\omega < \Delta_m$) behaviour of $\chi''(B_{2g})$ loses its linear character and becomes convex shaped in the normal state. This change signifies the loss of the nodes at $(\pi,\pi)/2$ as one moves from the superconducting state to the normal state. Thus the normal-state gap cannot have d-wave symmetry.

Based on the results of NMR experiments Williams et al. [14] have also concluded that the pseudogap has d-wave symmetry but is unrelated to the superconducting gap. They analyzed their data using a model developed by Loram et al. [28] in which the magnitude of the composite gap at any temperature is determined by (6). For comparison with this model the unscreened spectra can be estimated using equation (7). One finds that the inclusion of E_g in (7) leads to an increase in the frequency of the pair-breaking peak in the B_{2g} spectrum beyond that due to Δ alone, in contrast to our experimental results (Fig. 10). Another point of disagreement between the model and our results concerns the behaviour at T_c. If E_g and Δ had similar magnitudes the pairbreaking peak should exhibit a discontinous shift as the sample is warmed through T_c, rather than simply disappearing as is observed experimentally [29,32]. On the other hand, if E_g has d-wave symmetry the low frequency behaviour of the spectra should be unaffected by passage through the critical temperature since there would be nodes at $(\pi/2,\pi/2)$ both above and below T_c.

5.2. Pseudogap Energy E_g

ARPES experiments appear to provide the most direct and detailed measure of the magnitude and symmetry of energy gaps in the cuprates. The nature of the superconducting gap in optimally doped BSCCO has been carefully studied [5] using photoemission techniques and its magnitude determined from measurements of the leading edge shift of the electron current with respect to the Fermi energy. In experiments carried out on optimally doped BSCCO it is found that the superconducting gap is anisotropic with a maximum value located near the axes in reciprocal space and minima along the diagonals. The magnitude of the gap maximum is given [40] by $2\Delta_m \approx 8k_BT_c$. All of these features are in good agreement with the results of Raman scattering experiments [80]. The results of Raman measurements on optimally doped YBCO [77] and LSCO [73] are also consistent with a d-wave gap with maxima given by $2\Delta_m \approx 8k_BT_c$. The LSCO results have also been corroborated by recent photoemission experiments [46].

In several photoemission experiments on underdoped BSCCO [38-44] the normal state gap energy E_g has also been determined from measurements of the leading edge shifts of the current. In the (1,0) directions the leading edge shift is about 25meV at low temperatures in underdoped BSCCO, and remains constant at this value as the sample is warmed through T_C. The pseudogap appears to close gradually as the sample is warmed and disappears at $T \approx 250K$. It has been pointed out [5] that the leading edge shift underestimates E_g, and should be corrected for the spectrometer response. The resulting value for E_g may be as large as 35meV. We will thus assume that the ARPES value is $250 < E_g < 270cm^{-1}$. Tunneling measurements [48,49] in BSCCO yield a similar value and both techniques find that E_g increases as the doping level is decreased. Finally it must be noted that recent ARPES experiments [46] in LSCO have found what they have called a large pseudogap with $E_g \sim 800cm^{-1}$. In this case an inflection point in the current–energy curve, and not the leading edge shift, was used to determine a value for E_g.

In IR reflectivity experiments it is found that the scattering rate decreases anomolously below about $700cm^{-1} < \omega < 800cm^{-1}$ in a number of different compounds [3]. This energy was also found [3] to be approximately independent of doping in the underdoped region. Nemetschek et al. [32] identified this same energy below which a loss of spectral weight occurred in the B_{2g} Raman spectrum of underdoped BSCCO at low temperatures. A similar energy is also obtained from an analysis [78] of the scattering rates relevant to the B_{2g} spectrum of underdoped LSCO. Thus optical experiments suggest $E_g \approx 750cm^{-1}$ for the pseudogap, an energy scale that is about three times larger than that pertaining to superconductivity. Even if the value of $2E_g \approx 750$ cm^{-1} is reflected in the optical experiments the discrepancy between the two sets of results appears to be outside experimental uncertainties.

Finally an analysis of specific heat measurements [27] has led to the suggestion that $E_g \sim J(1 - p/p_{cr})$ where p is the number of holes per CuO_2 layer and p_{cr} is thought to lie on the overdoped side at about $p = 0.19$. The specific heat measurements thus suggest $E_g \sim J \approx 800$ cm^{-1} [83] at low doping levels.

The experimentally determined energy scales for the pseudogap thus appear to fall into two groups. ARPES and tunneling measurements on BSCCO yield $E_g \sim 250cm^{-1}$ while the specific heat and optical measurements on several different cuprates yield $E_g \sim 750cm^{-1} \sim J$, a much larger value.

From Figs 4 and 8 it is clear that there are no obvious gap-like features in the $\chi''(B_{1g})$ spectra that reflect either the smaller (30meV) or larger (100meV) values of E_g that are identified above. It is interesting to assume, however, that the PG might originate from short-range antiferromagnetic correlations which would lead to $E_g \approx J$, or one-magnon excitations. Single magnon excitations with large wavevector are not observed in the Raman spectra but in this case one could observe such excitations indirectly via two magnon scattering [83-85] which gives rise to a broad peak centered near 3J. This could occur, for example, if there were small antiferromagnetic correlated regions in underdoped, but still superconducting, compounds. Multimagnon peaks have been observed in underdoped LSCO [10] and YBCO [86] which suggests that magnetically correlated domains exist in the underdoped compounds. Such a scenario is also suggested by the results of recent muon scattering experiments [87]. Given the existence of such correlations we would expect the gap edge to occur in the B_{1g} spectra near the energy of the multimagnon peak or at about $3J \approx 0.3eV = 2400cm^{-1}$. To investigate this possibility in our samples we have obtained spectra at higher energies and typical B_{1g} spectra obtained from LSCO samples with x = 0.1 and 0.13 are shown in Fig. 14. It should be noted that the spectra have not been corrected for spectrometer response and thus the peak energy values are not reliable. It is clear, however, that the broad peak that is centered at about 300meV in the x = 0.1 spectra, weakens significantly as the doping level is increased to 0.13, and for optimal doping the response is completely flat out to $3000cm^{-1}$. Furthermore this peak represents the only gap-like feature in the B_{1g} spectra. Similar high energy spectra have been obtained from a series of underdoped YBCO compounds by Rubhausen et al. [86]. These aspects will be discussed in more detail in section 5.3.2.

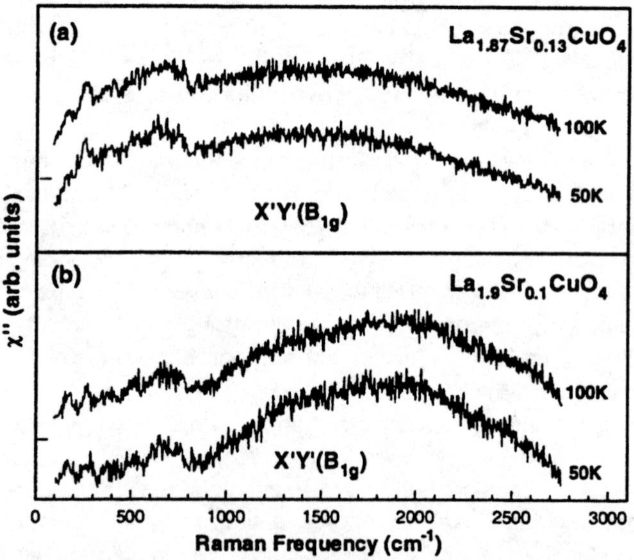

Figure 14. High energy B_{1g} Raman spectra of underdoped LSCO at 50K and 100 K for (a) x = 0.13 and (b) x = 0.1. The gap-like feature near 300meV corresponds to scattering by two-magnon excitations.

5.3. Variation of the Superconducting Gap and Pseudogap with Doping

5.3.1 Superconducting Gap

In optimally and overdoped compounds a measure of the magnitude of the superconducting gap ($2\Delta_m$) is provided [71,72,78] by the energy of the pairbreaking peak in the low temperature B_{1g} spectrum. From Figs. 10(c,d,e) and 15 we can see that the gap energy decreases from about $2\Delta_m \approx 8k_BT_c$ to about $6k_BT_c$ in the x = 0.22 sample. This apparent "collapse" of the gap is similar to the behaviour first observed in YBCO [76] and subsequently in BSCCO [88] and the Tl based compounds [89-91].

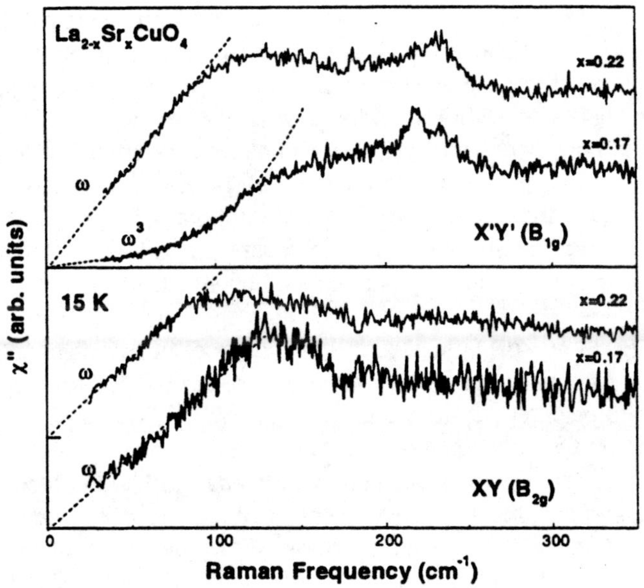

Figure 15. The low energy Raman spectra in overdoped (x = 0.22) (upper curves) and optimally doped (x = 0.17) LSCO (lower curves) at 15K in the B_{1g} (upper panel) and B_{2g} (lower panel) geometries. The dashed lines show the power law behaviour of the response functions at low energy. The B_{2g} spectrum of the overdoped crystal has been displaced for clarity.

The low temperature spectra obtained from the overdoped compound differ from the optimally doped spectra in an important aspect. This concerns the dependence of $\chi''(B_{1g})$ on frequency in the limit $\omega \to 0$. If the superconducting gap has d-wave symmetry the presence of nodes at $|k_x| = |k_y|$ leads to [80] $\chi''(B_{1g}) \propto \omega^3$ and $\chi''(B_{2g}) \propto \omega$. These expectations are clearly realized in the spectra obtained from optimally doped LSCO (Fig. 15). In spectra obtained from the 0.22 overdoped sample, $\chi''(B_{2g}) \propto \omega$ which implies the existence of nodes near $(\pi/2,\pi/2)$, but $\chi''(B_{1g}) \propto \omega$, which appears to be incompatible with the existence of nodes along the diagonal directions. It has been suggested [92,93] that the linear behaviour of $\chi''(B_{1g})$ at low frequencies could be due to the presence of disorder and/or scattering due to spin fluctuations. However agreement with the data requires scattering rates $1/\tau > \Delta_m$. It is also possible that the position of the nodes move away from $(\pi/2,\pi/2)$ as the doping level is increased, as is suggested by recent ARPES experiments [45,47]. Further work will be required to clarify this aspect of the overdoped spectra.

It is surprising that as soon as the doping level is reduced below optimum the superconductivity induced renormalization in the B_{1g} channel vanishes. The abruptness of this change is analogous to the sudden loss of strength in the B_{1g} phonon anomaly [94] in YBCO when the oxygen concentration is reduced below optimum. It is now clear that both phenomena can be attributed to an abrupt gapping of the quasiparticles located in $(\pi,0)$ regions. As a result, in the underdoped regime the B_{1g} Raman spectra do not provide direct information on the maximum gap magnitude Δ_m. However, an indirect estimate of the magnitude of the superconducting gap can be obtained from the low temperature B_{2g} spectra (Figs. 5,10a,10b). We first note that the low frequency linear behaviour (Fig. 5) of $\chi''(B_{2g})$ implies the existence of nodes near $(\pi/2,\pi/2)$ and hence d-wave symmetry. In the B_{2g} spectra (Fig. 5) obtained from underdoped YBCO the pairbreaking peak occurs at about $230\text{cm}^{-1} \approx 5k_BT_c$, which is similar to the ratios that are typically obtained in optimally doped spectra. This implies that the magnitude of the superconducting gap decreases in the underdoped regime. We can also see that the frequency of the pairbreaking peak occurs at about $120\pm20\text{cm}^{-1}$ in the two underdoped samples (Figs. 10a and 10b) but the peak frequency is not well enough defined to make any definitive statements. In ARPES measurements carried out on underdoped BSCCO Harris et al. [40] found that the superconducting gap energy increases in magnitude as the doping level was decreased below optimum, but the measured increase is only slightly greater than their energy resolution. Tunneling measurements [48] on BSCCO also revealed a small increase in the superconducting gap on the underdoped side. This scenario is thus quite different than the decreasing gap that is implied by the Raman measurements in YBCO (Fig. 5) and BSCCO [32]. The LSCO results might be in better accord with the ARPES picture but a definitive answer will require more accurate measurements of the pairbreaking frequency.

5.3.2 Pseudogap

The doping dependence of the pseudogap is more difficult to determine. However, as mentioned in section 5.2, the evidence obtained directly from $\chi''(B_{2g})$ and indirectly from $\chi''(B_{1g})$, yields an estimate of $E_g \approx J$ for the magnitude of the pseudogap. In this case we would expect the magnitude of the pseudogap to vary with doping in the same manner as the superexchange energy J. To obtain an estimate for the dependence of J on doping we can note that the energy of the multimagnon peak ($\approx$ 3J) decreases [10,84-86] by about 20% as p is increased from zero to near optimum ($\approx$0.14). That is in undoped compounds strong two-magnon peak occur at 3000cm^{-1} in LSCO [10,84,85] and at about 2600cm^{-1} in YBCO [85,86]. As the doping level is increased the magnitude of these peaks decreases rapidly but the peak frequency decreases more slowly; for example to about 2000cm^{-1} in nearly optimally doped YBCO [86]. Hence we would expect E_g to decrease with doping, on the underdoped side, but to still be rather large when p = 0.16 where the pseudogap becomes filled and disappears. Our view is that the pseudogap both fills and closes with doping, but becomes filled well before it closes. In this regard if the relation [27] $E_g \sim J(1 - p/p_{cr})$ is to provide a reasonable estimate for E_g a value of $p_{cr} \sim 0.3$ to 0.5 would be required.

6. COMPARISON WITH OTHER WORK

6.1. Comparison with Theory

From the above discussion it is clear that the Raman results obtained here from LSCO and YBCO, and Raman and IR measurements in BSCCO [3,32] provide a consistent picture in which the energy scale associated with the pseudogap is similar in all three compounds. Furthermore, the magnitude of the pseudogap is larger than that of the superconducting gap in all three compounds. Our results also indicate that the spectral weight depletion associated with the pseudogap is confined to regions of Fermi surface that are located near the (π,0) points and, in particular, does not appear to conform to a d-wave distribution. Given either one of the above differences one must conclude that the pseudogap and $\Delta(\mathbf{k})$ result from different mechanisms and since superconductivity appears to grow at the expense of the pseudogap in the overdoped region it appears that the two different mechanisms compete with each other for the available quasiparticles. These observations appear to preclude agreement with those models that are based on the premise of preformed pairs. This leaves models that involve a magnetic pairing scenario (section 2.2), which is also consistent with the proposition that $E_g \approx J$.

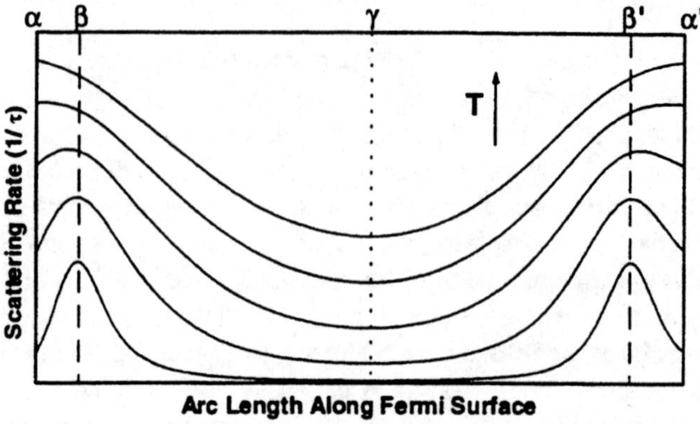

Figure 16. Quasiparticle scattering rate around a Fermi surface contour (αβγβ′α′ of FIG. 2) for different temperatures in the NAFL model [67].

Our experiments have clearly identified a loss of spectral weight from regions of the Fermi surface located near (π,0). This is consistent with the existence of an anisotropic scattering mechanism such as that incorporated in the NAFL model. Here the quasiparticles on regions of the Fermi surface near (π,0) can be coupled (Fig. 2) by the antiferromagnetic ordering vector **Q** = (π,π). This interaction leads to an effective scattering rate 1/τ that depends strongly on direction in k-space. To illustrate the variation of 1/τ with direction that is inherent to the NAFL model the results of a calculation by Devereaux and Kampf [67] are displayed in Fig. 16. The scattering rate is large in quasi-localized regions near (π,0) and small over a relatively wide arc of the Fermi surface centered at (π/2,π/2). It is evident that this dependence of scattering rate on angle could lead to a depletion of spectral weight that is quasi-localized near (π,0) in qualitative agreement with our Raman results. It should be mentioned that the calculations of 1/τ were carried out [67] with parameters that might be more appropriate to an optimally doped material. It is expected that the anisotropy {τ(π/2,π/2)/τ(π,0)} would become larger as the doping level is decreased.

Some other aspects of our results are also accounted for by the NAFL model. For example Pines [54] has predicted that only the cold quasiparticles should participate in the superconducting transition and that the hot quasiparticles should not be involved. These predictions are in direct correspondence with the observed renormalization in the B_{2g} channel and the invariance of $\chi''(B_{1g})$ on transition into the superconducting state.

On the other hand the crossover temperatures T_{cr} and T^* that have been incorporated [54,55] into the NAFL model cannot be readily identified from our spectra. We have found some evidence [95] for T_{cr} in overdoped LSCO and it is expected that $T_{cr} > 300K$, and thus outside the temperature range that we have investigated, in underdoped compounds. T^* however, which marks the transition into the pseudogap state, was determined to be about 200K from NMR measurements [18] carried out on underdoped LSCO. As mentioned previously there is a small loss of spectral weight in the B_{2g} channel below about 250K (Fig.9). There is also evidence of a redistribution or renormalization [78] of spectral weight in the B_{2g} spectra of underdoped LSCO at about 250K. These features could be a manifestation of the onset of the pseudogap phase as envisaged by Pines et al. [54-56]. It must be concluded, however, that our spectra do not provide a clear indication of an onset temperature T^*. In spite of this the NAFL model provides a qualitative explanation of many of the features in our spectra.

6.2. Comparison with Experiment

In this section we will attempt to reconcile our observations with other experiments. We will begin with, what is to us, the most serious discrepancy between our results and the ARPES measurements. As mentioned previously ARPES measurements in BSCCO give a leading edge shift $E_A \approx 30meV = 240cm^{-1}$ in spectra obtained from regions near the $(\pi,0)$ points. They also find that this gap decreases as the temperature increases and closes at about 250K. Since ARPES is a single particle spectroscopy we might expect to see some evidence of this feature in the Raman spectra at $2E_A \approx 60meV$ (or $500cm^{-1}$). It is puzzling that the thermally normalized B_{1g} Raman spectra ($\chi''(B_{1g})$) do not provide any obvious indication of a 60meV gap opening in either YBCO (Fig. 4b) or BSCCO [32] as the temperature is reduced from 300K. As noted in section 5.2 the overall depletion in the B_{1g} channel can be characterized by an energy scale $J \approx 100meV$, which is substantially greater than the ARPES energy.

It is interesting to note that the ARPES results seem to be in much better agreement with the intensity measurements (Fig. 4a) which are suggestive of a 35meV gap opening below about 250K. This comparison becomes even more interesting if we compare the YBCO spectra shown in Fig. 4(b) with normal state spectra obtained [77] from optimally doped samples. From Fig. 4b it is evident that, in addition to the overall depletion shown in Fig. 10, the underdoped spectra exhibit a further depletion below approximately $300cm^{-1}$, relative to spectra obtained from optimally doped compounds. That is in the underdoped compounds the scattered intensity increases linearly (Fig 4b) with frequency in the region $0 < \omega < 300cm^{-1}$, while in optimally doped spectra the scattered intensity increases much more rapidly in this same frequency region. Although this "gap" feature in the Raman spectrum coincides with E_A, and not $2E_A$ as expected, it appears to represent the only possible point of correspondence with the leading edge shift obtained in the ARPES experiments. We thus speculate that the added depletion below $300cm^{-1}$ is the pseudogap energy measured in the ARPES experiments on BSCCO [38-42]. One should also note that the low frequency Raman slope remains essentially constant as the temperature is varied between T_c and 300K, in contrast to the ARPES gap which closes at about 250K. We can also speculate that this onset temperature is an artifact [17] resulting from thermal broadening. On the basis of the specific heat results and NMR measurements carried out by Williams et al. [14], Tallon has concluded [14,17] that the pseudogap cannot be characterized by a well defined onset temperature T^*. They have suggested that T^* found in ARPES experiments is due to thermal broadening, perhaps as manifested in the spectra shown in Fig. 4a. Our results appear to support their contention, in that our B_{1g} spectra do not provide strong evidence for a well defined T^*. It is clear, however that further work will be required, not only to corroborate the above suggestion, but also to probe the physical origin of the additional depletion between $0\text{-}300cm^{-1}$. The overall depletion in the B_{1g} channel might also be reflected in some of the higher energy features of the photoemission spectra. For example, Ino et al. [46,47] obtained $E_g \approx J$ from measurements of an inflection point in ARPES spectra obtained from LSCO.

With respect to the symmetry of the pseudogap, the variation of the leading edge shift with direction in k-space [40,43], suggests that the pseudogap in BSCCO has d-wave symmetry. This observation is in direct contrast to both our Raman results (section 4.3) and those of Nemetschek et al. [32]. It must be noted, however, that the ARPES energy resolution might not be adequate to distinguish between d-wave symmetry and a gap profile determined by a variation of scattering rate such as that shown in Fig.16. In this regard one should also note that in the measurements of Harris et al. [40] the pseudogap amplitude is zero over an extended arc of the Fermi surface near $(\pi,\pi)/2$. If one uses their error bars in a favourable manner, their results appear to be quite consistent with the existence of an anisotropic scattering mechanism, as suggested by our Raman results. In this same vein Williams et al. [14] found that the assumption of d-wave symmetry for the pseudogap led to better agreement with their NMR results than did an s-wave gap. However, from an admittedly superficial examination of their results, it would appear that the assumption of an anisotropic scattering rate (Fig. 16) would provide equally good agreement.

We will now attempt to reconcile our results with those obtained from IR reflectivity experiments by Timusk and coworkers [3,19-21] and Raman experiments of Hackl and coworkers [32,33]. In IR experiments on underdoped YBCO, LSCO and BSCCO the presence of the pseudogap results in a depression of the frequency dependent scattering rate for energies below about 750cm^{-1}. The magnitude of the depression increases as the doping level is decreased and as the temperature is decreased. In contrast the characteristic onset energy is approximately the same in all three materials and is also independent of the doping level. In the Raman experiments [32] a small loss of spectral weight occurs in the B_{2g} channel for energies less than 750cm^{-1} and temperatures below 250K in both YBCO and BSCCO. In our B_{2g} spectra from underdoped LSCO (Fig. 9) one can also note that if the spectra are normalized at about 700cm^{-1}, the response function at lower energies decreases as the temperature is lowered below about 200K. A depression of the scattering rate, similar to that obtained from the IR spectra can be obtained [78] from a Kramers-Kronig transformation of the B_{2g} spectra shown in Fig. 9. The results obtained from the IR and B_{2g} Raman spectra can thus be said to be in good agreement and consistent with the suggestion [54,32] that the IR response is determined by cold quasiparticles.

We would now like to address the question of any connection between the spectral weight depletion observed in the B_{1g} channel and the above B_{2g} results. First, as noted above, the IR response is determined by the B_{2g} quasiparticles which is consistent with the observed [32] depletion of spectral weight in the B_{2g} channel. Second, as mentioned previously, the superexchange energy $J \approx$ 750cm^{-1}, which is the same energy scale of the effects in the IR [3] and B_{2g} spectra [32], is also indirectly reflected in the multi-magnon peak that is observed in the B_{1g} channel. On the other hand, however, in spectra obtained from the cold quasiparticles there appears [3] to be an onset temperature $T < 300$K associated with the scattering rate and spectral weight depletion. The low energy B_{1g} spectra ($\omega < 500$cm^{-1}) of underdoped YBCO, on the other hand, are almost independent of temperature. If one examines the higher energy ($500 < \omega < 900$cm^{-1}) portions of the spectra however (Fig. 4b) the intensity in this region increases marginally as T is reduced from 300K, and then decreases below about 250K and becomes constant below about 200K. We might speculate that the decrease in B_{1g} intensity below about 250K is related to the onset temperature observed in the B_{2g} channel. Although the variation is weaker (Fig.9), a similar intensity variation can be observed in the B_{1g} spectra obtained from LSCO. Further work is required to corroborate these observations, but such measurements might also produce a connection with the variation of the magnetic susceptiblity observed in NMR experiments. In summary a quantitative connection between the results obtained in the B_{1g} and B_{2g} channels is missing.

Loram et al. have carried out specific heat measurements [25-28] as a function of doping in a number of different cuprate systems. Their results represent a response to quasiparticle weight averaged over the complete Fermi surface. The depletion of spectral weight from the regions of the Fermi surface near $(\pi,0)$ should thus be reflected in their measurements. They have proposed [27] that $E_g \sim J(1 - p/p_{cr})$ where p_{cr} is the value of hole concentration at which the pseudogap "closes". On the other hand, our Raman results suggest that at optimum doping p_{opt}, where a superconductivity induced renormalization is observed in the B_{1g} channel (Fig. 10c), the pseudogap is "filled". Given that $J \approx 1000\ cm^{-1}$ in undoped LSCO and $E_g \approx 700\ cm^{-1}$ in the $x = 0.1$ sample (Fig. 14b) suggest $p_{cr} > p_{opt}$. Therefore we conclude that the pseudogap "fills" before it "closes". Thus our Raman results are in qualitative agreement with specific heat measurements [27] in terms of both magnitude and doping dependence.

7. CONCLUSIONS

Raman scattering experiments on YBCO and LSCO have produced results that provide important information about the electronic properties of the underdoped regime. Several features of the spectra change dramatically as the doping level in the high-T_c cuprates is reduced below optimum. The most obvious change concerns the renormalization that occurs in the B_{1g} channel when optimally doped and overdoped samples enter the superconducting state. In underdoped compounds the B_{1g} spectra are unaffected by the transition to the superconducting state and the expected 2Δ peak is absent. A reduction in the doping level below optimum also leads to a weakening of the low energy B_{1g} spectra, which is consistent with a significant loss of spectral weight from regions of the Fermi surface located near the axes in reciprocal space. The presence of this pseudogap can thus be characterized both by a depletion of spectral weight from regions of the Fermi surface located near the axes in reciprocal space, and *also by the absence of a superconductivity induced renormalization in the B_{1g} channel.*

In direct contrast to the B_{1g} channel, the B_{2g} spectra are essentially unaffected by reductions in the doping level below optimum. That is the low energy B_{2g} intensity is the same for all doping levels from 0.10 to 0.22. Furthermore a superconductivity induced renormalization of the B_{2g} spectrum is observed in all the crystals studied and the frequency of the resulting pair-breaking peak is the same throughout the underdoped regime. The normal state depletion of spectral weight is thus confined to the B_{1g} channel, a result that is not compatible with the assignment of d-wave symmetry to the pseudogap. A depletion of spectral weight from regions of the Fermi surface near the axes is, however, consistent with the existence of an anisotropic scattering mechanism such as that arising from interactions associated with short-range antiferromagnetic correlations. That is, quasiparticles on regions of the Fermi surface located near $(\pm\pi,0)$ and $(0,\pm\pi)$ can be strongly coupled by the antiferromagnetic ordering vector $\mathbf{Q} = (\pi,\pi)$. These "hot" quasiparticles [54,55] are effectively gapped and do not participate in the transition to the superconducting state. On the other hand "cold" quasiparticles located near the diagonal directions in k-space are much more weakly scattered, and, as evidenced by a superconductivity induced renormalization in the B_{2g} channel, are involved in the transition to the superconducting state. These features in the spectra can be adequately described by a model involving short-range antiferromagnetic correlations [54,55,62].

In conclusion, in the normal state of the underdoped cuprates, there is a spectral weight depletion that is confined to regions of the Fermi surface located near $(\pm\pi,0)$ and $(0,\pm\pi)$, and which is characterized by an energy scale $E_g \approx J > \Delta_m$. The Raman results thus suggest that the pseudogap and superconducting gaps are characterized by different energy scales and by different symmetries. This means that the observed depletion of B_{1g} spectral weight cannot be attributed to precursor pairing and that the pseudogap is unrelated to the superconducting gap.

8. ACKNOWLEGEMENTS

We have been extremely fortunate in that we have been able to study well characterized, exceptionally pure, high quality single crystals of both YBCO and LSCO. We are deeply indebted to Drs. Ruixing Liang, Doug Bonn and Walter Hardy at the University of British Columbia for supplying us with YBCO crystals, and to Prof. Kohji Kishio and his group at the University of Tokyo for the LSCO samples. We would like to note the assistance and advice we have received both from his present students, T. Sasagawa and Y. Togawa, and also from his ex-students, Drs. T. Kimura and M. Okuya. We would like to acknowledge many helpful discusssions with Dr. T. P. Devereaux and, in particular, to thank him for providing us with Figure 16 prior to publication. We have also benefited from discussions with Drs. Rudi Hackl, Robert Buckley, Jeff Tallon, Joe Trodahl, Grant Williams, Chris Kendziora and Tom Timusk. Finally the financial support of the Natural Sciences and Engineering Research Council of Canada is gratefully acknowledged.

REFERENCES

[1] J. G. Bednorz and K. A. Mueller, Z. Phys. **B64**, 189 (1986).

[2] J. Annett, N. Goldenfeld and A. J. Leggett, in Physical Properties of High Temperature Superconductors V, edited by D.M. Ginsberg, (World Scientific, 1997).

[3] T. Timusk and B. Statt, to be published in Reports Progress in Physics.

[4] M. Randeria, in Proc. of International School of Physics, Verenna, 1997, edited by G. Iadonisi and J. R. Schrieffer, (IOS Press, Amsterdam 1998); preprint (cond-mat/9710223).

[5] M. Randeria and J. C. Campuzano, preprint (cond-mat/9709107).

[6] P. B. Allen, Z. Fisk and A. Migliori, in Physical Properties of High Temperature Superconductors I, edited by D. M. Ginsberg, (World Scientific, 1989).

[7] Y. Iye, in Physical Properties of High Temperature Superconductors III, edited by D. M. Ginsberg, (World Scientific, 1992).

[8] I . Bozovic, D. Kirillov, A. Kapitulnik, K. Char, M. R. Hahan, M. R. Beasley, T. H. Geballe, Y. H. Kim, A. J. Heeger, Phys. Rev. Lett. **59**, 2219 (1987).

[9] D. Reznik, S. L. Cooper, M. V. Klein, W. C. Lee, D. M. Ginsberg, A. A. Maksimov, V. Puchkov, I. I. Tartaovskii, S. Cheong, Phys. Rev. B **48**, 7624 (1993).

[10] S. Sugai, S. Shamoto, and M. Sato, Phys. Rev. B **38**, 6436 (1988).

[11] W. W. Warren Jr., R. E. Walstedt, G. F. Brennert, R. J. Cava, R. Tycko, R. F. Bell, and G. Dabbagh, Phys. Rev. Lett. **62**, 1193 (1989).

[12] D. C. Johnston, Phys. Rev. Lett. **62**, 957 (1989).

[13] C. P. Schlicter, R. L. Corey, N. J. Curro, S. M. DeSoto, K. O'Hara, T. Imai, A. M. Kini, H. H. Wang, U. Geiser, J. M. Williams, K. Yoshimura, M. Katoh, and K. Kosuge, Philosophical Magazine B **74**, 545-561 (1996).

[14] G. V. M. Williams, J. L. Tallon, E. M. Haines, R. Michalak, and R. Dupree, Phys. Rev. Lett. **78**, 721(1997).

[15] J.L. Tallon, G.V.M. Williams, N.E. Flower, and C. Bernard, Physica C **282-287**, 236 (1997).

[16] J. L. Tallon, C. Bernard, H. Shaked, R. L. Hitterman, and J. D. Jorgensen, Phys. Rev. B **51**, 12911 (1995).

[17] J. L. Tallon, G. V. Williams and J. W. Loram, in Proc. of SNS'97 (Cape Cod, 1997) to appear in J. Phys. Chem. of Solids.

[18] H. Yasuoka, Physica C **282-287**, 119 (1997).

[19] A. V. Puchkov, P. Fournier, D. N. Basov, T. Timusk, A. Kapitulnik and N.N. Kolesnikov, Phys. Rev. Lett. **77**, 3212(1996); ibid **77**, 1853(1996).

[20] A.V. Puchkov, D.N. Basov and T. Timusk, J. Phys: Cond. Matt. **8**, 10049

(1996).
[21] T. Startseva, T. Timusk, A. V. Puchkov, D. N. Basov, H. A. Mook, M. Okuya, T. Kimura, and K. Kishio, Preprint (cond-mat/9812134).
[22] H. Takagi, B. Batlogg, R. J. Cava, H. L. Kao, J. Kwo, J. J. Krajewski and W. F. Peck, Phys. Rev. Lett. **69**, 2975(1992).
[23] B. Batlogg, H. Y. Hwang, H. Takagi, H. L. Kao, J. Kwo, and R. J. Cava, Physica C **235-240**, 130 (1994).
[24] H. Y. Hwang, B. Batlogg, H. Takagi, H. L. Kao, J. Kwo, R. J. Cava, J. J. Krajewski, and W. F. Peck, Jr., Phys. Rev. Lett. **72**, 2636 (1994).
[25] J.W. Loram, K.A. Mirza, J.R. Cooper, N. Athanassopoulou, and W.Y. Liang, p341 in Proc. of 10th Anniversary HTS Workshop, (World Scientific, Singapore, 1996).
[26] J. W. Loram, K.A. Mirza, J.R. Cooper, W.Y. Liang and J. M. Wade, J. of Supercond. **7**, 243 (1994); J. W. Loram, K. A. Mirza, and J. R. Cooper, Phys. Rev. Lett. **71**, 1740 (1993).
[27] J. W. Loram, K. A. Mirza, J. R. Cooper, and J. L. Tallon, in Proc. of SNS'97 (Cape Cod, 1997) to appear in J. Phys. Chem. of Solids.
[28] J. W. Loram, K. A. Mirza, J. R. Cooper, and J. L. Tallon, Physica C **282-287**, 1405 (1997).
[29] X. K. Chen, J. G. Naeini, K. C. Hewitt, J. C. Irwin, R. Liang, and W. N. Hardy, Phys. Rev. B **56**, R513 (1997).
[30] X. K. Chen, J. G. Naeini, J. C. Irwin, R. Liang and W.N. Hardy, Proc. of SNS'97, to appear in J. Phys. Chem. Of Solids.
[31] J. G. Naeini, X. K. Chen, J. C. Irwin, M. Okuya, T. Kimura, and K. Kishio, to be published (cond-mat/9804262).
[32] R. Nemetschek, M. Opel, C. Hoffmann, P. F. Muller, R. Hackl, H. Berger, L. Forro, A. Erb, and E. Walker, Phys. Rev. Lett. **78**, 4837 (1997).
[33] M. Opel, R. Nemetschek, C. Hoffmann, P. F. Muller, R. Hackl, H. Berger, L. Forro, A. Erb, and E. Walker, Proc. of SNS'97 (Cape Cod, 1997) to appear in J. Phys. Chem. of Solids.
[34] G. Blumberg, M. Kang, M. V. Klein, K. Kadowaki, and C. Kendziora, Science **278**, 1427 (1997).
[35] G. Blumberg, M. Kang, M. V. Klein, K. Kadowaki, and C. Kendziora, in Proc. of SNS'97 (Cape Cod, 1997) to appear in J. Phys. Chem. of Solids.
[36] J. W. Quilty, H. J. Trodahl and D. M. Pooke, Phys. Rev. B **57**, R11097 (1998).
[37] C. Kendziora, Proc. of SNS'97 (Cape Cod 1997), to appear in J. Phys. Chem. of Solids.
[38] D. S. Marshall, A.G. Loeser, Z.-X. Chen and D. S. Dessau, Phys. Rev. Lett. **76**, 4841 (1996).

[39] A. G. Loeser, Z.-X. Chen and D. S. Dessau, Science **273**, 325 (1996).
[40] J. M. Harris, Z.-X. Chen, P. J. White, D. S. Marshall, M. C. Schabel, J. N. Eckstein, and I. Bozovic, Phys. Rev. B **54**, R15665 (1996).
[41] H. Ding, T. Yokoya, J. C. Campuzano, T. Takahashi, M. Randeria, M. R. Norman, T. Mochiku, K. Kadowaki, and J. Giapintzakis, Nature **382**, 51 (1996).
[42] H. Ding, M. R.Norman, T. Yokoya, T. Takeuchi, M. Randeria, J. C. Campuzano, T. Takahashi, T. Mochiku, and K. Kadowaki, Phys. Rev. Lett. **78**, 2628 (1997).
[43] M. R. Norman, H. Ding, M. Randeria, and J. C. Campuzano, in Proc. of SNS'97 (Cape Cod, 1997) to appear in J. Phys. Chem. of Solids (cond-mat/9710185).
[44] M. R. Norman, H. Ding, M. Randeria, J. C. Campuzano,T. Yokoya, T. Takeuchi, T. Takahashi, T. Mochiku, K. Kadowaki, P. Guptasarma, and D.G. Hinks, Preprint (cond-mat/9710163).
[45] A. Fujimori, A. Ino, T. Mizokawa, C. Kim, Z.-X. Shen, T. Sasagawa, T. Kimura, K. Kishio, M. Takaba, K. Tamasaku, H. Eisaki, and S. Uchida, in Proc. of SNS'97 (Cape Cod, 1997) to appear in J. Phys. Chem. of Solids.
[46] A. Ino, T. Mizokawa, K. Kobayashi, A. Fujimori, T. Sasagawa, T. Kimura, K. Kishio, K. Tamasaku, H. Eisaki, and S. Uchida, Phys. Rev. Lett. **81**, 2124 (1998).
[47] A. Ino T. Mizokawa, K. Kobayashi, A. Fujimori, T. Sasagawa, T. Kimura, K. Kishio, K. Tamasaku, H. Eisaki, and S. Uchida, Phys. Rev. Lett. **79**, 2101 (1997).
[48] Ch. Renner, B. Revaz, J.-Y. Genoud, K. Kadowaki and O. Fischer, Phys. Rev. Lett. **80**, 149 (1998).
[49] N. Miyakawa, P. Guptasarma, J. F. Zasadzinski, D.G. Hinks and K. E. Grey, Phys. Rev. Lett. **80**, 157(1998).
[50] J. Maly, J. Boldizar, and K. Levin, preprint (cond-mat/9805018).
[51] V. J. Emery and S. A. Kivelson, Nature **374**, 434 (1995).
[52] V. J. Emery, S. A. Kivelson and O. Zachar, Phys. Rev. B **56**, 6120 (1997).
[53] M. Randeria, in "Bose-Einstein Condensation" edited by A. Griffin, D. Snoke and S. Stringari (Cambridge University Press, 1995).
[54] D. Pines, Physica C **282-287**, 273 (1997).
[55] D. Pines, Z. Phys. B **103**, 129 (1997).
[56] V. Barzykin and D. Pines, Phys. Rev. B **52**, 13585 (1995).
[57] Y. Zha, V. Barzykin and D. Pines, Phys. Rev. B **54**, 7561 (1996).
[58] J. Scmalian, D. Pines and B. Stojkovic, Phys. Rev. Lett. **80**, 3839 (1998).
[59] J. Schmalian, S. Grabowski and K.H. Bennemann, Phys. Rev. B **56**, R509 (1997).

[60] A. Chubukov, D. Pines and B. Stojkovic, J. Phys: Cond. Matt. **8**, 10017 (1996).
[61] A. V. Chubukov and D. K. Morr, Physics Reports **288**, 355(1997).
[62] P. A. Lee and X. G. Wen, Phys. Rev. Lett. **76**, 503 (1996).
[63] A. J. Millis and H. Monien, Phys. Rev. Lett. **72**, 2636 (1993).
[64] B. L. Altshuler, L. B. Ioffe and A. J. Millis, Phys. Rev. **B53**, 415 (1996).
[65] M. V. Klein and S. B. Dierker, Phys. Rev. B **29**, 4976 (1984).
[66] T. P. Devereaux and A. Kampf, in Proc. of SNS'97 (Cape Cod, 1997) to appear in J. Phys. Chem. of Solids .
[67] T.P. Devereaux and A. P. Kampf, preprint (cond-mat/9711039).
[68] A. Zawadowski and M. Cardona, Phys. Rev. B **42**, 10732 (1990).
[69] A. Virosztek and J. Ruvalds, Phys. Rev. B **45**, 347 (1992); J. Ruvalds and A. Virosztek, Phys. Rev. B **43**, 5498 (1991).
[70] A. A. Abrikosov and L. A. Fal'kovskii, Soviet Physics JETP **13**, 179 (1961).
[71] X. K. Chen, J. C. Irwin, R. Liang, and W. N. Hardy, J. Supercond. **7**, 435 (1994); Physica C **227**, 113 (1994).
[72] X. K. Chen, J. C. Irwin, H. J. Trodahl, T. Kimura, and K. Kishio, Phys. Rev. Lett. **73**, 3290 (1994).
[73] X. K. Chen, J. C. Irwin, H. J. Trodahl, T. Kimura, and K. Kishio, Physica C **295**, 80 (1998).
[74] Ruixing Liang, P. Dosanjh, D. A. Bonn, D. J. Baar, J. F. Carolan and W. N. Hardy, Physica C **195**, 51 (1992).
[75] T. Kimura, K. Kishio, T. Kobayashi, Y. Nakayama, M. Motohira, K. Kitazawa, and K. Yamafuji, Physica C **192**, 247 (1992).
[76] P. G. Radaelli, D. G. Hinks, A. W. Mitchell, Hunter , J. L. Wagner, B. Dabrowski, K. G. Vandervoort, H.K. Viswanathan, and J.D. Jorgensen, Phys. Rev. B **49**, 4163 (1994).
[77] X. K. Chen, E. Altendorf, J. C. Irwin, R. Liang and W. N. Hardy, Phys. Rev. B **48**, 10530 (1993).
[78] J. G. Naeini, X. K. Chen and J.C. Irwin, to be published.
[79] J. L. Tallon, C. Bernhard, H. Shakeel, R. L. Hitterman and J. D. Jorgensen, Phys. Rev. B **51**, 12911 (1995).
[80] T. P. Devereaux, D. Einzel, B. Stadlober, R. Hackl, D. H. Leach and J.J. Neumeier, Phys. Rev. Lett. **72**, 91 (1994).
[81] M. Opel, private communication.
[82] T. Katsufuji, Y. Tokura, T. Ido and S. Uchida, Phys. Rev. B **48**, 16131 (1993).
[83] J. L. Tallon, private communication.
[84] P. E. Sulewski, P. A. Fleury, K. B. Lyons, S.-W. Cheong and Z. Fisk, Phys. Rev. B **41**, 225 (1990).

[85] K. B. Lyons, P. A. Fleury, L. F. Schneemeyer, and J.V. Waszczak, Phys. Rev. Lett. **60,** 372 (1988).
[86] M. Rubhausen, C. T. Rieck, N. Dieckmann, K. O. Subke, A. Bock and U. Merkt, Phys. Rev. B **56,** 14797 (1997).
[87] Ch. Niedermayer, C. Bernhard, T. Blasius, A. Golnik, A. Moodenbaugh and J. I. Budnick, Phys. Rev. Lett. **80**, 3843 (1998).
[88] C. Kendziora and A. Rosenberg, Phys. Rev. B **52**, R9867 (1995).
[89] M. Kang, G. Blumberg, M. V. Klein, and N.N. Kolesnikov, Phys. Rev. Lett. **77**, 4434 (1996).
[90] L. V. Gasparov, P. Lemmens, M. Brinkman, N.N. Kolesnikov and G. Guntherodt, Phys. Rev. B **55**, 1223 (1997).
[91] L. V. Gasparov, P. Lemmens, N.N. Kolesnikov and G. Guntherodt, preprint (cond-mat/9809159).
[92] T.P. Devereaux, Phys. Rev. Lett. **74**, 4313 (1995).
[93] R. Hackl, G. Krug, R. Nemetschek, M. Opel and B. Stadlober in *Spectroscopic Studies of Superconductors,* I. Bozovic and D. van der Marel Eds., Proc. SPIE **2696**, 194 (1996).
[94] E. Altendorf, J. C. Irwin, R. Liang and W. N. Hardy, Phys. Rev. B **45**, 7551(1992); Phys. Rev. B **47**, 8140(1993).
[95] J. G. Naeini, X. K. Chen, K. C. Hewitt, J. C. Irwin, T. P. Devereaux, M. Okuya, T. Kimura, and K. Kishio, Phys. Rev. B **57**, R11077 (1998).

Studies of High Temperature
Superconductors
Volume 27

ISBN 1-56072-684-9

NMR Studies of the Normal-State Pseudogap in High Temperature Superconducting Cuprates

G. V. M. Williams

NZ Institute for Industrial Research, P.O. Box 31310, Lower Hutt, New Zealand.

1. Introduction.

After nearly twelve years of high temperature superconductivity (HTS) research there is still no consensus as to the pairing mechanism and the essential physics in the normal state. It is now generally recognised that a pseudogap exists in the normal state [1-4]. This gap was originally observed in nuclear magnetic resonance and inelastic neutron scattering studies and attributed to a "spin gap" which conflicted with heat capacity and susceptibility measurements where it was found that a gap exists in the spin and charge spectrum [1]. However, it has recently been shown by angle resolved photo-emission spectroscopy (ARPES) measurements that a normal-state pseudogap does exist in the charge spectrum [3,4].

There are now a number of conflicting models that attempt to account for the normal-state pseudogap including: short-range pairing correlations [5], formation of real-space pairs [6], condensation of singlet paired spinons in the spin-charge separation strong-correlation models of Fukuyama, Lee and coworkers [7,8], antiferromagnetic correlations [9], a charge-density wave [10,11], charge stripes [12] and superspin in the SO(5) model of Zhang [13]. All of these models can not be correct.

The main difficulty in understanding the HTS is their complex structural and electronic properties. The unit cell consists of one of more superconducting CuO_2 planes separated by insulated layers. The underdoped parent compound is an antiferromagnetic insulator and hole doping results in a 2D Fermi surface with antiferromagnetic correlations.

2. Evidence for a Normal-State Pseudogap.

Evidence for the normal-state pseudogap is seen in a variety of measurements as can be seen in figure 1 where (a) resistivity, (b) thermopower, (c) infra-red and (d) nuclear magnetic resonance data are plotted for the $YBa_2Cu_4O_8$ HTS. This HTS is underdoped and has a T_c of 81K. It contains two superconducting CuO_2 layers separated by Y and two filled and stoichiometric metallic CuO chains. In figure 1a the resistivity is plotted by subtracting the resistivity intercept and dividing by temperature which removes the high temperature linear temperature dependence. It can be seen that there is a decrease in $(R-R_0)/T$ for temperatures below ~250K which has been attributed to the normal-state pseudogap. The thermopower, S, is plotted in figure 1b for $YBa_2(Cu_{1-y}Zn_y)_4O_8$ where it can be seen that all the thermopower curves have departed from the common curve for $T \leq 210K$. It should be noted that the effect of Zn substitution is to dramatically reduce T_c consistent with unitary scattering in a superconductor with a $d_{x^2-y^2}$ order parameter [14].

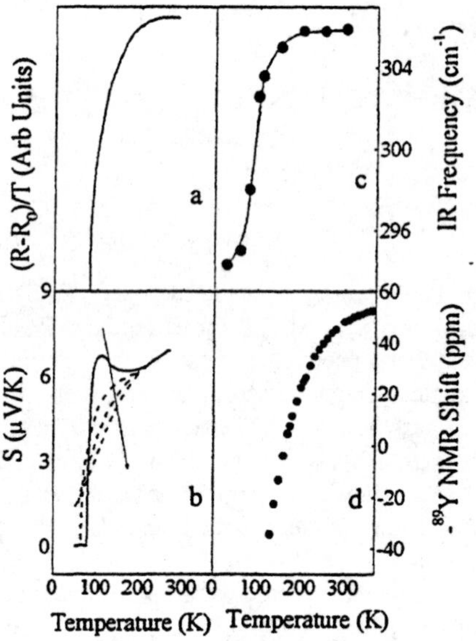

Figure 1: Plot of the temperature dependence of the (a) resistivity, (b) thermopower, (c) IR mode position and (d) ^{89}Y NMR shift for the $YBa_2Cu_4O_8$ HTSC. In (b) data on $YBa_2(Cu_{1-z}Zn_z)_4O_8$ is also included where the arrow indicates increasing Zn concentration.

The behavior in figure 1b has been used as evidence for a normal-state pseudogap where the gap magnitude does not depend on the Zn concentration but that Zn induces a filling in of the normal-state density of states (DOS) [15]. Figure 1c shows the temperature dependence of an infra-red active phonon as a function of temperature. It is clear that there is phonon mode softening above T_c. The ^{89}Y NMR shift is shown in figure 1d where is can be seen that the NMR shift decreases with decreasing temperature. This temperature dependent change has been attributed to the normal-state pseudogap and will be discussed later.

It can be seen in figure 2 that the normal-state pseudogap is also observed in the electronic entropy and susceptibility [16,17]. In figure 2a the electronic entropy, S, is plotted as S/T for $YBa_2Cu_3O_{7-\delta}$ and the spin susceptibility, χ_s, is plotted as $a_W\chi_s$ where a_w is the Wilsons ratio for weakly interacting Fermions. The arrows indicate decreasing δ and hence increasing hole concentration. This HTS has two superconducting CuO_2 planes separated by Y and a metallic CuO chain where the occupancy of the chain oxygen site can be altered by annealing. The decrease in S/T and χ_s with decreasing temperature have again been attribute to a normal-state pseudogap. The appearance of a gap from S/T data with measures all spin and charge degrees of freedom and χ_s which measures the real part of the dynamic spin susceptibility at **q**=(0,0) indicates that the gap is in both the spin and charge degrees of freedom and the gap is not just a spin gap as originally assumed.

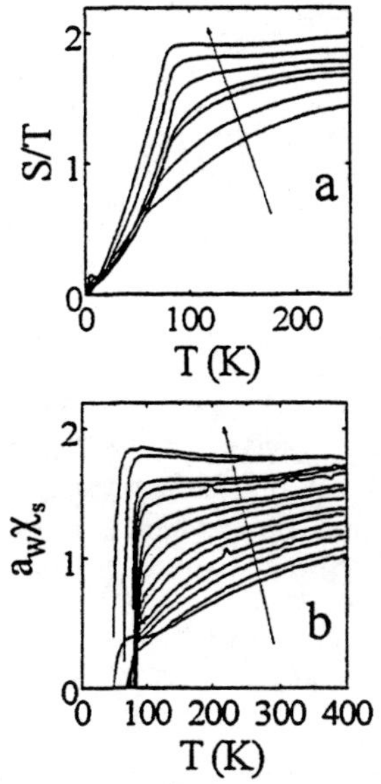

Figure 2: Plot of the temperature dependence of (a) the electronic entropy, S, divided by temperature and (b) the spin susceptibility, χ_s, multiplied by the Wilsons ration, a_W. The S/T and $a_W\chi_s$ units are mJ/g.at.K^2 [16].

Direct evidence of the normal-state pseudogap has been provided by ARPES measurements on the $Bi_2Sr_2CaCu_2O_{8+\delta}$ HTS. This HTS has two superconducting CuO_2 layers separated by SrO and BiO insulating layers. The ARPES data clearly shows that the normal-state pseudogap exists and has a $d_{x^2-y^2}$ like symmetry where $E_g(\mathbf{k})=|E_g(\cos(k_xa)-\cos(k_ya))|$ [3,4]. A normal-state pseudogap with $d_{x^2-y^2}$ like symmetry has also been observed in the NMR Knight shift [18] and ESR [19] data.

3. Crossover Temperatures in the Normal-State.

It is fashionable to describe normal-state data above T_c in terms of two crossover or onset temperatures [5,9,20,21]. The lower temperature, T_L, is variously attributed to the opening of a spin gap, the opening of a pseudogap in the normal-state DOS originating from a charge density wave instability or short range pairing correlations. A number of definitions of T_L has been defined including the position of the maximum in $(^{63}T_1T)^{-1}$ [22,23], where $^{63}T_1$ is the copper spin lattice relaxation rate, the temperature at which $^{63}T_1T$ departs from linearity [24] or the temperature where anomalies in the NMR/NQR (nuclear quadrupole resonance) data [25]. Each definition results in different values of T_L (160K [22], 180K [25] or 215K [26]). In the nearly antiferromagnetic Fermi liquid model (NAFL), T_L is the temperature at which the normal-state pseudogap opens [9,24] (this is at odds with heat capacity [1,17], tunneling [27] and Raman [28] data which show that the pseudogap opens at a higher temperature). An anitiferromagnetic-correlation pseudoscaling regime is assumed in the intermediate temperature region where $T_L<T<T_U$, while the upper temperature T_U marks the crossover from pseudoscaling to mean-field behavior. The NAFL model also predicts distinct scaling regimes for $^{63}T_1T/T_{2G}$ and $^{63}T_1T/T_{2G}^2$ where T_{2G} is the gaussian component of the copper spin-spin relaxation rate [29].

The interpretation of the NMR data in terms of crossover temperatures is at odds with recent high resolution ^{89}Y NMR measurements on $YBa_2Cu_4O_8$ plotted in figures 3a. The ^{89}Y NMR data can be understood by noting that from the Mila-Rice Hamiltonian it can be shown that the NMR shift can be expressed as [31],

$$^{89}K = \frac{\sum_j A_j}{\gamma_n \gamma_e \hbar^2} \chi_s + \sigma \qquad 1.$$

where A_j are the hyperfine coupling constants (negative for ^{89}Y), γ_n is the nuclear gyromagnetic ratio, γ_e is the electron gyromagnetic ratio, χ_s is the static spin susceptibility and σ is the temperature independent chemical shift. The first term is know as the Knight

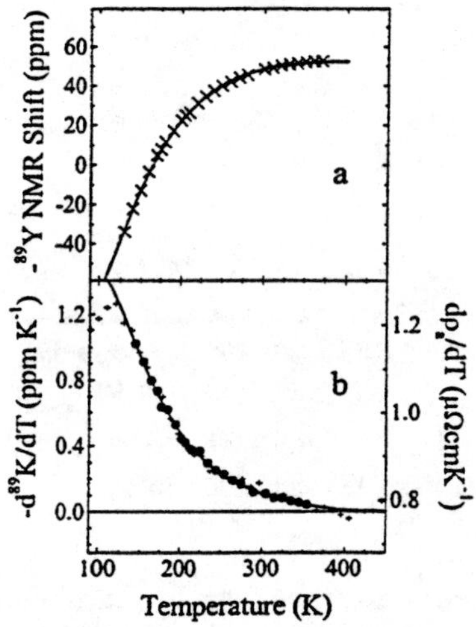

Figure 3: (a) Plot of the ^{89}Y NMR shift against temperature for $YBa_2Cu_4O_8$. The solid curve is the scaling curve described later [30]. (b) Plot of the derivative of the NMR shift data in (a) (solid circles). The solid curve is the derivative of the scaling curve in (a). Also included is the derivative of the resistivity in the a direction from a $YBa_2Cu_4O_8$ single crystal (+ [32]).

shift, K_s, as is directly proportional to the static spin susceptibility. For a metal $\chi_s = \mu_B^2 \int N(E)(-\frac{\partial f}{\partial E})dE$ where N(E) is the density of states and f(E) is the Fermi function and hence a gap in the charge excitations leads to a reduction in the NMR Knight shift. In figure 3b it is apparent that there is no kink in ^{89}K that can be attributed to a T_L. Here the derivative of the NMR shift is plotted as well as the resistivity data of Hussey *et al.* [32] from measurements on a single crystal.

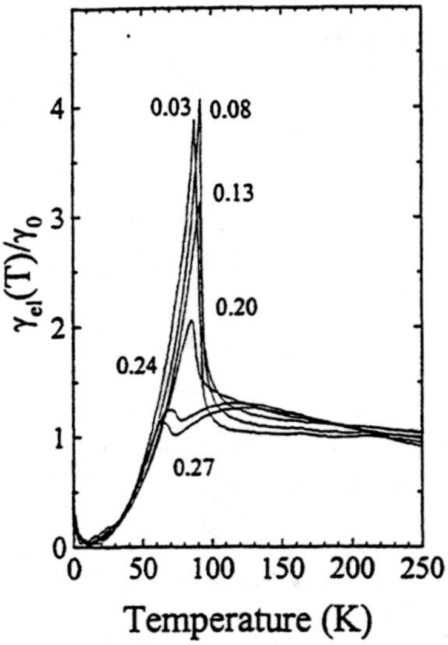

Figure 4: Plot of the normalised γ_{el} against temperature for $YBa_2Cu_3O_{7-\delta}$ for δ values shown [33].

There are also no kinks in heat capacity data at the expected lower crossover temperature as can be seen in figure 4 where we plot $\gamma_{el}=C_{el}/T$ against temperature for $YBa_2Cu_3O_{7-\delta}$. Thus the data in figures 3 and 4 force us to conclude that there are no

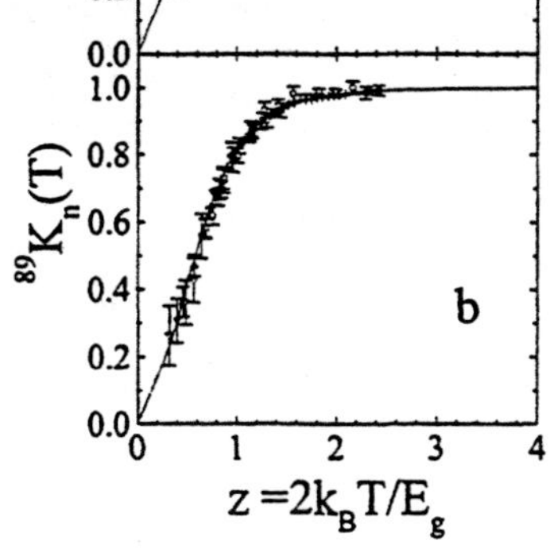

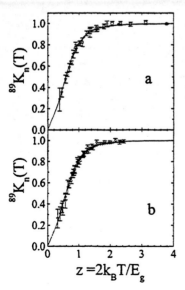

Figure 5: (a) Plot of the scaled ^{89}Y NMR shift, $^{89}K_n(T)$, against the scaling parameter, $z=2k_BT/E_g$, for $Y_{0.8}Ca_{0.2}Ba_2Cu_3O_{7-\delta}$ with T_c and p values of 86K, p=0.173 (open circle), 83.2K, p=0.136 (open square), 65.8K, p=0.105 (open up triangle) and 47.5K, p=0.086 (open down triangle). (b) Plot of $^{89}K_n(T)$ against $z=2k_BT/E_g$ for $Y_{0.9}Ca_{0.1}Ba_2Cu_3O_{7-\delta}$ with T_c and p values of 84.9K, p=0.135 (open circles), 65K, p=0.099 (open squares), 57K, p=0.082 (open up triangles) and <4K, p=0.053 (open down triangles). The solid curves in (a) and (b) are the scaling curves described in the text [33].

crossover temperatures.

The absence of crossover temperatures is evident in the scaling of the NMR Knight shift shown in figure 5 for $Y_{1-x}Ca_xBa_2Cu_3O_{7-\delta}$ [33]. Here the normalised ^{89}Y NMR shift, $^{89}K_n(T)$ is plotted for a wide range of doping concentrations against a scaling parameter $z=2k_BT/E_g$ where E_g is associated with the pseudogap energy. This scaling is not expected in the two crossover temperature models but is expected if there is an underlying energy scale associated with the normal-state pseudogap. A crossover only exists in the sense that a low temperature expansion gives a linear ^{89}K while a high temperature expansion gives a temperature independent ^{89}K. Thus a crossover between the low and high temperature expansions will occur when $T \sim E_g/2k_B$.

The departure from linearity in the ($^{63}T_1T$) data can be accounted for by the normal-state pseudogap without introducing crossover temperatures. A lower crossover temperature was deduced from the ($^{63}T_1T$) data for $YBa_2Cu_4O_8$ plotted in figure 6a (open [26] and full circles [34]). However when $1/^{63}T_1$ and ^{89}K are plotted on the same graph as shown in figure 6b then it can be seen that both $1/^{63}T_1$ and ^{89}K have the same temperature dependence consistent with the absence of crossover temperatures. It is shown in figure 6a that removing the normal-state pseudogap, as observed in the static spin susceptibility, by plotting $^{63}T_1T\,^{89}K_s(T)/^{89}K_s(\infty)$ also removes the apparent lower crossover temperature in ($^{63}T_1T$). This result is similar to the key observation made by Takigawa *et al.* [35] but has been largely ignored. They showed that the ratio $^{17}T_1/^{63}T_1$, where $^{17}T_1$ is the ^{17}O spin-lattice relaxation rate, is quite featureless at the T_L observed in $(^{63}T_1T)^{-1}$ and noted that "this suggests a possibility that the peak in $(^{63}T_1T)^{-1}$ is a combined effect of the T dependence of χ_{spin} and the development of AF correlations and may not require a spin gap to open around 150K". The importance of the relations, $(^{63}T_1)^{-1} \propto K_s$ and $(^{17}T_1T)^{-1} \propto K_s$ can be understood by noting that quite generally, $(T_1T)^{-1}$, can be expressed as [29],

$$(T_1T)^{-1} = \frac{k_B}{2\mu_B{}^2\hbar^2}\sum_{\mathbf{q}}|A(\mathbf{q})|^2\frac{\chi''(\mathbf{q},\omega)}{\omega} \qquad 2.$$

where $|A(\mathbf{q})|$ is the form factor expressed as $A(\mathbf{q})=\sum_j A_j \exp(i\mathbf{q}\cdot\mathbf{r}_j)$, μ_B is the Bohr magneton and $\chi''(\mathbf{q},\omega)$ is the imaginary part of the dynamical spin susceptibility. Using the Mila-Rice Hamiltonian and accounting for the antiferromagnetic correlations it can be show that $(^{17}T_1T)^{-1}$ probes $\chi''(\mathbf{q},\omega)$ about $\mathbf{q}=(0,0)$ while $(^{63}T_1T)^{-1}$ probes $\chi''(\mathbf{q},\omega)$ about $\mathbf{q}=(\pi,\pi)$ [31]. Therefore, the observation that $(^{63}T_1)^{-1} \propto K_s$ and $(^{17}T_1T)^{-1} \propto K_s$ indicates that the pseudogap is observed for all $\mathbf{q}$. This is consistent with the analysis of S/T and χ_s plotted in figure 2 which show that the normal-state pseudogap is observed in the spin and charge spectrum [16].

Recently Corey *et al.* [26] and Curro *et al.* [34] have presented a scaling analysis of $^{63}T_1$ and T_{2G} data from $YBa_2Cu_4O_8$ in terms of two crossover temperatures. However, the data can equally be analysed in terms of no crossover temperatures [33]. This is apparent by first noting that the NAFL model uses a phenomenological dynamical spin susceptibility which can be written as [21],

$$\chi_s(\mathbf{q},\omega) = \frac{a_0\chi_s(T)\xi^2}{[1+(\mathbf{Q}-\mathbf{q})^2 - i\omega/\omega_{sf}]} + \frac{\chi_s(T)}{1-i\omega/\Gamma_0}, \qquad 3.$$

where **Q** is the antiferromagnetic wavevector, ξ is the antiferromagnetic correlation length in units of the average ab plane lattice parameter, ω_{sf} is the paramagnon frequency and Γ_0 is the temperature-independent effective bandwidth. The first term accounts for the strong antiferromagnetic correlations about $\mathbf{Q}=(\pi,\pi)$ while the second term is the Fermi-liquid term. We have included $\chi_s(T)$ as a factor in the first term, as originally proposed, because this is consistent with the analysis above which shows that the pseudogap exist for all **q**. Inserting equation 3 into equation 2, using the Mila-Rice Hamiltonian and in the limit of $\xi >> 1$ leads to $(^{63}T_1)^{-1}=a_1(T/\omega_{sf})\chi_s(T)$ and $(^{17}T_1T)^{-1}=a_2\Gamma_0$. Taking $\omega_{sf}\propto T$ (as is apparent in

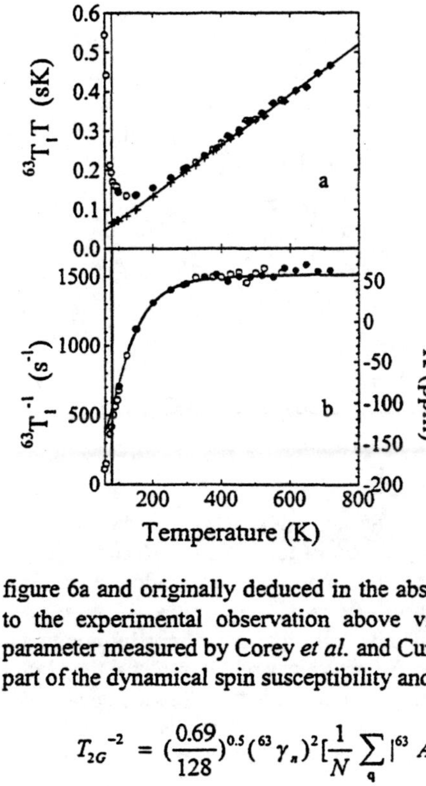

Figure 6: (a) Plot of $^{63}T_1T$ (open [26] and filled circles [34]) and $^{63}T_1T^{89}K_s(T)/^{89}K_0$ (+) against temperature for $YBa_2Cu_4O_8$. (b) Plot of $(^{63}T_1)^{-1}$ against temperature using the data in (a). Also plotted is ^{89}K (dark solid curve) and the scaling curve (solid curve) [33].

figure 6a and originally deduced in the absence of the normal-state pseudogap [37]) leads to the experimental observation above viz. $(^{63}T_1)^{-1}\propto K_s$ and $(^{17}T_1T)^{-1}\propto K_s$. The other parameter measured by Corey *et al.* and Curro *et al.* is T_{2G} which is proportional to the real part of the dynamical spin susceptibility and can be written as [29],

$$T_{2G}^{-2} = \left(\frac{0.69}{128}\right)^{0.5}(^{63}\gamma_n)^2\Big[\frac{1}{N}\sum_{\mathbf{q}}|^{63}A_{eff}(\mathbf{q})|^4\chi'(\mathbf{q},0)^2 - \Big(\frac{1}{N}\sum_{\mathbf{q}}|^{63}A_{eff}(\mathbf{q})\chi'(\mathbf{q},0)\Big)^2\Big] \qquad 4.$$

where $^{63}A_{eff}(\mathbf{q})$ is the effective ^{63}Cu form factor. Using the Mila-Rice Hamiltonian and in the limit of $\xi >> 1$ it can be shown that $(T_{2G})^{-2}=a_3\chi_s(T)\xi$ where a_3 is temperature independent. The resultant temperature dependence of ξ^{-1} is shown in figure 7 where χ_s was obtained from the scaling curve in figure 5. It is clear that there are no well defined crossover temperatures in ξ^{-1}.

Magnetic scaling behaviour has been assumed in the normal-state NAFL model, expressed as $\omega_{sf} \propto \xi^{-z}$. In the quantum critical scaling regime z=1 while in the mean field regime z=2 [29]. Thus $\omega_{sf}\xi^2$ is expected to be temperature independent for $T>T_U$ (~500K for $YBa_2Cu_4O_8$ [26]) and $\omega_{sf}\xi$ is expected to be temperature independent for $T_L<T<T_U$ (T_L=215K for $YBa_2Cu_4O_8$ [26]). However it is apparent in figure 6 that $\omega_{sf}(\propto {}^{63}T_1T\,{}^{89}K_s(T)/{}^{89}K_s(\infty))$ can be written as $\omega_{sf}=a_4T$ and thus $\omega_{sf}\xi$ and $\omega_{sf}\xi^2$ reduce to a_4T/ξ^{-1} and a_4T/ξ^{-2} respectively. Consequently, scaling of this nature is only emphasising

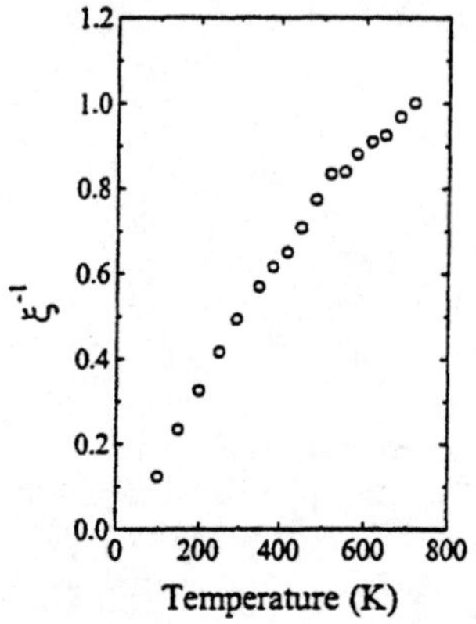

Figure 7: Plot of the $YBa_2Cu_4O_8$ normalised inverse antiferromagnetic correlation length, ξ^{-1}, against temperature.

different temperature regions of ξ^{-1} and cannot be used to obtain well-defined upper and lower crossover temperatures.

4. Origin of the Normal-State Pseudogap.

There is currently no theoretical model of the normal-state pseudogap that can account for all the experimental data. The problem lies in the complex electronic and magnetic behavior. For example, ARPES measurements show the absence of quasiparticle peaks above T_c and near $\mathbf{k}=(\pm\pi,0)$ and $\mathbf{k}=(0,\pm\pi)$, the very region in k-space where E_g is a maximum [38]. Interpretations of this behavior include collective excitations leading to a significant reduction in quasiparticle lifetimes with the possibility of a non-Fermi liquid in this region [38] or strong interactions with collective excitations that lead to a decrease in spectral weight at the quasiparticle peak in the ARPES spectra [39]. There is also evidence from tunneling and ARPES measurements of scattering from collective excitations below T_c which has been attributed to a spin-gap below T_c [40,41,42]. One ARPES study also found evidence for Fermi surface evolution in the normal-state where the Fermi surface progressively appears with increasing temperature [43].

A functional form for the scaling curve in figure 5 can be obtained from the Pauli spin susceptibility, $\chi_s = \mu_B^2 \int N(E)(-\frac{\partial f}{\partial E})dE$, and assuming a triangular density of states that fills in with increasing temperature. This leads to

$$^{89}K=N_0[1-1/z\times\tanh^n(1/z)\ln(\cosh(1/z))]+{}^{89}\sigma, \qquad 5.$$

where $z=k_BT/E_g$ and E_g is the pseudogap energy defined as the energy where the density of

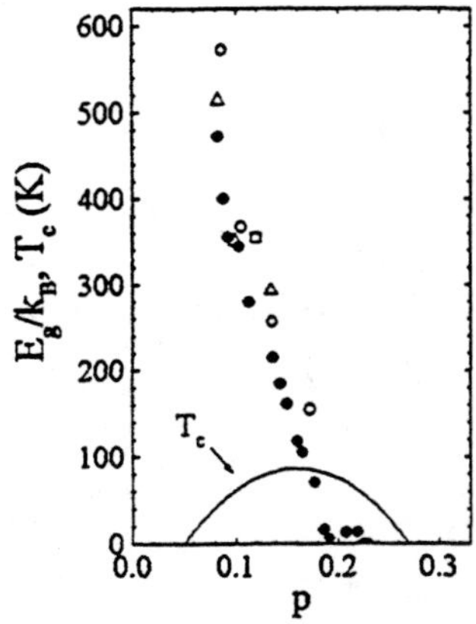

Figure 8: Plot of the hole concentration dependence of T_c (solid curve), E_g determined from the scaling of the ^{89}Y NMR data for $Y_{0.9}Ca_{0.1}Ba_2Cu_3O_{7-\delta}$ (open up triangles [33]), $Y_{0.8}Ca_{0.2}Ba_2Cu_3O_{7-\delta}$ (open circles [33]) and $YBa_2Cu_4O_8$ (open square) and E_g determined from the heat capacity data for $Y_{0.8}Ca_{0.2}Ba_2Cu_3O_{7-\delta}$ (filled circles [42]).

states begins to fall linearly with energy. This scaling curve and the associated density of states contain the essential experimental observations of a linear density of states and NMR shift at low temperatures and a temperature independent NMR shift and electronic entropy at high temperatures. It can be seen figure 3 and figure 5 that this scaling curve does indeed fit the data with n=4.55. We emphasise that scaling the experimental data it is only the hole concentration dependence and not the absolute magnitude that can be determined. This is obvious because one curve must be chosen to scale the other curves against. Thus using a different form for the DOS will result in a different absolute magnitude.

It can be seen in figure 8 that the deduced normal-state pseudogap energy decreases with increasing hole concentration, p, and is comparable to E_g as determined from heat capacity data [44]. In particular, E_g is zero for $p>0.19$. This observation is consistent with Raman [28,45], ARPES [46] and Hall effect [47] measurements.

Isotope effect measurements have been made in the normal-state in an attempt to ascertain the origin of the normal-state pseudogap. The importance of isotope effect measurements is apparent by noting that isotope effect measurements were of crucial importance in establishing the phonon-induced weak coupling BCS model of superconductivity [48]. In the BCS model the isotope effect derives from the superconducting transition temperature, T_c, being proportional to the Debye temperature. As the Debye temperature is proportional to the $M^{1/2}$, where M is the atomic mass, the isotope effect coefficient, $\alpha\equiv-\ln T_c/d\ln M=0.5$. The later inclusion of the coulomb interaction resulted in predicted α values of less than 0.5 and enabled a reasonably good fit to the isotope effect data where low isotope effect coefficients correspond to low T_c values [49]. The situation is completely different in the HTS were the oxygen isotope effect is small near optimal doping and maximum T_c (α_O~0.05 for $YBa_2Cu_3O_{7-\delta}$ with T_c=91K [50])

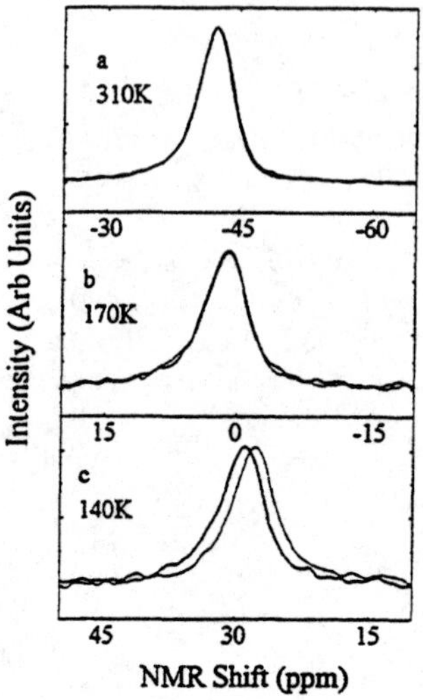

Figure 9: Plot of the ^{89}Y NMR spectra at the temperatures indicated for ^{16}O exchanged $YBa_2{}^{63}Cu_4O_8$ (dark solid curves) and ^{18}O exchanged $YBa_2{}^{65}Cu_4O_8$ (light solid curves).

and increases dramatically for lower hole concentrations and smaller T_c values (α_O~0.46 for $YBa_2(Cu_{0.87}Co_{0.13})_3O_{7-\delta}$ with T_c=22.67K [50]). Even strong coupling calculations assuming phonon-mediated pairing fail to account for the isotope effect in the HTSC.

Oxygen isotope effect measurements have been made on ^{16}O and ^{18}O exchanged $YBa_2Cu_4O_8$ [30]. Raman measurements indicated that the ^{18}O sample was 90% exchanged. ^{89}Y NMR magic angle spinning measurements were used to obtain the NMR shift in the normal-state. Typical ^{89}Y NMR magic angle spinning spectra are shown in figure 9 where it can be seen that there is no oxygen isotope induced shift in the normal-state for the 170K and 310K spectra.

This is seen more clearly in figure 10 where ΔK_s is plotted against temperature. If an isotope effect existed in the normal state pseudogap its coefficient can be written as α_{Eg}=-dln(E_g)/dlnM and hence $\Delta E_g/E_g=-\alpha_{Eg}\Delta M/M$. Using the experimental observation that $^{89}K_s={}^{89}K_s(z)$ it can easily be shown that an isotope effect in E_g will lead to a shift in the ^{89}Y NMR Knight shift of $\Delta^{89}K_s = (-z\frac{\partial K_s}{\partial z})\frac{\Delta E_g}{E_g}$ and hence $\Delta^{89}K_s = (-z\frac{\partial K_s}{\partial z})\alpha_{E_g}\frac{\Delta M}{M}$ which also removes the dependence on the absolute magnitude of the normal state pseudogap. Using equation 2 for the scaling function and the experimental α_O value of α_O=(0.076±0.010)K it can be seen that the data cannot be accounted for by assuming an isotope effect in the normal state pseudogap with the same value as that in T_c. The origin

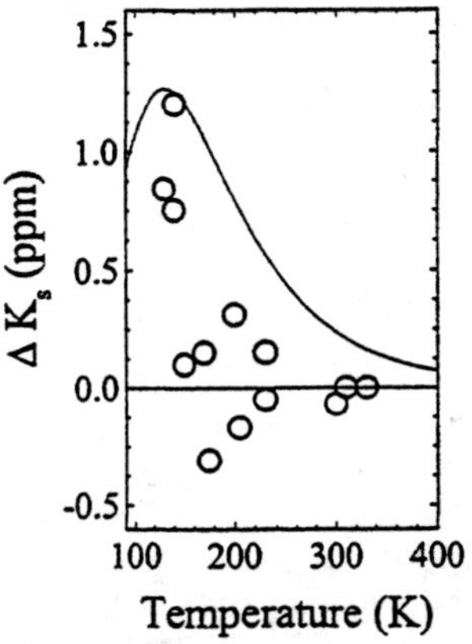

Figure 10: Plot of the isotope induced shift in the Knight shift, ΔK_s, obtained from ^{89}Y NMR measurements plotted against temperature for oxygen isotope effect measurements on $YBa_2Cu_4O_8$ (open circles). The solid curve is the expected shift if the normal-state oxygen isotope effect coefficient is the same as the oxygen isotope effect coefficient in T_c.

of the positive effect for temperatures less than 150K is unknown.

The absence of an isotope effect in the normal-state for temperatures above 150K with the same magnitude as the isotope effect in T_c points to correlations of predominately electronic origin. It is also inconsistent with models which attribute the normal-state pseudogap to precursor superconducting pairing without long range phase coherence.

5. Relationship between the Normal-State Pseudogap and the Superconducting Order Parameter. Considerable importance has been placed on models that assume that the normal-state pseudogap arises from precursor superconducting pairing [5]. However the absence of an oxygen isotope effect in the normal-state above 150K [30] and the scaling of S/T below T_c but not above T_c, shown in figure 11 [16], clearly show that the corelations responsible for superconductivity and the normal-state pseudogap are independent and competing. In figure 11 the electronic entropy for $Y_{0.8}Ca_{0.2}Ba_2Cu_3O_{7-\delta}$ is shown scaled against $z=2k_BT/\Delta_0$ where Δ_0 is the superconducting gap. It is apparent that the data scale below T_c but not above T_c.

Loram *et al.* [1] have developed a simple model that includes the independence of the corelations responsible for the normal-state pseudogap and superconductivity. In this model the quasiparticle dispersion can be written as,

$$E(\mathbf{k}) = [\varepsilon(\mathbf{k})^2 + \Delta'(\mathbf{k})^2 + E_g(\mathbf{k})^2]^{1/2} \qquad 6.$$

where $\varepsilon(\mathbf{k})$ is the quasiparticle dispersion in the absence of superconductivity or the normal-state pseudogap, $\Delta'(\mathbf{k})$ is the superconducting order parameter and $E_g(\mathbf{k})$ is the normal-state pseudogap. This model accounts for the experimentally observed decrease in the specific heat jump with decreasing hole concentration shown in figure 12a where γ_{el} from heat capacity measurements on $YBa_2Cu_3O_{7-\delta}$ is plotted against temperature. The calculated γ_{el} is shown in figure 12b using $\varepsilon(\mathbf{k}) = \hbar^2k^2 / 2m^*$, $\gamma_{el} = \partial S_{el} / \partial T$ and

$$S_{el} = -k_B \int N(E)\{f(E)\ln[F(E)] + [1 - f(E)]\ln[1 - f(E)]\}dE \qquad 7.$$

It is apparent that this simple model reproduces the decrease in the specific heat jump at T_c with decreasing hole concentration.

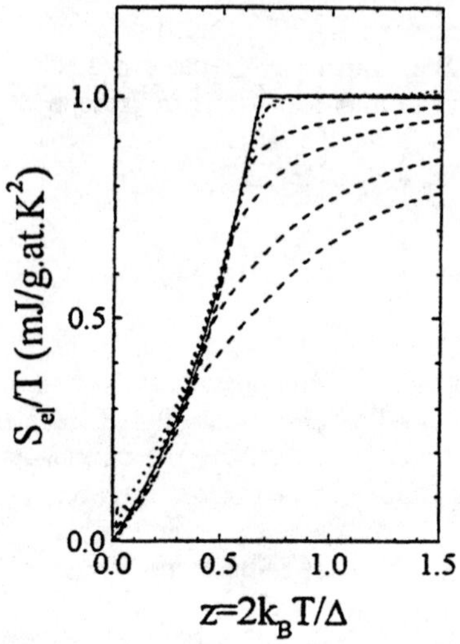

Figure 11: Plot of S/T against the scaling parameter $z=2k_BT/\Delta_0$ for $Y_{0.8}Ca_{0.2}Ba_2Cu_3O_{7-\delta}$ [15]. The dotted curves are for overdoped samples and the dashed curves are for underdoped samples. The solid curve is S/T expected in the absence of the normal-state pseudogap [16].

The close relationship between S/T and χ_s mentioned earlier, $S/T=a_W\chi_s$, is also

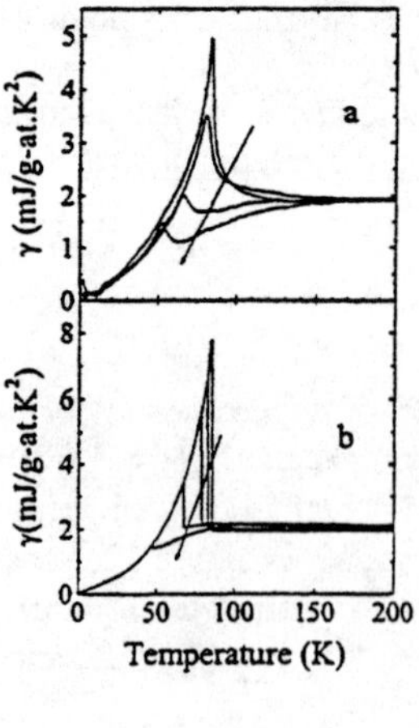

Figure 12: (a) Plot of the normalised γ_{el} against temperature for $YBa_2Cu_3O_{7-\delta}$ with δ values shown. (b) Plot of γ_{el} against temperature using the model described in the text. The arrow indicates increasing E_g.

evident in the NMR data. Using $\gamma_{el} = \partial S/\partial T$, $S/T = a_w\chi_s$, and $(^{63}T_1)^{-1} \propto K_s$ it is easy to

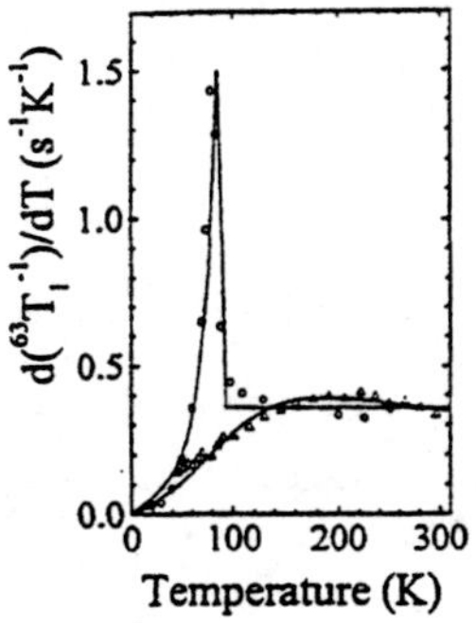

Figure 13: Plot of $d(^{63}T_1^{-1})/dT$ against temperature for $YBa_2Cu_3O_{6.63}$ (open circles) and $YBa_2Cu_3O_{6.63}$ (open up triangles) using the data of Takigawa *et al.* [35].

show that $\gamma_{el} \propto \partial(^{63}T_1^{-1}) / \partial T$. It can be seen in figure 13 that this is consistent with the data. Here $d(^{63}T_1^{-1})/dT$ is plotted for $YBa_2Cu_3O_{6.63}$ (open circles [33]) and $YBa_2Cu_3O_7$ (open up triangle [35]).

6. Implication of the Normal-State Pseudogap.

Tallon *et al.* have recently noted that T_c is suppressed more rapidly in underdoped than in overdoped $Y_{1-x}Ca_xBa_2(Cu_{1-y}Zn_y)_3O_{7-\delta}$ [51] and $BiSr_2Ca(Cu_{1-y}Zn_y)_2O_8$ [52] samples.

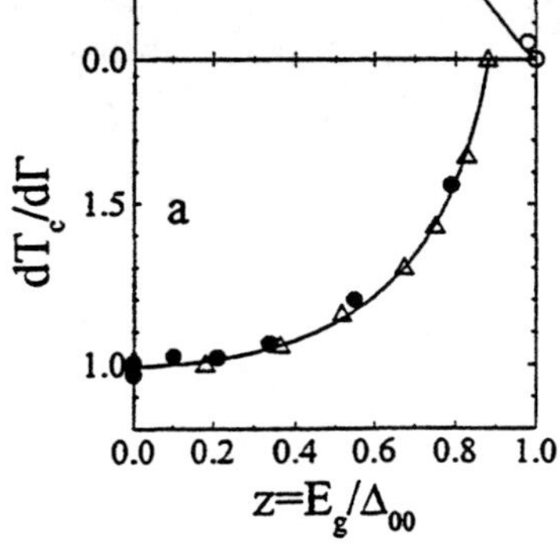

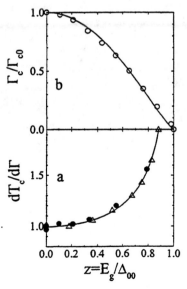

Figure 14: (a) Plot of the calculated $dT_c/d\Gamma(z)$ scaled by $dT_c/d\Gamma(0)$ against $z=E_g/\Delta_{00}$ (open up triangles). Also shown is the experimental data for $Y_{1-x}Ca_xBa_2(Cu_{1-y}Zn_y)_3O_{7-\delta}$ (filled circles). The solid curve is described in the text. (b) Plot of the calculated values of Γ_c/Γ_{c0} against z. The solid curve is $\Gamma_c/\Gamma_{c0}=[1-(E_g/\Delta_{00})^2]^{5/4}$ [54].

In particular, they observed a strong increase in $dT_c/dy(p)$ for small y and for $p<0.19$ consistent with the opening the normal-state pseudogap for $p<0.19$ mentioned above. They found that.

$$\frac{dT_c}{dy(p)} = a_5\{1 - [\frac{E_g(p)}{\Delta_{00}(p)}]^2\}^{0.5} \qquad 8.$$

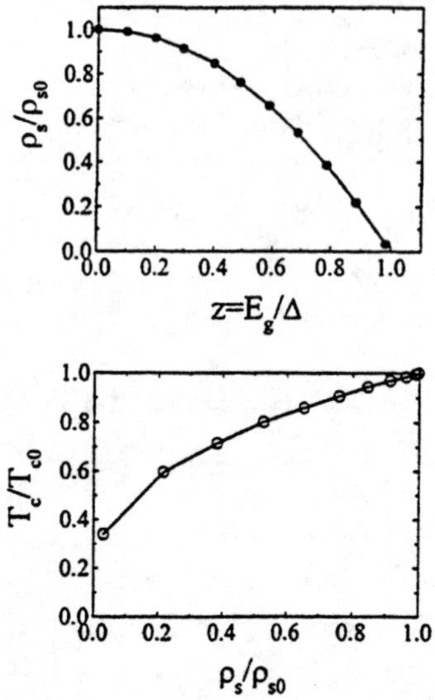

Figure 15: (a) Calculated plot of ρ_s against z where ρ_s is scaled by ρ_s when z=0. (b) Calculated plot of T_c/T_{c0} against $\rho_s/\rho_s(z=0)$ where T_{c0} is T_c when ρ_s=0 [54].

provides a good description of the data where $E_g(p)$ is the magnitude of the normal-state pseudogap and $\Delta_{00}(p)$ is the magnitude of the superconducting gap at T_c=0 and in the absence of pairbreaking. It is possible to show using the unitary scattering (strong scattering), $d_{x^2-y^2}$ model of Sun and Maki [53] but including the normal-state pseudogap that this relationship is expected [54]. This can be shown by starting with the following equation for the order parameter,

$$\Delta'(\mathbf{k}) = -\pi T N_0 \sum_{\mathbf{k}} \left\langle \frac{V(\mathbf{k},\mathbf{k}')\Delta'(\mathbf{k}')}{\sqrt{\tilde{\omega}_n^{\ 2} + E_g(\mathbf{k})^2 + \Delta'(\mathbf{k})^2}} \right\rangle \qquad 9.$$

where the average is over the Fermi surface, N_0 is the DOS at the Fermi level and $\tilde{\omega}_n$ are the renormalised Matsubara frequencies. When the normal-state pseudogap is included $\tilde{\omega}_n$ becomes, in the unitary limit,

$$\tilde{\omega}_n = \omega_n + \Gamma \left\langle \frac{\tilde{\omega}_n}{\sqrt{\tilde{\omega}_n^{\ 2} + E_g(\mathbf{k})^2 + \Delta'(\mathbf{k})^2}} \right\rangle^{-1} \qquad 10.$$

where $\omega_n = \pi T(2n-1)$ and Γ is the scattering rate parameter expressed as $\Gamma = n_i/\pi N_0$ where n_i is the two dimensional impurity concentration. Γ_c/Γ_{c0} and the initial $dT_c/d\Gamma$ are obtained from the self consistent solutions to equations 9 and 10 and shown in figure 14 as a function of $z = E_g/\Delta_{00}$, where Γ_c is the critical Γ at which $T_c=0$ and Γ_{c0} is the critical Γ at which $T_c=0$ and when $E_g=0$. It can be seen that the effect of the normal-state pseudogap is to reduce Γ_c/Γ_{c0} and increase $dT_c/d\Gamma$. Included in figure 14a is the data of Tallon *et al.* [51] using $z=3.08-15.4p$ (open circles). The solid line in figure 14a is $dT_c/dz \propto (1-z^2)^{a5}$ where $a_5=0.45$, close to the $a_5=0.5$ obtained by Tallon *et al.* It can be seen that this gives a good fit to the data.

The normal-state pseudogap can also account for some of the decrease in the superconducting condensate density, ρ_s ($\propto 1/\lambda^2$ where λ is the penetration depth). This can be shown by calculating ρ_s in a manner similar to Kim *et al.* [55] and also included the normal-state pseudogap leading to,

$$\rho_s = 2N_0 v_F^{\,2} \pi m_e T \sum_n \int_0^{2\pi} \frac{d\theta}{2\pi} \frac{\Delta'(\theta)^2 \cos^2(\theta)}{(\tilde{\omega}_n^{\,2} + E_g(\theta)^2 + \Delta'(\theta)^2)^{3/2}} \qquad 11.$$

where v_F is the 2D Fermi velocity and m_e is the electron mass. It can be seen in figure 15a that ρ_s is predicted to decrease as E_g increases [54]. The corresponding Uemura plot is shown in figure 15b where T_c is plotted against ρ_s. Experimentally T_c is approximately linear with ρ_s on the underdoped side.

The effect of the normal-state pseudogap is also seen in the superconducting condensate energy, U, as can be seen in figure 16a where U(z) is plotted against z obtained from $U = \int_0^{T_c} (S_n(T') - S_s(T'))dT'$ where S_n is the electronic entropy calculated in the absence of superconductivity and S_s is the electronic entropy calculated in the

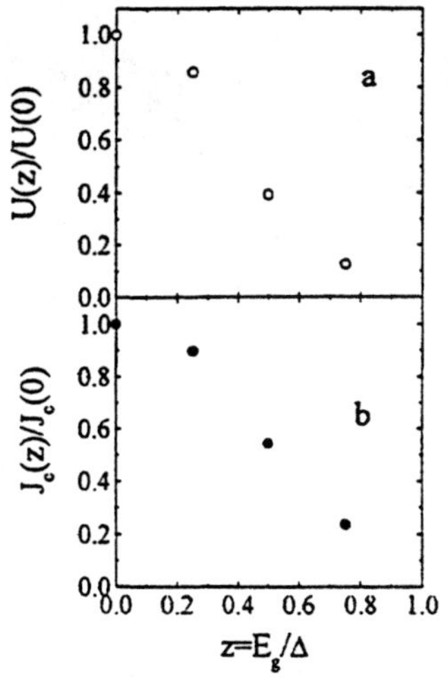

Figure 16: (a) Plot of the superconducting condensate energy against $z=E_g/\Delta$. (b) Plot of the critical superconducting current density, J_c, against z.

superconducting state. It can be seen that the condenstate energy decreases with increasing E_g as has been observed experimentally [44].

This model also predicts that the critical current should be a maximum near p=0.19 where E_g=0 and not at maximum hole doping (p=0.16). This can be shown in a simple model by defining the critical current, J_c, as $J_c \propto H_c/\lambda$. The result is shown in figure 16b where H_c is obtained by modeling the electronic entropy and λ is obtained by modeling the superconducting condensate density. It can be seen that, within this simple model, J_c is predicted to be a maximum when E_g=0.

7. Conclusions.

A number of conclusions can be drawn concerning the normal-state pseudogap. Firstly, it is apparent that there are no crossover or onset temperatures and, therefore, complex theoretical scenarios based on crossover or onset temperatures need to be revised. Secondly, the normal-state pseudogap does not appear to originate from phonons or precursor superconducting pairing. Furthermore, the normal-state pseudogap correlations compete with superconductivity leading to a reduction in T_c. Finally, the normal-state pseudogap accounts for the hole concentration dependence of the decline in T_c by impurities and provides a partial explanation of the Uemura curve. The disappearance of the normal-state pseudogap for p>0.19 indicates that maximum, ρ_s, U and J_c should occur near p=0.19 rather than maximum T_c (p=0.16).

References.

1. J. W. Loram, K. A. Mirza, J. R. Cooper, W. Y. Liang and J. M. Wade, J. Supercond. **7**, 243 (1994).
2. B. Batlogg, H. Y. Hwang, H. Takagi, R. J. Cava, H. L. Kao and J. Kwo, Physica C **235-240**, 130 (1994).
3. A. G. Loeser, Z. –X. Zhen, D. S. Dessau, D. S. Marshall, C. H. Park, P. Fournier and A. Kapitulnik, Science **273**, 325 (1996).
4. H. Ding T. Yokoya, J. C. Campuzano, T. Takahashi, M. Randeria, M. R. Norman, T. Mochiku, K. Kadowaki and J. Giapintzakis, Nature **382**, 51 (1996).
5. V. J. Emery and S. A. Kivelson, Nature **374**, 434 (1993).
6. A. S. Alaxandrov, V. V. Kabanov and N. F. Mott, Phys. Rev. Lett. **77**, 4796 (1996).
7. H. Fukuyama, H. Kohno and T. Tanamoto, J. Low Temp. Phys. **95**, 309 (1994).
8. P. A. Lee and X. G. Wen, Phys. Rev. Lett. **76**, 503 (1996).
9. D. Pines, Physica C **282-287**, 273 (1997).
10. T. Dahm. D. Manske and L. Tewordt, Phys. Rev. B **56**, 11419 (1997).
11. I. Eremin, M. Eremin, S. Varlamov, D. Brinkmann, M. Mali and J. Roos, Phys. Rev. B **56**, 11305 (1997).
12. U. Lõw, V. J. Emery, K. Fabricius and S. A. Kivelson, Phys. Rev. Lett. **72**, 1918 (1994).
13. S. –C. Zhang, Science **275**, 1089 (1997).
14. C. Bernhard, J. L. Tallon, C. Bucci, R. De. Renzi, G. Guidi, G. V. M. Williams and Ch. Niedermayer, Phys. Rev. Lett. **77**, 2304 (1996).
15. J. L. Tallon, J. R. Cooper, P. S. I. P. N. de Silva, G. V. M. Williams and J. W. Loram, Phys. Rev. Lett. **75**, 4114 (1995).

16. J. L. Tallon, J. W. Loram , G. V. M. Williams and C. Bernhard, (submitted to Phys. Rev. Lett.).
17. J. W. Loram, K. A. Mirza, J. M. Wade, J. R. Cooper , N. Athanassopoulou and W. Y. Liang, *"Advances in Superconductivity VII"*, (Springer-Verlag, Tokyo, 1995) p75.
18. G. V. M. Williams, J. L. Tallon, E. M. Haines , R. Michalak and R. Dupree, Phys. Rev. Lett. **78**, 721 (1997).
19. A. Jánossy, T. Fehér, G. Oszlányi and G. V. M. Williams, Phys. Rev. Lett. **79**, 2726 (1997).
20. A. Millis, L. B. Ioffe and H. Monien, J. Phys. Chem. Solids **56**, 1641 (1995).
21. D. Pines, Z. Phys. B **103**, 129 (1997).
22. I. Tomeno, T. Machi, K. Tai, N. Koshizuka, S. Kambe, A. Hayashi, Y. Ueda and H. Yasuoka, Phys. Rev. B **49**, 15327 (1994).
23. Y. Yasuoka, Physica C **282-287**, 199 (1997).
24. A. Chubukov, D. Pines and B. Stojkovic, J. Phys. Condens. Matter **8**, 1 (1996).
25. A. Suter, M. Mali, J. Roos, D. Brinkmann, J. Karpinski and E. Kaldis, Phys. Rev. B **56**, 5542 (1997).
26. N. J. Curro, T. Imai, C. P. Slichter and B. Dabrowski, Phys. Rev. B **56**, 877 (1997).
27. Ch. Renner, B. Revaz, J.-Y. Genoud, K. Kadowaki, and Ø. Fischer, Phy. Rev. Lett. **80**, 149 (1998).
28. J. W. Quilty, H. J. Trodahl and D. M. Pooke, Phys. Rev. B **57**, 11097 (1998).
29. V. Barzykin and D. Pines, Phys. Rev. B **52**, 13585 (1995).
30. G. V. M. Williams, J. L. Tallon, J. W. Quilty, H. J. Trodahl and N. E. Flower, Phys. Rev. Lett. **80**, 377 (1998).
31. A. J. Millis, H. Monien and D. Pines, Phys. Rev. B **42**, 167 (1990).
32. N. E. Hussey, K. Nozawa, H. Takagi, S. Adachi and K. Tanabe, Phys. Rev. B **56**, 11423 (1997).
33. G. V. M. Williams, J. L. Tallon and J. W. Loram, Phys. Rev. B (to be published).
34. R. L. Corey, N. J. Curro, K. O'Hara, T. Imai, C. P. Slichter, K. Yoshimura, M. Katah and K. Kosuge, Phys. Rev. B **53**, 5907 (1996).
35. M. Takigawa, A. P. Reyes, P. C. Hammel, J. D. Thompson, R. H. Heffner, Z. Fisk, and K. C. Ott, Phys. Rev. B **43**, 247 (1991).
36. F. Mila and T. M. Rice, Physica C **157**, 561 (1989).
37. H. Monien, D. Pines and M. Takigawa, Phys. Rev. B **43**, 248 (1991).
38. Z. –X. Shen and J. R. Schrieffer, Phys. Rev. Lett. **78**, 1771 (1997).
39. M. R. Norman, M. Randeria, H. Ding, J. C. Campuzano (unpublished).
40. Anjan K. Gupta and K. –W. Ng, Phys. Rev. B **58**, 8901 (1998).
41. M. R. Norman, H. Ding, J. C. Campuzano, T. Takeuchi, M. Randeria, T. Yokoya, T. Takahashi, T. Mochiku and K. Kadowaki, Phys. Rev. Lett. **79**, 3506 (1997).
42. M. R. Norman and H. Ding, Phys. Rev. B **57**, 11089 (1998).
43. M. R. Norman, H. Ding, M. Randeria, J. C. Campuzano, T. Yokoya, T. Takeuchi, T. Takahashi, T. Mochiku, K. Kadowaki, P. Guptasarma and D. G. Hinks, (to be published in Nature).
44. J. W. Loram, K. A. Mirza, J. R. Cooper and J. L. Tallon, Physica C **282-287**, 1405 (1997).

45. J. G. Naeini, X. K. Chen, J. C. Irwin, M. Okuya, T. Kimura and K. Kishio (submitted to Phys. Rev. Lett.).
46. A. ino, T. Mizokawa, K. Kobayashi, A. Fujimori, T. Sasagawa, T. Kimura, K. Kishio, T. Tamasaku, H. Eisaki and S. Uchida, Phys. Rev. Lett. **81**, 2124 (1998).
47. H. V. Hwang, B. Batlogg, T. Takagi, H. L. Kao, J. Kwo, R. J. Cava, J. J. Krajewskiu and W. F. Peck, Phys. Rev. Lett. **72**, 2636 (1994).
48. J. Bardeen, Phys. Rev. **79**, 167 (1950).
49. G. Gladstone, M. A. Jensen and J. R. Schrieffer in *"Superconductivity"* edited by R. D. Parks (Marcel Dekker Inc., New York, 1969), pp767.
50. J. R. Franck in *"Physical Properties of High Temperature Superconductors IV"*, edited by D. M. Ginsberg (World Scientific, Singapore, 1994), pp189.
51. J. L. Tallon, C. Bernhard, G. V. M. Williams and J. W. Loram, Phys. Rev. Lett. **79**, 5294 (1997).
52. J. L. Tallon, Phys. Rev. Lett. (to be published).
53. Y. Sun and K. Maki, Phys. Rev. B **51**, 6059 (1995).
54. G. V. M. Williams, E. M. Haines and J. L. Tallon, Phys. Rev. B **57**, 146 (1998).
55. H. Kim, G. Preosti and P. Muzikar, Phys. Rev. B **49**, 3544 (1994).

Studies of High Temperature
Superconductors
Volume 27

ISBN 1-56072-684-9

SOME THEORETICAL MODELS FOR THE PSEUDOGAP IN HTSC

K. P. SINHA

Department of Physics, Indian Institute of Science, Bangalore 560 012, India
And
Jawaharlal Nehru Centre for Advanced Scientific Research, IISc. Campus, Bangalore 560 012, India

1. INTRODUCTION

The discovery of high T_c superconductors (HTSC) in layered cuprate systems made over ten years ago has led to a deluge of experimental and theoretical researches all over the world [1,2]. While newer families of cuprates with rising critical temperature T_c have been prepared, measurements of other physical properties have revealed many anomalous results both in the superconducting and normal states. These have posed serious theoretical challenges towards formulating the mechanisms of pairing and other anomalous behaviour. Many theoretical models have been suggested and only a few are likely to survive in the teeth of some reliable experimental data. The central issue is to observe the evolution of electronic structure with hole doping near the filling controlled metal-insulator transition (MIT). First there were doubts whether or not these doped cuprates constitute regular Fermi liquids. Ideas of Luttinger liquids and other exotic forms of quasiparticle states were suggested [3].

2. EXPERIMENTAL EVIDENCE OF PSEUDOGAP

However, the existence of a Fermi surface in the metallic regime of the high T_c materials has been now firmly established experimentally [4,5]. Extensive high resolution angle-resolved photoemission, scanning tunneling microscopy and inelastic neutron scattering studies have been carried out on $YBa_2Cu_3O_7$(YBCO), $Bi_2Sr_2CaCu_2O_{8+\delta}$ (Bi 2212) and the $La_{2-x}Sr_xCuO_4$ (LSCO) systems [4-9]. These studies reveal the appearance of a pseudogap in the density of states before the critical temperature T_c is approached from above. This pseudogap also opens up below a characteristic temperature T* for each system. Accordingly, the opening of this kind of pseudogap is considered to be a precursor effect of the superconducting phase fluctuations [11]. Furthermore, the fact that the pseudogap is accompanied by a predominantly incoherent quasiparticle spectra in some regions of the Brillouin Zone is a very significant experimental discovery and may hold the crucial clue to the mechanism of high-T_c superconductors (HTSC).

The appearance of a sharp dispersionless peak in photo emission spectra in $Bi_2Sr_2CaCu_2O_{8+\delta}$ (T_c = 87K) along Γ-$\overline{M}$-Z, i.e., (0,0) – (π,0) – (2π,0) in the normal (105 K) and superconducting state has some special features [10]. The peak at $\overline{M}$ which is visible at about the energy 40 meV in the normal state sharpens in the superconducting state. We shall see, in the context of the lochon model, that the above result suggests strong local pair correlations in the normal state which amplify as one goes to the superconducting state [11].

Tunneling spectra and neutron scattering results on YBCO also show such peaks around 40 meV [6-8]. The pseudo-gap has also been observed by the measurement of nuclear spin-lattice relaxation rate in bilayer 123 system and single layer 214 systems [12]. The temperature at which this pseudogap opens (T_{pg}) is determined at the peak of $1/T_1T$ versus T, where $1/T_1$ is the spin-lattice relaxation rate. This peak temperature is comparable but larger than the superconducting T_c of systems such as $YBa_2Cu_4O_8$, $YBa_2Cu_3O_7$, $Tl_2Ba_2CuO_6$ and $La_{2-x}Sr_xCuO_4$ [12] (see Fig. 1).

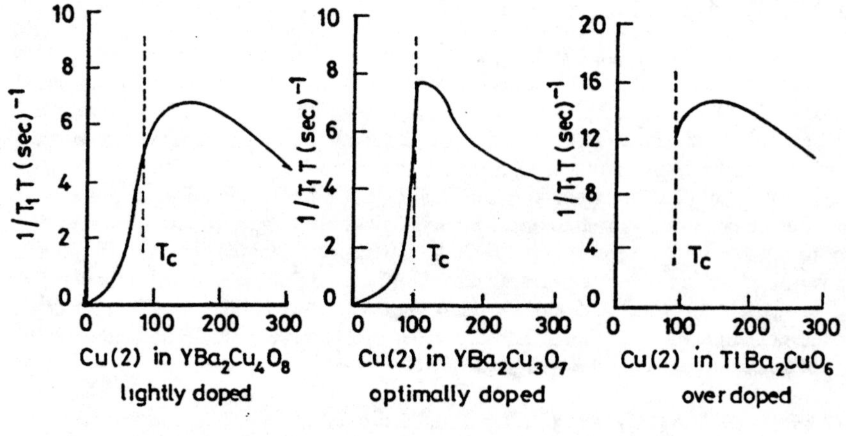

Fig. 1: Temperature dependencd of $1/T_1T$ for Cu(2) sites in CuO_2 planes by NMR (After Yasuoka [12]).

Ding et al [5] have made a careful spectroscopic (ARPES) study of the pseudogap in the normal state of underdoped high T_c superconductors (mainly $Bi_2\,Sr_2\,Ca\,Cu_2O_{8+\delta}$) as a function of doping. The results are best summarized in the form of a schematic phase diagram

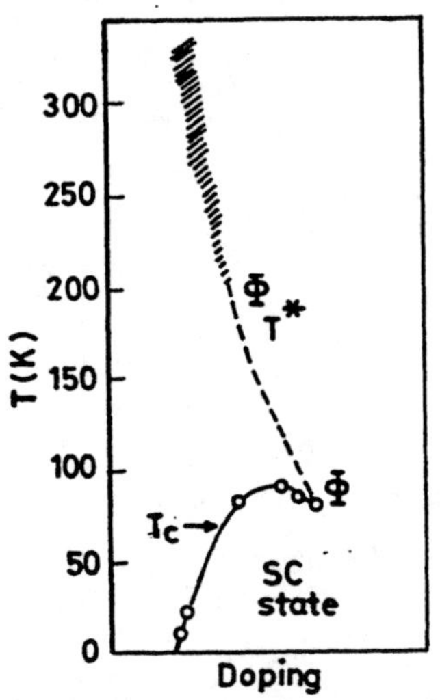

Fig. 2: Schematic phase diagram for Bi 2212 as a function of doping. Measured, T_c is denoted by open circles and ϕ are T^* at which pseudogap closes. For the T_c = 10K, the symbol at 301 K is a lower bound of T^*. The portion between T^* and T_c is the unusual "normal state" having a pseudogap in the excitation spectrum (Adapted from Ding et al. [5]).

The important point emerging out of these experimental studies is that T* is larger for the under doped samples than for higher doped samples. For the T_c = 10K sample the pseudogap is quite large in the normal state with T* > 301 K. The gapless Fermi surface is not recovered even at 301. Ding et al. [5] infer the shape and the size of the Fermi surface from the minimum gap locus. It is found that the minimum gap locus for the T_c = 10K sample is a large barrel as in the optimal and lightly – under doped samples. Its volume is smaller for the 10K sample than the T_c = 83K sample. This is an expected result.

Norman et al. [10] found unusual dispersion and line shape of the photoemission spectra in the superconducting state of $Bi_2\ Sr_2\ CaCu_2O_{8+\delta}$ (Bi 2212). Below T_c two features near the (π,0) point of the Brillouin Zone are seen. There is a sharp peak at low energy and a bump at a higher binding energy. It is found that the sharp peak persists at low energy on moving towards the point (0,0). On the other hand, the broad bump displays appreciable dispersion. This correlates significantly with the normal state dispersion.

The temperature dependence of the line shape in Bi 2212 is quite dramatic. The broad normal state spectrum near (π,0) point develops into a sharp peak below $T < T_c$ at the energy 40 meV. (See Fig. 3).

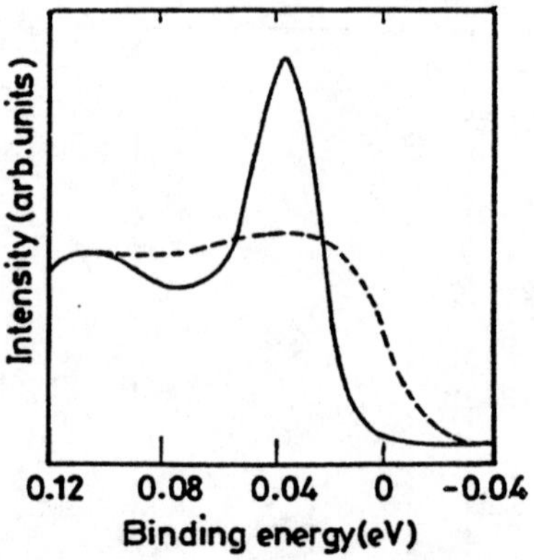

Fig. 3: Results at (π,o) point in the normal state (105 K, dashed line) and in the superconducting state (13 K, solid line) for Bi 2212 sample (T_c = 87 K) (After Norman et al. [10]).

The most important aspect of the results of Norman et al. [10] is the dispersionless nature of the sharp peak observed by them. They further plotted the position of the low energy peak and higher binding energy hump as a function of the energy of the single broad peak in the normal state. This shows a strong resemblance to the predicted feature of electrons interacting with a sharp mode in the superconducting state. An adaptation of their plot is shown in Fig. 4.

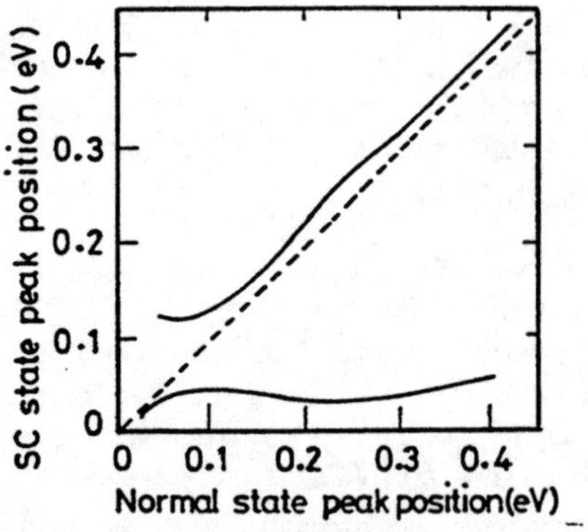

Fig. 4: Solid line is based on the experimental data of Norman et al. [10]. The dotted line denotes the normal state dispersion.

Norman et al. [10] conclude with the remark that they have found the presence of a persistent low energy phase in the photoemission spectra in Bi 2212 in the superconducting (SC) state. This exists over a large momentum range near the $\overline{M}(\pi,0)$ point. It is inferred from the dispersion and the higher binding energy hump as a function of momentum that the electrons in the SC state are interacting with a mode of resonant character with energy near $1.3\Delta_M$ where Δ_M is the SC energy gap at $\overline{M}$ point. This is close to 40 meV. They further emphasize that the electron self-energy is dominated by electron-electron interaction. This is consistent with an electron-electron origin to the pairing. We will see later on that the fermion-lochon (local charged boson) interaction is the kind of mechanism which involves pair wise electron-electron interaction.

At this stage a brief account of the resonance peak observed by other techniques will be in order. Inelastic neutron scattering experiments first demonstrated the existence of a sharp collective mode ("resonance peak") in the superconducting state of optimally doped (YBCO) i.e. $YBa_2Cu_3O_7$ [8,13]. Recent experiments show that this feature exists in the under doped $YBa_2Cu_3O_{6+x}$ also [14,15]. However, in the underdoped compounds the resonance peak appears even in the normal state but is considerably broadened [15]. This is similar to the ARPES result on Bi 2212 given by Norman et al. [10].

Tunneling experiments on Bi 2212 by Renner et al. [6] also finds the resonance peak but is not consistent with the picture in which ω_{res} decreased with decreasing doping [6].

We will now consider various theoretical models that have been advanced to explain the pseudogap and the resonance peak ending with an extended account of the lochon-fermion model.

3. THEORETICAL MODELS

Many theoretical models have been put forward. In what follows only a few plausible ones will be discussed.

(a) Interlayer Tunneling Model

Yin et al. [19] considered a model within the context of inter layer tunneling theory of high temperature superconductors. They consider a reduced Hamiltonian in a subspace in which both the states ($\underline{k}\uparrow$) and ($-\underline{k}\downarrow$) are both simultaneously occupied or unoccupied.

$$H_{red} = \Sigma \; \varepsilon_{\underline{k}} C^{\dagger}_{\underline{k}\sigma i} C_{\underline{k}\sigma i} - \Sigma V_{\underline{k},\underline{k}'} C^{\dagger}_{k\uparrow i} C^{\dagger}_{-\underline{k}'\downarrow i} C_{-k'\downarrow i} C_{k'\uparrow i}$$

$$- \Sigma \; T_J [C^{\dagger}_{\underline{k}\uparrow i} C^{\dagger}_{-\underline{k}\downarrow i} C_{-\underline{k}\downarrow j} C_{k\uparrow j} + H.C]., \qquad (3.1)$$

where ($C^{\dagger}_{\underline{k}\sigma i}$, $C_{k\sigma i}$) are fermion (creation, annihilation) operators for state $|\underline{k}\sigma i>$, i = 1,2 is the layer index, σ = spin, $\underline{k}$ = in plane wave vector, $\varepsilon_{\underline{k}}$ is the single particle energy and V is the in-plane pairing interaction and T_J is the Josephson type inter-layer tunneling matrix element. In the mean field analysis they find the gap equation

$$\Delta_{\underline{k}} = (1 / 1-\chi_{\underline{k}} T_J(\underline{k})(\Sigma V_{\underline{k},\underline{k}'} \chi_{\underline{k}'} \Delta_{\underline{k}'} \qquad (3.2)$$

where $\chi_k = (1/2\ E_k) \tan h\ (E_k/2T)$ is the pair susceptibility and $E_k = [(\varepsilon_k - \mu)^2 + \Delta^2_k]^{1/2}$, μ being the chemical potential. Further the factorization $V_{k,k'} = V g_k g_{k'}$ was resorted to by assuming that $g_k = 1/2[\cos(k_x a) - \cos(k_y a)]$ has the d-wave symmetry. The full gap at T = 0 on the Fermi surface, taking the gap to be real turns out to be

$$\Delta_{kF} = g_{kF}\Delta_o + (T_J(k_F)/2)\ \mathrm{sgn}(\Delta_{kF}); \qquad (3.3)$$

Δ_o is a positive definite integral.

For the above model the imaginary part of the spin susceptibility $\chi(q,\omega)$ their expression is

$$\chi(q,\omega) = \Sigma\ [A^{+}_{k,q}\ F^{-}_{k,q}/\Omega^{1}_{k,q}(\omega)] + (A^{-}_{k,q}(1 - F^{+}_{k,q})/2 \times \{(1/\Omega^{2+}_{k,q}(\omega)) - (1/\Omega^{2-}_{k,q}(\omega))\}] \qquad (3.4)$$

Here

$$A^{\pm}_{k,q} = ½[1 \pm (\varepsilon_k - \mu)(\varepsilon_{k+q} - \mu) + \Delta_k \Delta_{k+q})/E_k E_{k+q})]$$

$$\Omega^{1}_{kq}(\omega) = \omega - (E_{k+q} - E_k) + i\delta$$

$$\Omega^{2\pm}_{k,q}(\omega) = \omega \pm (E_{k+q} + E_k) + i\delta \qquad (3.5)$$

$F^{\pm}_{k,q} = f(E_{k+q}) \pm f(E_k)$; f(x) = the Fermi function. For computation they choose the inplane one electron dispersion as $\varepsilon_k = -2t_1[\cos(k_x a) + \cos(k_y a)] + 4t_2 \cos(k_x a)\cos(k_y a)$. The values of the parameters are $t_1 = 0.25$ eV, $t_2 = 0.45\ t_1$, and $\mu = -0.315$ eV which corresponds to an open Fermi surface with band filling of 0.86; V = 0.2 eV, N(0) = 0.92. For $T_J = 0.075$ eV the Imχ at T = 0 is shown in the Fig. 5.

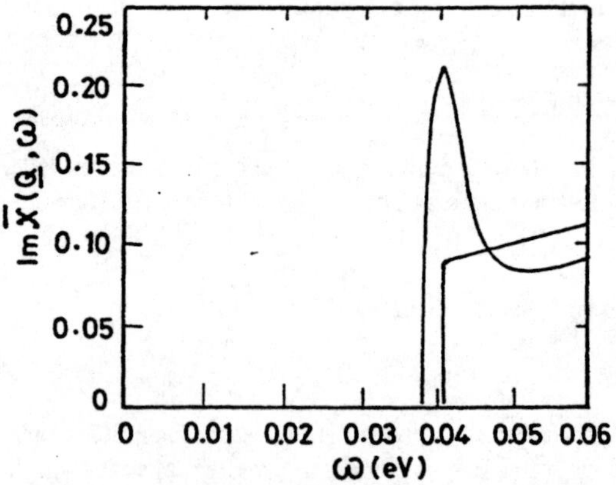

Fig. 5: $I_m\chi$ at T = 0 for T_J = .075. The step discontinuity at the edge is for the BCS theory (T_J = 0). Adpated from Yin et al. [19].

They also computed Im χ for $T \neq 0$. The result at T = 20 K and T = 0 are almost indistinguishable. The unusual peak in the neutron scattering at 40 meV is thought to arise from the inter-layer tunneling model in contrast to the BCS model which shows only a step discontinuity. The domination of T_J makes the density of states sharply peak at $T_J/2$. The intensity and the position of the peak normalized to zero temperature values decreased with increasing temperature. Its position at T = 0 is 41.2 meV. They claim that this vindicates the interlayer tunneling theory of high temperature superconductors.

(b) Collective Excitation coupling to Quasi particles.

Shen and Schrieffer [20] studied the anomalous momentum, temperature and doping dependence of the spectral photoemission line shape in data from $Bi_2Sr_2CaCu_2O_{8+\delta}$ (Bi 2212). They focus their attention on the anisotropic excitation pseudogap in the normal state of under doped Bi 2212. The broad feature at 100-200 meV that is always present near $(\pi,0)$ is absent in spectra at the Fermi surface along (o,o) to (π,π) directions in under doped samples. In over doped samples the features are absent in both these directions. They suggest that these results arise from a stronger dressing of the photo hole for $\underline{k} \cong (\pi,0)$ in the underdoped materials than in other cases. The hole couples strongly to collective modes of momentum $\underline{q}$ whose spectral function $\chi''(q,\omega)$ peaks near $\underline{Q} = (\pi, \pi)$ for the underdoped case. This coupling is weak because $\chi''(\underline{q}, \omega)$ is weak and broad in momentum for the over doped case. There is no discussion of the nature of the collective excitations which couple strongly to quasi particles. These collective excitations provide the glue that leads to pairing of quasi particles. Treating these collective excitations as some kind of bosons they calculate photo hole spectral function on the basis of a coupled fermion-boson model with the choice of band structure corresponding to the Fermi surface given in their Fig. 1 [20]. The quasi particle peak appears when the resonance condition $\omega - \varepsilon_k - \Sigma_1(k, \omega) = 0$ is satisfied for the case when the level width $\Sigma_2(k, \omega)$ is small. The self-energies $\Sigma_1(k,\omega)$ and $\Sigma_2(k,\omega)$ are calculated within the rainbow approximation [20]. The main difference between phonons and the envisaged collective excitation is the following. The phonon anomalies in conventional superconductors have their signature in the energy axis. The collective excitations, on the other hand, have their characteristic features both in the momentum and the energy spread. They find that the quasiparticle excitation spectrum cannot be resolved from the higher energy loss features in the normal state. However, below T_c it becomes resolution limited sharp peak with a dip separating it from the loss features. The striking fact is that in the underdoped samples the gap (pseudogap) already opens in the normal state.

(c) Spin-fermion Model

Recently Morr and Pines [21] have put forward the view that the resonance peak observed in inelastic neutron scattering experiments on underdoped and optimally doped samples of $YBa_2Cu_3O_{6+x}$ comes from spin-wave excitation. Their model is based on spin-fermion interactions. The spin-wave mode dispersion is taken as

$$\omega_{\underline{q}}^2 = \Delta_{sw}^2 + C_{sw}(\underline{q} - \underline{Q})^2 \qquad (3.6)$$

where Δ_{sw} is the spin-wave gap, C_{sw} is the spin wave velocity and $Q = (\pi, \pi)$. Usually, for systems having strong antiferromagnetic correlations, the dispersion of spin wave modes is linear i.e, $\omega_q \alpha q$ [22]. It Is further assumed by them that at high temperatures the spin wave mode is strongly damped owing to its coupling to planar quasiparticles. But in the superconducting state the spin damping is taken to be minimal. Thus the resonance should be observable if the condition $\Delta_{sw} < \omega_c \approx 2\Delta_{sc}$. They claim that in under doped systems, the spin damping present at higher temperatures is reduced. Accordingly the resonance mode remains visible. The spin wave mode in optimally doped systems is overdamped and hence invisible.

The bonding and anti-bonding tight binding quasi particle bands for a two-layer system such as $YBa_2Cu_3O_{6+x}$ are

$$\varepsilon_k = -2t_1[\cos(k_x a) + \cos(K_y a)] - 4t_2 \cos(k_x a)\cos(k_y a) \pm t_\perp - \mu, \qquad (3.7)$$

where, as given earlier, t_l and t_2 are the hopping matrix elements in the in-plane nearest and next-nearest neighbours respectively ant $t_\perp$ is the transfer integral between nearest neighbors on different planes. Using the spin-fermion model of Monthoux and Pines [23], the spin-wave propagator, χ, is written in [21] as

$$\chi^{-1} = \chi_c^{-1} - \mathrm{Re}\Pi - i\mathrm{I_m}\Pi \quad , \qquad (3.8)$$

In the above χ_o is the bare propagator and Π is the irreducible particle-hole bubble. The form of (χ_o^-1 - ReΠ) is chosen by them [21] in such a way that they reproduce the inelastic neutron scattering results in the normal state of the under doped $YBa_2Cu_3O_{6+x}$ systems. Thus

$$\chi_o^{-1} - \mathrm{Re}\Pi = [1 + \xi^2(q - Q)^2 - (\omega^2/\Delta_{sw})^2] / \alpha\xi^2 \quad , \qquad (3.9)$$

ξ being the magnetic correlation length, $\Delta_{sw} = C_{sw}/\xi$, α is a constant.

After making several assumptions [21], only the imginary part of Π, which describes the damping due to the decay of spin excitation into a particle – hole pair, is calculated. The calculation is confined to the odd channel which involves quasi particle excitation between the bonding and antibonding bands. To the lowest order in the spin-fermion coupling g_{sf} (for $\omega > 0$) and in the superconducting state

$$\mathrm{Im}\Pi_{odd} = (3\pi g_{sf}^2/8)\,\Sigma[1 - f(E^+_{k+q}) - f(E^-_k)]\,x$$

$$[1 - (\varepsilon^+_{k+q}\varepsilon^-_k + \Delta_{k+q}\Delta_k)/E^+_{k+q}E^-_k]\,\delta(\omega - E^-_k - E^+_{k+q})$$

$$+ [f(E^-_k) - f(E^-_{k-q})]\,[1 + (\varepsilon^+_{k+q}\varepsilon^-_k + \Delta_{k+q}\Delta_k)/E^+_{K+q}E^-_k]$$

$$x\,\{\delta(\omega + E^-_k - E^+_{k+q}) - \delta(\omega - E^-_k + E^+_{k+q})\} \quad ; \qquad (3.10)$$

as before f(x) is the Fermi function and $E^\pm_k = [(\varepsilon_k^\pm)^2 + |\Delta_k|^2]^{1/2}$ is the dispersion of the bonding and anti-bonding bands in the superconducting state. They assume a d-wave gap

$\Delta_k = \Delta_{sc}[(\cos(k_xa) - \cos(k_ya)]/2$. In Fig. 6 below their calculations of $Im\Pi_{oud}$ at $Q = (\pi, \pi)$ as a function of frequency for the normal (solid line) and superconducting states are shown.

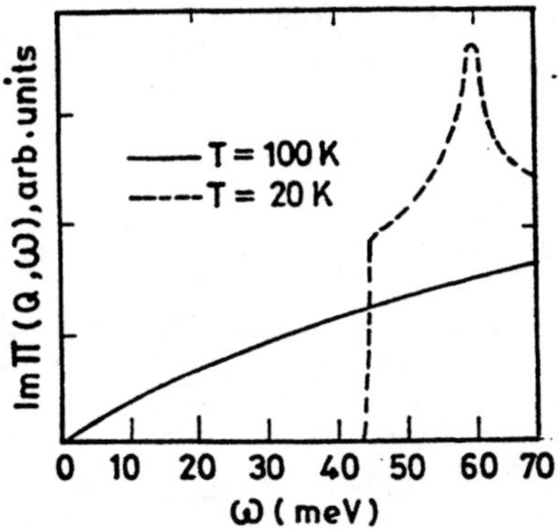

Fig. 6: $I_m\Pi_{odd}$ at Q (π,π). Adapted from Morr & Pines [21].

The results are for $YBa_2Cu_3O_7$ using the values $t_1 = 300$ meV, $t_2 = 0.40\ t_1$, $t_\perp = 0.3t_1$, $\mu = -1.27t_1$. These correspond to a 22% hole concentration in the planes. $\Delta_{sc}(T = 0) \approx 25$ meV. They have taken that $2\Delta_{sc}$ has the same value from the underdoped to overdoped regions. However, Δ_{sw} increases linearly in this region.

Having determined the behaviour of $Im\Pi_{odd}$ at $Q = (\pi, \pi)$, the results for χ_{odd} at $Q = (\pi, \pi)$ as a function of frequency is obtained. The relationship

$$\chi_{odd}\,(Q_1\ \omega = \Delta_{sw}) = [Im\ \Pi_{odd}(Q, \Delta_{sw})]^{-1} \qquad (3.11)$$

is used in the computation. In Fig. 7, the results are shown.

The solid line gives the normal state behaviour and the dashed one for the superconducting state. Their argument is that in the normal state, the spin excitations are over damped. Hence χ'' shows a flat maximum at $\omega = 20$ meV. In the superconducting state this spin damping is so strongly reduced, that the spin-wave mode becomes very sharp at a frequency chosen to be at 41 meV to have agreement with experiment. However, several conditions are imposed and the parameters are adjusted to have agreement. The claim that spin-wave model provides a natural explanation is not sustainable. There are other models, which will be discussed in the following:

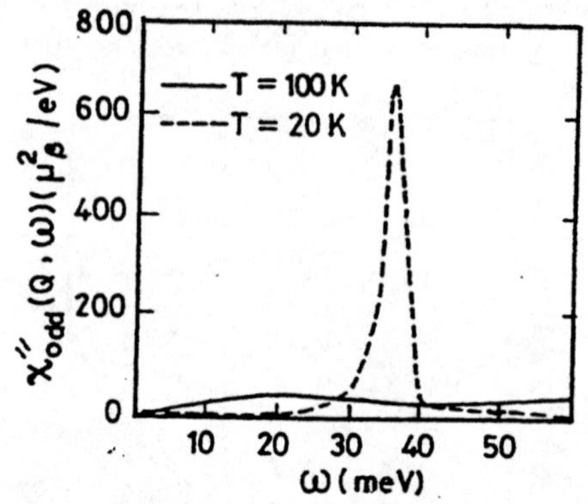

Fig. 7: χ'' at Q (π,π) as a function of frequency.

(a) Lochon(Boson)-Fermion Model

The pairing interaction mediated by lochons (local charged bosons or local singlet pairs or bipolarons) has a long history. It was first suggested, over thirty years ago, for the pairing of fermions in conventional superconductors to achieve the enhancement of superconducting transition temperature [24,2]. The model envisages the existence of centers or complexes which can harbour lochons (local boson, pairs or sometimes refers to as negative U centres) which can undergo double charge fluctuation in interaction with fermions of the metallic matrix of the system. The interaction mechanism involves the splitting of a lochon (local boson) into a pair of fermions (belonging to a wide band) and the inverse process in which there is a confluence of a fermion pair to give the localized boson. The discovery of high temperature cuprate superconductors led to the revival of this mechanism by several groups from 1987 onwards [2,25-32,11].

The Hamiltonian for layered cuprates is given by (confining to two layers)

$$H = \Sigma\ \varepsilon_{\underline{k}}(n_{i\underline{k}\sigma}) + \Sigma\ E_L\ b_L^{+} b_L + \Sigma\ g_{Li}(\underline{k})\ (C^{+}_{i\underline{k}\uparrow}\ C^{+}_{i,-\underline{k}\downarrow}\ b_L + h.c.)\quad , \qquad (3.12)$$

where $n_{i\underline{k}\sigma} = C^{+}_{i\underline{k}\sigma}\ C_{i\underline{k}\sigma}$ and $C^{+}_{i\underline{k}\sigma}$ $(C_{i\underline{k}\sigma})$ denote the fermion creation (annihilation) operator in the state $|i\underline{k}\sigma>$; as before $\underline{k}$ is the wave vector, σ spin index for fermions in the ith conduction plane, $\varepsilon_{\underline{k}}$ = single particle energy (relative to the chemical potentia) and is taken independent of the layer index. The entities

$$b_L^{+} = C^{+}_{L\uparrow}\ C^{+}_{L\downarrow},\ b_L = C_{L\downarrow}C_{L\uparrow} \qquad (3.13)$$

are lochon creation and annihilation operators. They are composites of fermions in the singlet spin state and localized in the orbital state |L> at site L ; E_L represents the lochon energy $g_{Li}(\underline{k})$ is the coupling constant for the interaction between lochon (L) and fermions in the ith conduction layer. It has been shown else where that the fermion-lochon interaction has the general form [11, 32, 33]

$$g_{Li}(\underset{\sim}{k}) = \phi_{\underset{\sim}{k}i} g \ , \tag{3.14}$$

where

$$\phi_{\underset{\sim}{k}i} = m_s \, \phi_{s\underset{\sim}{k}i} + m_d \, \phi_{d\underset{\sim}{k}i}$$

with $\phi_{s\underset{\sim}{k}i} = [\cos(k_x a) + \cos(k_y a)]_i.$

$$\phi_{dki} = [\cos(k_x a) - \cos(k_y a)]_i, \tag{3.15}$$

a = lattice constant of the square.

The important point is that fermion-lochon interaction permits both s-wave and d-wave pairing. The mixing coefficients m_s and m_d for normalized $\phi_{\underset{\sim}{k}}$ must satisfy

$$|m_s|^2 + |m_d|^2 = 1 \ , \tag{3.16}$$

The intra layer and interlayer pairing interaction is obtained by the standard canonical transformation [25,33]. The transformed and reduced Hamiltonian is

$$\begin{aligned} H = {} & \Sigma \ \varepsilon_{\underset{\sim}{k}} \, n_{i\underset{\sim}{k}\sigma} + \Sigma \, E_L b_L^{+} b_L \\ & - \Sigma \ V_{ii} \, (\underset{\sim}{k}, \underset{\sim}{k}') \, C^{+}_{i\underset{\sim}{k}'\uparrow} \, C^{+}_{i,-k'\downarrow} \, C_{i\text{-}k\downarrow} \, C_{i,\underset{\sim}{k}\uparrow} \\ & - \Sigma \, V_{ij}(\underset{\sim}{k}, \underset{\sim}{k}') \, C^{+}_{j\underset{\sim}{k}'\uparrow} \, C^{+}_{i\text{-}\underset{\sim}{k}'\downarrow} \, C_{j,\text{-}\underset{\sim}{k}\downarrow}, \, C_{j,\underset{\sim}{k}\uparrow}, \end{aligned} \tag{3.17}$$

where

$$V_{ii} = [g_{Li}(\underset{\sim}{k}) \, g_{Li}(\underset{\sim}{k}')]/E_L$$

$$V_{ij} = [g_{Li}(\underset{\sim}{k}) \, g_{Lj}(\underset{\sim}{k}')]/E_L \tag{3.18}$$

and E_L is the energy of the lochon mode. It is interesting to observe that the interlayer pairing (the last term in Eqn. (3.17)) looks similar in appearance to the pairing induced by Josephson tunneling considered by Yin et al. [19], (in eq. 3.1). In the lochon model the pairing is mediated by lochon centers which are located in the intervening polarizable dielectric layers. Lochons can induce both intralayer and interlayer pairing. Even in systems having one conducting layer per unit cell, the interaction mediated by lochon modes can be very strong unlike weak Josephon tunneling. The gap equation at T = 0 and on the Fermi surface will have the form

$$\Delta \, (\underset{\sim}{k}_F) = \phi_{\underset{\sim}{k}_F}(\Delta_o + \Sigma \ \ \phi_{\underset{\sim}{k}'_F} \Delta_l/2), \tag{3.19}$$

where Δ_o is a positive quantity involving intralayer contribution and $\Delta_l = g^2/E_L$.

The second term in (3.19) involves the inter-layer contribution. As discussed in [11], the lochon model will have a singularity like feature and the density of states peaks near the Fermi level. In the above model this amounts to two particle resonance states. There is strong local pair correlations in the normal state which amplify as one goes to the superconducting state as indeed seen in experiments. The peak at M visible at above 40 meV in the normal state sharpens in the superconducting state. These modes are identified with lochon (local pair fluctuations) modes and the effect is enhanced in intensity below T_c owing to fermion-lochon interaction when more Cooper pairs are formed. The calculation of susceptibility parallels that of Yin et al. [19]. By solving the gap equation for various values of Δ_1 and fermion-lochon coupling constant λ_L, the peak is obtained for a reasonable values of the parameters involved. The reason is the density of states [11].

$$N(\varepsilon_F) = 2/\pi D \ln |D/\varepsilon_F|, \tag{3.20}$$

where D is the width of the singularity like feature near the Fermi energy.

Domanski et al. [34] have used an equivalent model but call it boson-fermion model. In the atomic limit they calculate the spectral properties of the fermions. They find that on lowering the temperature the features develop into a three pole structure in the vicinity of the Fermi level. This three pole structure arises from the local bonding, antibonding and non-bonding states between bosons (lochons) and fermions. Thus the pseudogap in the density of states of the fermions is connected with the strong local pair correlations in the normal state. However, in the normal state global phase coherence is absent. It develops only in the superconducting state below T_c. Ranninger and Romano [35] have recently extended this treatment of boson(lochon)-fermion, the pseudogap and the incoherent quasiparticle features in high T_c superconductors. The model is essentially the lochon-fermion model to examine the interrelation between interaction except that local bosons are called localized bipolarons. Earlier they had treated bipolarons as quasiparticles without any internal structure [35]. This was generalized by taking into account the internal polaronic structure of the bipolaronic bosons. These bosons are now composed of charge and lattice degrees of freedom existing together in a coherent quantum state.

In the site representation the boson(lochon) fermion model is written as

$$\begin{aligned} H = {} & (W-\mu)\,\Sigma\, C^{+}_{i\sigma} C_{i\sigma} - t\ \Sigma\ C^{+}_{i\sigma} C_{j\sigma} \\ & + (E_B - 2\mu)\ \Sigma\, b^{+}_i b_i + v\,\Sigma\,[b^{+}_i C_{i\downarrow} C_{i\uparrow} + C^{+}_{i\uparrow} C^{+}_{i\downarrow} b_i] \\ & - \hbar\omega_o \alpha \Sigma\, b^{+}_i b_i\,(a_i + a^{+}_i) + \hbar\omega_o\,\Sigma(a^{+}_i a_i + ½) \end{aligned} \tag{3.21}$$

The fermion and boson creation operators have been defined before. Here W is the bare fermionic half bandwidth, the boson(lochon) energy level is denoted by E_B and the boson-fermion pair exchange coupling constant by v. The chemical potential μ is common to both fermions and bosons. Note that indices i denote effective sites of units made of adjacent clusters of the metallic fermions and dielectric bosonic subsystem. Boson and fermion operators are assumed to commute with each other owing to small overlap of the oscillator wave functions at different sites. Various eigenstates of the above Hamiltonian are considered and the pair distribution functions (PDF) are calculated within this manifold. The parameters are chosen as follows:

hole concentration ≈ 0.25, total concentration of particles n_{tot} = 2. The lochon (bipolaron) level E_B is put above the bare electronic level W. The precise position of lochon level is adjusted such that

$$E_B = 2W + \hbar\omega_o\alpha^2 - \delta E_B \tag{3.22}$$

with $\delta E_B = 0.025$, giving $n_F \approx 0.75$. Further in units of W, $\alpha = 2.5$, $v = 0.25$, $\omega_o = 0.1$, and $\delta E_B = 0.025$, $\xi = X\,(M\omega_o/\hbar)^{1/2}$, dimensionless parameter, M = mass of the oscillator. In Fig. 8, the pair distribution function is illustrated for various temperatures in units of W. (adapted from Ranninger and Romano [35]). PDF shows a double peak structure and

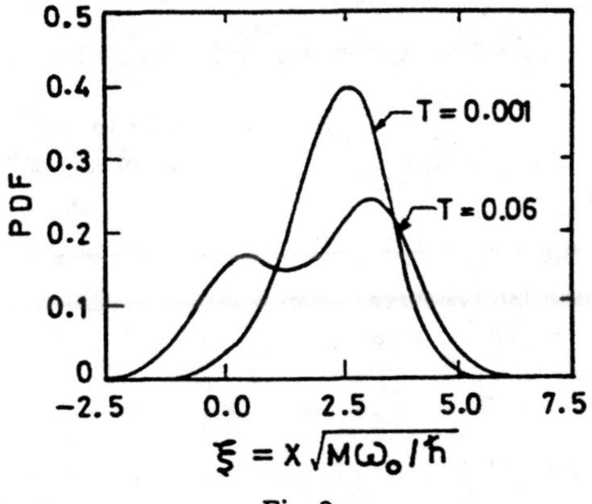

Fig. 8.

changes into a single peak structure as the temperature is lowered below T^*, the temperature below which the pseudogap opens up. The two peak positions correspond to two local lattice deformations alternately occupied by lochons (local pairs). There are experimental indications of such dynamical local lattice fluctuations (see [35] for references).

The intensity of the photo emission spectrum $I_{PES}(\omega)$ is evaluated from a single site boson(lochon)-fermion system. This is given by $I_{PES}(\omega) = I_E(\omega)f(\omega)$, where $f(\omega)$ is the Fermi distribution function and I_E is the emission part of the total one particle fermionic spectral function. I_{PES} is calculated for different temperatures (in units of W). It is found that for high temperature ($T \simeq 0.06$) a broad spectral function is observed which is close to a typical Fermi liquid. As the temperature is lowered the spectral function starts showing a pseudogap. At the same time a broad incoherent contribution appears which extends over energy region of the order of half band width ($\simeq$ 0.5 eV). Further, it is almost temperature independent at low temperatures. This feature is vindicated by experiment [35]. All the above aspects are depicted in Fig. 9,which is adapted from Ranninger & Romano [35].

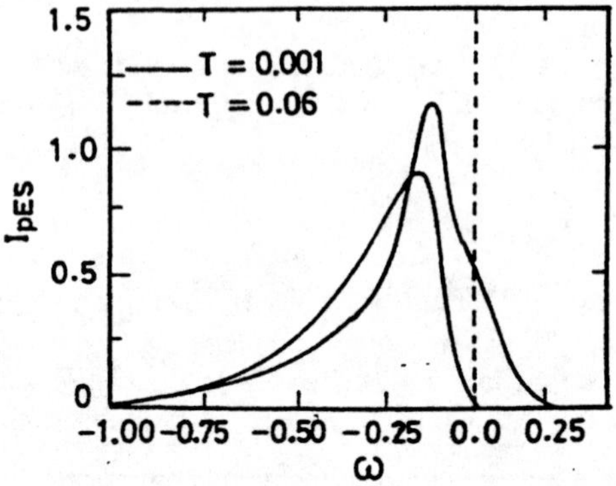

Fig.9: I_{PES} versus ω. $\Delta\omega = 0.05$. As before $\alpha = 2.5$, $\nu = 0.25$, $\omega_o = 0.1$, $\delta E_B = 0.025$.

The temperature behaviour of the pseudogap is also shown in their original figure [35]. The evolution of the electronic density of states as a function of temperature is shown in Fig. 10, as adapted from [35].

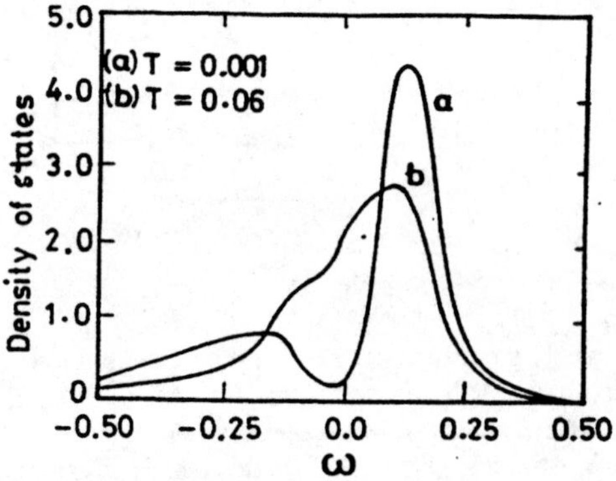

Fig. 10: $\Delta\omega = 0.05$; α, σ, ω_o and δE_B are given the same values as before. Adapted from [35].

4. CONCLUDING REMARKS

In the foregoing section, we have discussed experimental evidences of pseudogap and the appearance of a resonance peak in cuprate superconductors in underdoped and optimally doped systems. These features are among the most important signatures of high

T_c superconductors. Various theoretical models have been suggested by different research groups to explain these features. These can be broadly described as arising from i) final state interaction between the fermionic particles [16-18], (ii) band structure anomalies [36], (iii) interlayer Josephson type tunneling [19], iv) coupling of electrons to collective modes such as in particle-particle channel [20], or spin-wave mode brought about by strong antiferomagnetic correlations [21] and v) fermion-lochon (local charged boson) model [2,11,24-35]. This model is also referred by other authors as boson-fermion model [28,31]. These bosons are charged and arise from local pairs in the singlet state, also referred to as bipolarons.

In this model the temperature dependence of the pseudogap is connected with the incoherent part of the quasiparticle spectrum. The appearance of the pseudogap happens because of the resonant exchange between otherwise free unpaired fermions and localized fermions pairs in the singlet state (called lochons or bipolarons). As this is driven by insulator-metal crossover the pseudogap can open above the superconducting phase transition T_c. Ranninger and Romano [35] relate the broad incoherent part of the spectrum to phonon shakeoff effects. The double peak of the pair-distribution function arises from the temperature fluctuations of the local lattice deformation associated with polarons.

Thus lochon (boson) – fermion model is a strong contender for the correct theory of HTSC's and can well explain the opening of pseudogaps well above T_c.

5. ACKNOWLEDGEMENT

The author would like to thank the University Grant Commission, New Delhi, India for a contingency grant to support this work.

REFERENCES

[1]. J.G. Bednorz and K.A. Muller, Z. Phys. **64**, 189 (1986).
[2]. K.P. Sinha and S.L. Kakani, High Temperature Superconductivity: Current Results and Novel Mechanisms (Nova Science Publishers, Inc., New York 1994).
[3]. P.W. Anderson, Science **256**, 1526 (1992).
[4]. D.S. Marshall et al., Phys. Rev. Let. **76**, 4841 (1996).
[5]. H. Ding et al., Nature (London) **382**,, 51 (1996); Phys. Rev. **B55**, 14872 (1997).
[6]. Chi. Renner et al., Phys. Rev. Let. **80**, 149 (1998).
[7]. Y. de Wilde et. al., Phys. Rev. Let. **80**, 153 (1998).
[8]. H.F. Fong et al., Phys. Rev. Lett. **75**, 321 (1995); Phys. Rev. **B54**, 6708 (1996).
[9]. A. Ino et al. Preprint, University of Tokyo, Tokyo, Japan, Cond-mat/980 6341, 29 June, (1998).
[10]. M.R. Norman et al., Phys. Rev. Lett. **79**, 3506 (1997).
[11]. K.P. Sinha, Mod. Phys. Lett. **B12**, 1 (1998).
[12]. H. Yusuoka, Hyperfine Interactions, **105**, 27 (1997).
[13]. J. Rossat-Mignod et al., Physica (Amsterdam) **185C-189C**, 86 (1991).
[14]. P. Dai et al., Phys. Rev. Lett., **77**, 5425 (1996).
[15]. P. Bourges et al., Europhys. Lett. **38**, 313 (1997).

[16]. I.I. Mazin and V.M. Yakovenko, Phys. Rev. Lett. **75**, 4134 (1995).
[17]. D.Z. Liu et al., Phys. Rev. Lett. **75**, 4130 (1995).
[18]. A. Millis and H. Monien, Phys. Rev. **B54**, 16172 (1996).
[19]. Lan Yin et al., Phys. Rev. Lett. **78**, 3559 (1997).
[20]. Z.-X. Shen and J.R. Schrieffer, Phys. Rev. Lett., **78**, 1771 (1997)
[21]. D.K. Morr and D. Pines, Phys. Rev. Lett. **81**, 1086 (1998).
[22]. K.P. Sinha and N. Kumar, Interactions in Magnetically ordered solids (Oxford University Press, Oxford, 1980).
[23]. P. Monthoux and D. Pines, Phys. Rev. **B47**, 6069 (1993)
[24]. B.N. Ganguly, U.N. Upadhyaya and K.P. Sinha, Phys. Rev. **146**, 317 (1996).
[25]. K.P. Sinha and M. Singh, J. Phys. **C21**, L231 (1988).
[26]. K.P. Sinha, Physica, **B163**, 664 (1990).
[27]. K.P. Sinha, Sol. Stat. Commun. **79**, 735 (1991).
[28]. J.R. Friedberg et al., Phys. Lett. **152A**, 417 (1991).
[29]. Y. Bar-Yam, Phys. Rev. **B43**, 359, 2601 (1991).
[30]. D.M. Eagles, Physica, **C211**, 319 (1993).
[31]. J. Ranninger and J.M. Robin, Physica, **C235**, 279 (1995).
[32]. C.P. Enz, Phys. Rev. **B54**, 3589 (1996).
[33]. K.P. Sinha and A.S. Vytheeswaran, Sol. Stat. Commun. **99**, 845 (1996).
[34]. T. Domanski et al., Sol. Stat. Commun. **105**, 473 91998).
[35]. J. Ranninger and A. Romano, Phys. Rev. Lett. **80**, 5643 (1998).
[36]. N. Bulut and D. Scalapino, Phys, Rev. **B53**, 5149 (1996).

Studies of High Temperature
Superconductors
Volume 27

ISBN 1-56072-684-9

THE FLUCTUATION-INDUCED PSEUDOGAP IN THE OPTICAL CONDUCTIVITY OF HIGH T_c SUPERCONDUCTORS

FRANCESCA FEDERICI

Theoretical Physics Group, School of Physics and Astronomy, University of Birmingham, Edgbaston, Birmingham B15 2TT, UNITED KINGDOM

ANDREI A. VARLAMOV

Department of Theoretical Physics, Moscow Institute of Steel and Alloys, Leninskii Prospect 4, Moscow 117936, RUSSIA

1 INTRODUCTION

The extensive experimental investigation into high temperature superconductors (HTS) carried out in the last ten years has emphasized a variety of unusual properties in the normal state of these compounds: the peak in the c-axis resistivity above T_c [1, 2, 3]; the giant magnetoresistance observed in a wide temperature range above the transition [4, 5, 6]; the deviation from the Korringa law in the temperature dependence of the NMR relaxation rate [7]; the opening of a large pseudogap in the c-axis optical conductivity at temperatures well above T_c [8, 9]; the anisotropic gap observed in the electron spectrum by angular resolved photoemission experiments [10]; the gap-like tunneling anomalies [11, 12, 13, 14, 15, 16]; the anomalies in the thermoelectric power [17, 18], the Hall effect [19, 20, 21, 22] and the heat transport [23, 24].

Many authors attribute these effects to the opening of a "pseudogap" in the electronic spectrum above T_c and most of the different interpretations proposed rely on unconventional theories of superconductivity based on ideas of spin-charge separation, preformed Cooper pairs, polarons, etc.(see for instance [25]).

The study of superconducting fluctuation effects in HTS represents a different approach: it develops the perturbation theory for interacting electrons in the normal phase of a strongly anisotropic superconductor in the optimally or overdoped part of the phase diagram where the Fermi surface is well developed. The only hypothesis about the electron interaction is that it is attractive and leads to the appearance of superconductivity with Cooper pairs of charge $2e$ at temperatures below T_c; for our purposes it is not necessary to specify the origin of the interaction. Obviously perturbation theory requires the magnitude of the effects to be small and this presents a serious limitation on the proposed theory. Nevertheless we believe it is important to understand how smeared out the transition point in the HTS compounds is, how to separate the fluctuation contributions from the normal state ones and what microscopic information can be extracted from the analysis of the fluctuation corrections in different physical characteristics of superconductors.

Before analysing the fluctuation effects in some detail it is necessary to point put why the thermodynamic fluctuation of the order parameter of the superconducting transition are important in HTS. In fact it is well known that in bulk samples of conventional superconductors the critical temperature T_c sharply divides the superconducting and the normal phases and such behavior is well reproduced by both the Ginzburg-Landau phenomenological theory (1950) and the BCS microscopic theory of superconductivity (1957). Consistently the first numerical estimation of the temperature range of fluctuation effects, proposed by Ginzburg in 1960 [26], showed that the fluctuation correction to the heat capacity of a bulk clean conventional superconductor is relevant in a range of temperature which is many orders of magnitude smaller than the experimentally accessible one:

$$\frac{\delta T}{T_c} \sim \left(\frac{T_c}{E_F}\right)^4 \sim \left(\frac{a}{\xi_0}\right)^4 \sim 10^{-12} \div 10^{-14} \tag{1}$$

where a is the interatomic distance, E_F is the Fermi energy and ξ_0 is the superconductor coherence length at zero temperature. This is why fluctuation phenomena in conventional superconductors were ignored for a long time.

A new interest in fluctuation effects on the superconducting transition emerged in the 1950s and 1960s, with the formulation of the microscopic theory of superconductivity and the theory of type-II superconductors, when the search for high-T_c superconductivity attracted attention towards dirty systems and the properties of superconducting films and filaments. In fact the effective or real reduced dimensionality of these systems indicated the possibility of observing an increased role of fluctuation effects. The consistent microscopic theory of fluctuations in the normal phase of a superconductor in the vicinity of the critical temperature was formulated in 1968 by L. G. Aslamazov and A. I. Larkin [27] who not only confirmed Ginzburg's evaluation [26] of the temperature range fluctuationsin a bulk clean superconductor, but also showed very interesting results for low dimensional or dirty superconducting systems: the exponent ν of the ratio (a/ξ_0) in (1) drastically decreases with the effective dimensionality of the electron motion, from $\nu = 4$ for 3D to $\nu = 1$ for 2D. Moreover one source of the effective increase of the strength of fluctuation effects is the decrease of the coherence length, which occurs in dirty superconductors because of the diffusive character of the electronic motion. These considerations lead immediately to the conclusion that in the HTS compounds, characterized by an extremely anisotropic electronic spectrum and a very small coherence length (as well as by an high value of T_c and a low charge carrier density) the fluctuation temperature range can be estimated as tens of degrees and clearly detectable effects are expected.

We now describe some of the general characteristics of the thermal fluctuations effects above the critical temperature in the particular case of dc electrical conductivity. In the first approximation there are three different effects. The first one, a direct contribution, consists in the appearance of nonequilibrium Cooper pairs with the characteristic lifetime $\tau_{GL} = \pi\hbar/8k_B(T - T_c)$ in the vicinity of the transition. In spite of their finite lifetime, a non-zero number (dependent on the proximity to T_c) of such pairs is always present in the normal phase without the estabilishment of a long range order in the system. It is important to notice that in the 2D case, the most appropriate for HTS compounds, the density of Cooper pairs decreases extremely slowly as a function of temperature: $\sim \ln(T_c/(T - T_c)$. This is why it is not surprising that precursor effects of superconductivity can often be detected in the normal phase well above T_c, especially in underdoped samples. The presence of nonequilibrium Cooper pairs gives rise, for instance, to the appearance of the precursor effect of the Meissner-Ochsenfeld anomalous diamagnetism in the normal phase, detected as an anomalous increase of the diamagnetic susceptibility [28] at the edge of the transition. As far as conductivity is concerned a new, non-dissipative, channel of charge transfer has been opened above T_c. This direct fluctuation contribution to the conductivity is called paraconductivity or the Aslamazov-Larkin (AL) contribution [27].

Another consequence of the appearance of fluctuating Cooper pairs above T_c is the decrease of the one-electron density of states at the Fermi level. Indeed, if some electrons are involved in the pairing they cannot simultaneously participate in charge transfer and heat capacity as one-particle excitations. Nevertheless the total number of electronic states cannot be changed by the Cooper interaction and only a redistribution of the levels along the energy axis is possible [29, 30] . In this sense one can speak about the opening of a fluctuation pseudogap at the Fermi level. This indirect fluctuation effect causes a reduction of the normal state conductivity known as the density of states (DOS) renormalisation. It is a negative correction and is much less singular in $(T-T_c)^{-1}$ than the AL contribution, so that, in the vicinity of T_c, it is usually omitted. However, in many cases [31, 32, 33, 34, 35], when for various reasons the main, most singular corrections are suppressed, the DOS correction becomes of major importance. This is the case for many anomalies observed in the normal state of HTS such as the quasiparticle current in tunnel structures, the c-axis transport, the NMR relaxation rate and the thermoelectric power.

The third, purely quantum, fluctuation contribution is generated by the coherent elastic scattering of the pair electrons with the same impurity. This is the anomalous Maki-Thompson (MT) contribution [36, 37] which often turns out to be important in conductivity and other transport phenomena at the edge of the transition. Its temperature singularity near T_c is similar to that of the paraconductivity, but this contribution is extremely sensitive to electron phase-breaking processes. In HTS materials there are several sources of strong pair-breaking above T_c, such as localized magnetic moments, thermal phonons etc. Thus the MT contribution turns out to be depressed by these phase-breaking processes and can usually be omitted. Nevertheless in some special cases, like the NMR relaxation rate, it has to be taken into account even in its overdamped form.

Finally, for completeness, we have to mention the regular part of the Maki-Thompson diagram which is much less singular and has an origin similar to the DOS renormalization contribution.

The thorough analysis of the fluctuation contributions and their mutual competition allow the qualitative, and in many cases quantitative explanation of many phenomena such as the behavior of the c-axis resistance [3, 31, 38, 39, 40, 41]; the giant growth of the c-axis resistance peak in the presence of an external magnetic field applied along the c-axis [32, 41, 42, 43]; the anomalous negative magnetoresistance observed above T_c in BSCCO samples [5, 6, 44, 45]; the decrease of the thermoelectric power at the edge of transition [46, 47, 48, 49, 50]; the temperature dependence of the NMR rate $1/T_1T$ [51, 52]; finally the observed pseudogap-like structure in the far infra-red optical conductivity along the c-axis [53] which will be described in detail in the next section.

For a complete review of fluctuation theory results and their comparison with experimental data we refer to [54].

In the next section we will focus on the fluctuation effect on the optical conductivity, showing the details of diagrammatic calculations and the comparison of our result with the experimental data.

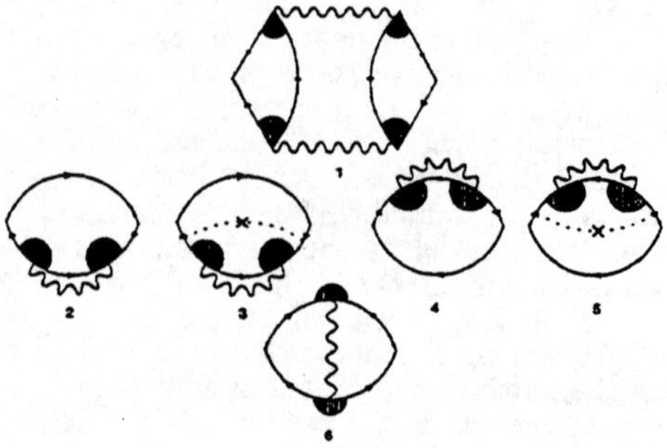

Figure 1: We show the leading Feynman diagrams contributing to the optical conductivity. The wavy lines indicate the fluctuation propagators; the thin solid lines with arrows stand for the impurity-averaged normal-state electron Green's functions; the shaded partial circles are the vertex corrections arising from impurities; the dashed curves with central crosses are additional impurity renormalizations. Diagram 1 is the Aslamazov-Larkin contribution, diagrams 2-5 are the corrections from the density of states renormalization and diagram 6 is the Maki-Thompson diagram.

2 OPTICAL CONDUCTIVITY

We analyse the ac fluctuation conductivity tensor for a layered superconductor taking into account all contributions and paying attention to the most interesting case of *c*-axis polarization of the field. For completness, the *ab*-plane results of the old paper of Aslamazov and Varlamov [42] will be re-examined and discussed in application to the novel HTS layered systems.

2.1 THE MODEL AND SOME DEFINITIONS

The optical conductivity of layered superconductors can be expressed by the retarded analytical continuation of the current-current correlator (electromagnetic response operator) $Q^{(R)}(\omega)$:

$$\mathrm{Re}\left[\sigma_{\alpha\beta}(\omega)\right] = -\frac{\mathrm{Im}\left[Q^{(R)}_{\alpha\beta}(\omega)\right]}{\omega} \tag{2}$$

For the detailed description of the model and the diagrammatic presentation of the electromagnetic response operator tensor $Q_{\alpha\beta}$ we refer to [32]. The first order Feynman diagrams for the linear response operator are shown in Fig. 1.

We assume the electron spectrum of the layered metal is of the form

$$\xi(\mathbf{p}) = \epsilon_0(\mathbf{p}) + J\cos(p_z s) - E_{\mathrm{F}}, \tag{3}$$

where $\epsilon_0(\mathbf{p}) = \mathbf{p}^2/(2m)$, $p \equiv (\mathbf{p}, p_z)$, $\mathbf{p} \equiv (p_x, p_y)$ is a two-dimensional, intralayer wavevector, and J is an effective quasiparticle nearest-neighbour interlayer hopping energy. The Fermi surface defined by the condition $\xi(p_F) = 0$ is a corrugated cylinder, and E_F is the Fermi energy. This model spectrum is most appropriate for highly anisotropic layered materials, for which $J/E_F \ll 1$.

As is well established now, the electron mean free path in HTS layered single crystals or epitaxial films is of the same order as or several times larger than the coherence length $\xi_{ab}(0)$, so the parameter $T_c\tau \sim 1$ and the theory has to be constructed for an arbitrary impurity concentration.

Intralayer quasiparticle scattering is included in the single quasiparticle normal state Green's function by means of the relaxation time τ:

$$G(\mathbf{p}, \omega_n) = \frac{1}{i\tilde{\omega}_n - \xi(\mathbf{p})}, \tag{4}$$

where $\tilde{\omega}_n = \omega_n[1 + 1/(2|\omega_n|\tau)]$.

The "Cooperon" [35] (triangle vertex accounting for the interference in the impurity averaging of the pairs of Green's functions), which is necessary in the following calculations, may be expressed for an arbitrary impurity concentration [32, 42] as:

$$C(\mathbf{q}, \omega_n, \omega_{n'}) = \left[1 - \frac{\Theta(-\omega_n \omega_{n'})}{\tau(\tilde{\omega}_n - \tilde{\omega}_{n'})}\left(1 - \frac{\langle[\xi(\mathbf{p}) - \xi(\mathbf{q}-\mathbf{p})]^2\rangle}{(\tilde{\omega}_n - \tilde{\omega}_{n'})^2}\right)\right]^{-1} \tag{5}$$

where $\Theta(x)$ is the Heaviside step function, and $\langle\cdots\rangle$ denotes an average over the Fermi surface. Performing the Fermi surface average with the spectrum (3), we find:

$$\langle[\xi(\mathbf{p}) - \xi(\mathbf{q}-\mathbf{p})]^2\rangle = \frac{1}{2}\left(v_F^2\mathbf{q}^2 + 4J^2\sin^2(q_z s/2)\right) \equiv \tau^{-1}D\hat{Q}^2 \tag{6}$$

where $v_F = |\mathbf{p}_F|/m$ is the magnitude of the Fermi velocity parallel to the layers. In (5), we have made the assumption $\tau D\hat{Q}^2 \ll 1$, which we suppose throughout this manuscript; its limits have been discussed in [51]. The fluctuation propagator $L(\mathbf{q}, \omega_\mu)$ in the vicinity of T_c has the form :

$$L^{-1}(\mathbf{q}, \omega_\mu) = -\rho\left[\epsilon + \psi\left(\frac{1}{2} + \frac{\omega_\mu}{4\pi T} + \frac{4\eta D\hat{Q}^2}{\pi^2 v_F^2 \tau}\right) - \psi\left(\frac{1}{2}\right)\right], \tag{7}$$

where $\epsilon = \ln(T/T_c) \approx (T - T_c)/T_c$ for $T - T_c \ll T_c$, $\psi(x)$ is the digamma function, $\rho = N(0) = m/(2\pi s)$ is the single-spin quasiparticle normal density of states, and

$$\eta = -\frac{v_F^2\tau^2}{2}\left[\psi\left(\frac{1}{2} + \frac{1}{4\pi\tau T}\right) - \psi\left(\frac{1}{2}\right) - \frac{1}{4\pi\tau T}\psi'\left(\frac{1}{2}\right)\right] \tag{8}$$

is the positive constant which enters into the current expression in the phenomenological GL theory in two dimensions [55].

2.2 PARACONDUCTIVITY

Let us first examine the AL contribution (diagram 1 of Fig. 1) to the ac fluctuation conductivity. The general expression for the appropriate contribution to the electromagnetic response operator as a function of the Matsubara frequencies of the external electromagnetic field ω_ν is [32]:

$$\begin{aligned} Q^{\mathrm{AL}}_{\alpha\beta}(\omega_\nu) &= 2e^2T\sum_{\omega_\mu}\int\frac{d^3q}{(2\pi)^3}B_\alpha(\mathbf{q},\omega_\mu,\omega_\nu)L(\mathbf{q},\omega_\mu) \\ &\times \; L(\mathbf{q},\omega_\mu+\omega_\nu)B_\beta(\mathbf{q},\omega_\mu,\omega_\nu), \end{aligned} \tag{9}$$

The Green's function block is defined as:

$$\begin{aligned} B_\alpha(\mathbf{q},\omega_\mu,\omega_\nu) &= T\sum_{\omega_n}\int\frac{d^3p}{(2\pi)^3}v_\alpha(p)C(\mathbf{q},\omega_{n+\nu},\omega_{\mu-n})C(\mathbf{q},\omega_n,\omega_{\mu-n}) \\ &\times \; G(\mathbf{p},\omega_{n+\nu})G(\mathbf{p},\omega_n)G(\mathbf{q}-\mathbf{p},\omega_{\mu-n}). \end{aligned} \tag{10}$$

In the vicinity of T_c, for frequencies $\omega \ll T$, the leading singular contribution to the response operator $Q^{AL\,(R)}_{\alpha\beta}$ comes from the fluctuation propagators in (9) rather than from the frequency dependences of the B_α blocks, so we can neglect its frequency dependence [42]. This approximation leads to

$$\begin{aligned} B_\alpha(\mathbf{q},0,0) &= -2\rho\frac{\eta}{v_F^2}\frac{\partial}{\partial q_\alpha}\langle[\xi(\mathbf{p})-\xi(\mathbf{q}-\mathbf{p})]^2\rangle \\ &= -2\rho\frac{\eta}{v_F^2}\begin{cases} sJ^2\sin(q_z s) & \text{for } \alpha = z \\ v_F^2 q_\alpha & \text{for } \alpha = x,y \end{cases} \end{aligned} \tag{11}$$

Using these expressions in (9) followed by analytical continuation of the external Matsubara frequencies to the imaginary axis and integration over momenta, one can find the explicit expression for the imaginary part of the retarded electromagnetic response operator[1] for real frequencies $\omega \ll T$:

$$\begin{aligned} \mathrm{Im}\left[Q_\perp^{AL(R)}(\omega)\right] &= \frac{e^2T}{4\pi s}\left(\frac{s^2}{\eta}\right)\left(\frac{16T_c}{\pi\omega}\right)\mathrm{Re}\left\{\left(\frac{\pi\omega}{16T_c}\right)^2-\left(\epsilon-\frac{i\pi\omega}{16T_c}+\frac{r}{2}\right)\right. \\ &\times \left.\left[\Delta D_2\left(\epsilon-\frac{i\pi\omega}{16T_c}\right)-\left(\frac{r}{2}\right)^2\Delta D_1\left(\epsilon-\frac{i\pi\omega}{16T_c}\right)\right]\right\} \end{aligned} \tag{12}$$

[1]It is necessary to mention that the direct calculation of the expression (9) leads to the appearence of divergent expressions in ReQ. Nevertheless, as was shown in [42], the thorough summation of all diagrams from the first order of the perturbation theory for Q before momentum integration leads to the exact cancellation of Re $[Q^{\mathrm{fl}}(0)]$. Namely this fact justifies the possibility of the further calculation of different diagrammatic terms to Q^{fl} separately.

and

$$\mathrm{Im}\left[Q_{\parallel}^{AL(R)}(\omega)\right] = \frac{2e^2T}{\pi s}\mathrm{Im}\left\{\left[1+i\left(\frac{16T_c}{\pi\omega}\right)\left(\epsilon+\frac{r}{2}\right)\right]\right.$$
$$\left.\times\left[\Delta D_1\left(\epsilon-\frac{i\pi\omega}{16T_c}\right)\right]+i\left(\frac{16T_c}{\pi\omega}\right)\left[\Delta D_2\left(\epsilon-\frac{i\pi\omega}{16T_c}\right)\right]\right\} \tag{13}$$

where $D_1(z) = 2\ln\left[\sqrt{z}+\sqrt{(z+r)}\right]$, $D_2(z) = -\sqrt{z(z+r)}$, $\Delta D_1(z) = D_1(z) - D_1(\epsilon)$, $\Delta D_2(z) = D_2(z) - D_2(\epsilon)$ and $r = 4\eta J^2/v_F^2$. The value $r \sim \xi_c^2(0)/s^2$ is the usual anisotropy parameter [29] characterizing the dimensional crossover from the 2D to the 3D regime in the thermodynamic fluctuation behavior at T_c (except for $\sigma_\perp$, for which the crossover is from 0D to 3D at T_c). The expressions presented above solve the problem of the frequency dependence of the paraconductivity tensor in the general form for $\epsilon \ll 1$ and $\omega \lesssim T$ for an arbitrary relation between ϵ, r and ω, but they are too cumbersome.

Let us concentrate on the most interesting case for the HTS analysis of $2D$ fluctuations where $\xi_c(T) \ll s$ $(r \ll \epsilon)$ and $\sigma_\perp^{\mathrm{AL}}$ are suppressed by the necessity of the independent tunneling of each electron participating in the fluctuation pairing from one CuO_2 layer to the neighbouring one [31, 57]. The approximation $r \ll \epsilon$ considerably simplifies the expressions (12) and (13)[2] and, at the same time, it keeps their validity up to frequencies comparable to T_c:

$$\begin{aligned}\sigma_\perp^{AL(2D)}(\epsilon,\omega) &= \frac{e^2 s}{64\eta}\left(\frac{r}{2\epsilon}\right)^2\frac{1}{\tilde{\omega}^2}\ln\left(1+\tilde{\omega}^2\right) \\ &= \sigma_\perp^{AL(2D)}(\epsilon,0)\begin{cases}1-\dfrac{\tilde{\omega}^2}{2} & \text{for } \tilde{\omega}\ll 1\\ \dfrac{2}{\tilde{\omega}^2}\ln\tilde{\omega} & \text{for } \tilde{\omega}\gg 1\end{cases}\end{aligned} \tag{14}$$

and

$$\begin{aligned}\sigma_\parallel^{AL(2D)}(\epsilon,\omega) &= \frac{e^2}{16s}\frac{1}{\epsilon}\left\{\frac{2}{\tilde{\omega}}\arctan\tilde{\omega}-\frac{1}{\tilde{\omega}^2}\ln(1+\tilde{\omega}^2)\right\} \\ &= \sigma_\parallel^{AL(2D)}(\epsilon,0)\begin{cases}1-\dfrac{\tilde{\omega}^2}{6} & \text{for } \tilde{\omega}\ll 1\\ \dfrac{\pi}{\tilde{\omega}} & \text{for } \tilde{\omega}\gg 1\end{cases}\end{aligned} \tag{15}$$

where $\tilde{\omega} = \dfrac{\pi\omega}{16(T-T_c)}$.

Two considerations follow from the expressions obtained. Firstly, the paraconductivity begins to decrease rapidly with the increase of frequency for $\omega \gtrsim T - T_c$; the critical exponents of this power decrease coincide with those in the ϵ-dependence of dc-conductivity tensor components: $\nu_\parallel = 1$ (2D fluctuations) and $\nu_\perp = 2$ (0D fluctua-

[2] The second expression coincides with that one obtained in [42, 56].

tions). Secondly, the assumption to neglect the ω-dependence of the Green's functions blocks evidently breaks down at frequencies $\omega \gtrsim T$ and this dependence only has the effect of accelerating the decrease.

2.3 DENSITY OF STATES CONTRIBUTION

The four main diagrams of the DOS contribution to the electromagnetic response operator tensor are presented in Fig. 1 (2-5). The general expression for the DOS contribution to $Q_{\alpha\beta}(\omega)$ from diagram 2 is:

$$\begin{aligned} Q_{\alpha\beta}^{DOS(2)}(\omega_\nu) &= 2e^2T\sum_{\omega_\mu}\int\frac{d^3q}{(2\pi)^3}L(\mathbf{q},\omega_\mu)T\sum_{\omega_n}\int\frac{d^3p}{(2\pi)^3}v_\alpha(\mathbf{p})v_\beta(\mathbf{p}) \\ &\times\; C^2(\mathbf{q},\omega_n,\omega_{\mu-n})G^2(\mathbf{p},\omega_n)G(\mathbf{q}-\mathbf{p},\omega_{\mu-n})G(\mathbf{p},\omega_{n+\nu}), \end{aligned} \tag{16}$$

The external frequency ω_ν enters the expression (16) only by the Green's function $G(\mathbf{p},\omega_{n+\nu})$ and it is not involved in the $\mathbf{q}$ integration. Therefore, near T_c we can choose the propagator frequency $\omega_\mu = 0$, even in the case of an arbitrary external frequency. In the same way it can be treated the contribution from diagram 3 of Fig. 1.

The diagrams 2, 4 and 3, 5 of Fig. 1 are topologically equivalent and so one might think that they give equal contributions to $\sigma(\omega)$. Nevertheless the thorough analysis of the anayitical continuation over the external frequency shows[3] that their contributions are slightly different and for the total DOS contribution to conductivity one finds:

$$\mathrm{Re}\begin{pmatrix}\sigma_\perp^{\mathrm{DOS}}(\omega)\\ \sigma_\parallel^{\mathrm{DOS}}(\omega)\end{pmatrix} = -\frac{e^2}{2\pi s}\begin{pmatrix}s^2J^2\\ v_F^2\\ 1\end{pmatrix}\ln\left[\frac{2}{\sqrt{\epsilon+r}+\sqrt{\epsilon}}\right]\kappa(\omega,T,\tau), \tag{17}$$

where

$$\begin{aligned} \kappa(\omega,T,\tau) &= \frac{Tv_F^2}{\eta}\frac{1}{(\tau^{-2}+\omega^2)^2}\left\{\frac{4}{\tau}\left[\psi\left(\frac{1}{2}\right)-\mathrm{Re}\,\psi\left(\frac{1}{2}-\frac{i\omega}{2\pi T}\right)\right]\right. \\ &+ \frac{\tau^{-2}+\omega^2}{4\pi T\tau}\frac{1}{\omega}\mathrm{Im}\,\psi'\left(\frac{1}{2}-\frac{i\omega}{2\pi T}\right)+(\tau^{-2}-\omega^2)\frac{1}{\omega}\left[\mathrm{Im}\,\psi\left(\frac{1}{2}-\frac{i\omega}{2\pi T}\right)\right. \\ &- \left.\left.2\,\mathrm{Im}\,\psi\left(\frac{1}{2}-\frac{i\omega}{4\pi T}+\frac{1}{4\pi T\tau}\right)\right]\right\}. \end{aligned} \tag{18}$$

We stress that, in contrast to (12) and (13), this result has been found using only the assumption $\epsilon \ll 1$, so it is valid for any frequency, any impurity concentration and any dimensionality of the fluctuation behavior. The function $\kappa(\omega,T,\tau)$ can be easily used to fit experimental data. Nevertheless we present the asymptotics of the expression

[3]This fact has not been taken into account before and it led to the lack of the factor 1/2 in the dirty and clean limit of the DOS contribution [31, 32]. We want to thank D. Livanov who attracted our attention to this circumstance.

(18) for clean and dirty cases. In the dirty case

$$\kappa_{\mathrm{d}}\left(\omega, T \ll \tau^{-1}\right) = \frac{T v_{\mathrm{F}}^2}{2\eta} \begin{cases} \frac{\tau}{(2\pi T)^2}\left|\psi''\left(\frac{1}{2}\right)\right| & \text{for } \omega \ll T \ll \tau^{-1} \\ \frac{\tau}{\omega^2} & \text{for } T \ll \omega \ll \tau^{-1} \\ -\frac{\pi}{\omega^3} & \text{for } T \ll \tau^{-1} \ll \omega \end{cases} \tag{19}$$

and in the clean case

$$\kappa_{\mathrm{cl}}\left(\omega, T \gg \tau^{-1}\right) = \frac{T v_{\mathrm{F}}^2}{2\eta} \begin{cases} \frac{\pi\tau^2}{4T} & \text{for } \omega \ll \tau^{-1} \ll T \\ -\frac{\pi}{4\omega^2 T} & \text{for } \tau^{-1} \ll \omega \ll T \\ -\frac{\pi}{\omega^3} & \text{for } \tau^{-1} \ll T \ll \omega \end{cases} \tag{20}$$

2.4 MAKI-THOMPSON CONTRIBUTION

The total contribution of the MT-like diagrams to $\sigma_{\alpha\beta}(\omega)$ has been analysed in [32] for the case of zero frequency and the frequency dependence of $\sigma_{\|}(\omega)$ has been studied in [42]. In [32] it was shown that actually the *regular* part of MT diagram can almost always be omitted. So we will concentrate on the *anomalous* MT contribution (Fig. 1 diagram 6).

In [42] it was demonstrated that in the case of quasi two-dimensional electron motion (3) there is no formal necessity to introduce the pairbreaking time τ_φ because the Maki-Thompson logarithmic divergency is automatically cut off due to the possible interlayer hopping. Nevertheless all evidence shows that the intrinsic pair-breaking in HTS is so strong that $\tau_\varphi \sim 2 \div 5 \cdot 10^{-13} s$ and we must consider the overdamped regime where the MT contribution does not manifest itself noticeably in the ϵ dependence of conductivity [32] (the major part of the experimental results can be explained in terms of AL or AL and DOS contributions). Anyway we are interested in this contribution because of its frequency dependence which evidently determines another characteristic scale $\omega_{\mathrm{MT}} \sim \tau_\varphi^{-1}$, in addition to the previous three ($T - T_c$, T, τ^{-1}) we have introduced.

The general expression of the *anomalous* MT contribution to the electromagnetic operator tensor is [32]:

$$Q_{\alpha\beta}^{\mathrm{MT}}(\omega_\nu) = 2e^2 T \sum_{\omega_\mu} \int \frac{d^3q}{(2\pi)^3} L(\mathbf{q}, \omega_\mu) I_{\alpha\beta}(\mathbf{q}, \omega_\mu, \omega_\nu), \tag{21}$$

where

$$\begin{aligned} I_{\alpha\beta}(\mathbf{q}, \omega_\mu, \omega_\nu) &= T \sum_{\omega_n} \int \frac{d^3p}{(2\pi)^3} v_\alpha(\mathbf{p}) v_\beta(\mathbf{q}-\mathbf{p}) C(\mathbf{q}, \omega_{n+\nu}, \omega_{\mu-n-\nu}) C(\mathbf{q}, \omega_n, \omega_{\mu-n}) \\ &\times \; G(\mathbf{p}, \omega_{n+\nu}) G(\mathbf{p}, \omega_n) G(\mathbf{q}-\mathbf{p}, \omega_{\mu-n-\nu}) G(\mathbf{q}-\mathbf{p}, \omega_{\mu-n}). \end{aligned} \tag{22}$$

After the integration over $\mathbf{p}$ momentum and the summation over $\omega_n$in the range $\omega_n \in$

$[-\omega_\nu, 0)$ (*anomalous* part), one finds:

$$\begin{pmatrix} Q_\perp^{\mathrm{MT(an)}}(\omega_\nu) \\ Q_\parallel^{\mathrm{MT(an)}}(\omega_\nu) \end{pmatrix} = e^2 T\tau \left[\psi\left(\frac{1}{2} + \frac{\omega_\nu}{2\pi T}\right) - \psi\left(\frac{1}{2}\right) \right]$$
$$\times \int \frac{d^3 q}{(2\pi)^3} \begin{pmatrix} J^2 s^2 \cos q_\perp s \\ v_F^2 \end{pmatrix} \frac{1}{\left(\omega_\nu + \tau_\varphi^{-1} + D\hat{Q}^2\right)\left(\epsilon + \eta q^2 + r \sin^2(q_\perp s/2)\right)} \tag{23}$$

At this stage of the calculations we artificially introduce the phase-breaking time in the "Cooperon" vertices. Carrying out the integration and separating the real and the imaginary parts we have:

$$\mathrm{Re} \begin{pmatrix} \sigma_\perp^{\mathrm{MT(an)}}(\omega) \\ \sigma_\parallel^{\mathrm{MT(an)}}(\omega) \end{pmatrix} = \frac{e^2}{2\pi s} \begin{pmatrix} \frac{s^2}{2\eta} \\ 1 \end{pmatrix} \frac{T}{\omega} \mathrm{Im} \left\{ \frac{\psi\left(\frac{1}{2} - \frac{i\omega}{2\pi T}\right) - \psi\left(\frac{1}{2}\right)}{\frac{i\pi\omega}{8T_c} + \epsilon - \gamma} \right.$$
$$\times \left. \begin{pmatrix} -\Delta D_2\left(-\frac{i\pi\omega}{8T_c} + \gamma\right) + \left(\frac{i\pi\omega}{8T_c} + \epsilon - \gamma\right) \\ \Delta D_1\left(-\frac{i\pi\omega}{8T_c} + \gamma\right) \end{pmatrix} \right\} \tag{24}$$

where $\gamma = \dfrac{\pi}{8T_c\tau_\varphi}$. In the two-dimensional overdamped regime ($r \ll \epsilon \lesssim \gamma$) the expression (24) gives the following limits:

$$\sigma_\perp^{MT(an)(2D)}(\omega) = \frac{e^2 s}{2^7 \eta} \frac{r^2}{\gamma\epsilon} \begin{cases} 1 & \text{for } \omega \ll \tau_\varphi^{-1} \\ \left(\dfrac{8T_c\gamma}{\pi\omega}\right)^2 & \text{for } \omega \gg \tau_\varphi^{-1} \end{cases} \tag{25}$$

$$\sigma_\parallel^{MT(an)(2D)}(\omega) = \frac{e^2}{8s} \begin{cases} \dfrac{1}{\gamma} \ln\left(\dfrac{\gamma}{\epsilon}\right) & \text{for } \omega \ll \tau_\varphi^{-1} \\ \dfrac{4T_c}{\omega} & \text{for } \omega \gg \tau_\varphi^{-1} \end{cases} \tag{26}$$

We recall that the expression (24) has been obtained without any limitation on frequency. The assumption we have made throughout this chapter is that $\tau D\hat{Q}^2 \ll 1$ which does not affect our results for the AL and the DOS contributions over the full range of frequency, temperature and impurity concentration but considerably influences the MT contribution. In fact, as was shown in [51], in the ultra-clean (or non-local) limit, when $T\tau > 1/\sqrt{\epsilon}$, the assumption $\tau D\hat{Q}^2 \ll 1$ is violated for the MT contribution and the results obtained are not valid in that limit. Nevertheless one can see that this non-local situation can only be realized in the clean case ($T\tau \gg 1$) and for temperatures in the range $1/(T\tau)^2 \ll \epsilon \ll 1$. We suppose $T\tau \sim 1$, as it is in the case of HTS, and that excludes the non-local limit from our analysis.

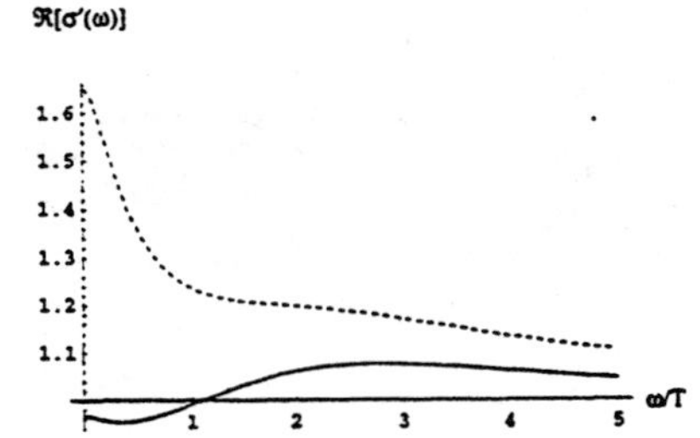

Figure 2: The plot shows the dependence of the real part of conductivity, divided by the Drude normal conductivity, on ω/T, $\Re\left[\sigma'(\omega)\right] = \mathrm{Re}\left[\sigma(\omega)\right]/\sigma^{\mathrm{n}}$. The dashed line refers to the ab-plane component of the conductivity tensor whose Drude normal conductivity is $\sigma^{\mathrm{n}}_{\|} = \rho e^2 \tau v_{\mathrm{F}}^2$. The solid line refers to the c-axis component whose Drude normal conductivity is $\sigma^{\mathrm{n}}_{\perp} = \sigma^{\mathrm{n}}_{\|} J^2 s^2 / v_{\mathrm{F}}^2$. In this plot we have put $T\tau = 0.3, E_{\mathrm{F}}/T = 50, r = 0.01, \epsilon = 0.04, T\tau_{\varphi} = 4$.

2.5 DISCUSSION

We first consider each fluctuation contribution separately and then discuss their interplay in $\mathrm{Re}\left[\sigma_{\perp}(\omega)\right]$. Because of the large number of parameters present in the expressions we restrict our consideration to the c-axis component of the conductivity tensor in the region of 2D fluctuations (above the Lawrence-Doniach crossover temperature). The in-plane component will be summarised at the end of this section.

The AL contribution describes the fluctuation condensate response to the applied electromagnetic field. The component of the current associated with it can be treated as the precursor phenomenon of the screening currents in the superconducting phase. Above T_c the binding energy of the virtual Cooper pairs gives rise to a pseudogap of the order of $T - T_c$, so it is not surprising that at higher frequencies the AL contribution decreases with the further increase of ω. Actually $\omega^{\mathrm{AL}} \sim T - T_c$ is the only relevant scale for σ^{AL}: its frequency dependence does not contain T, τ_{ϕ} or τ. The independence from the latter mathematically represents the fact that elastic impurities do not represent obstacles for the motion of Cooper pairs. The interaction of the electromagnetic wave with the fluctuation Cooper pairs in some way resembles the anomalous skin-effect where its reflection is determined by the interaction with the free electron system.

The relevant characteristic scales in the frequency dependence of *anomalous* MT contribution are $T - T_c$ and τ_{ϕ}^{-1}. In the case of HTS, where τ_{ϕ}^{-1} has to be estimated as at least $0.1 T_c$ for temperatures up to $5 \div 10$ K above T_c, the MT contribution is overdamped, it is determined by the value of τ_{ϕ} and it almost does not depend on temperature.

The density of states fluctuation renormalization contribution to $\mathrm{Re}\left[\sigma(\omega)\right]$ is negative at low frequencies ($\omega \ll \tau^{-1}$) and this results in the increase of the surface impedance, or in other words the decrease of the reflectance. Nevertheless the applied electromagnetic field affects the electron distribution and at high frequencies $\omega \sim \tau^{-1}$ the DOS contribution changes its sign. It is worth noting that this contribution, being a one-electron effect, depends on the impurity scattering in a similar way to the normal Drude conductivity. The decrease of $\mathrm{Re}\left[\sigma^{\mathrm{DOS}}(\omega)\right]$ starts at frequencies $\omega \sim \min\{T, \tau^{-1}\}$ which for HTS are much higher than $T - T_c$ and τ_{φ}^{-1}.

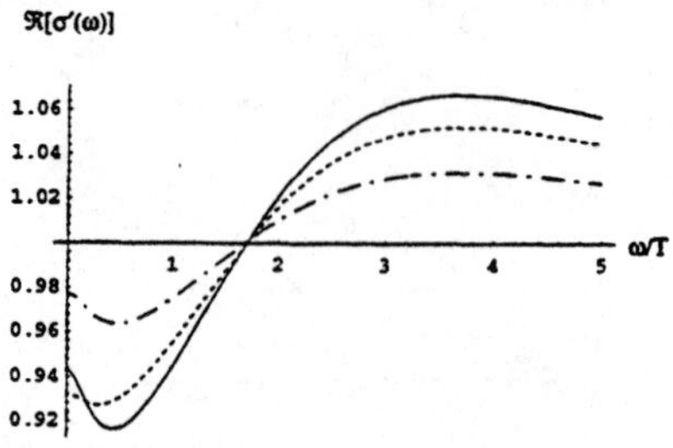

Figure 3: The behaviour of the c-axis component of conductivity frequency dependence for different values of temperature is shown. The solid line refers to $\epsilon = 0.04$; the dashed line refers to $\epsilon = 0.06$; the dot-dashed line refers to $\epsilon = 0.08$. $T\tau = 0.2$ for all the curves. The other parameters of this plot are the same used in Fig. 2.

The scenario of $\mathrm{Re}[\sigma_{\perp}^{\mathrm{tot}}]$ ω-dependence with the most natural choice of parameters ($r \ll \epsilon \lesssim \tau_{\varphi}^{-1} \ll \min\{T, \tau^{-1}\}$) is presented in Fig. 2.

The positive AL and MT effects are well pronounced at low frequencies against a background of the DOS contribution which remains a negative constant in this region. Then at $\omega \sim T - T_c$ the former decays and $\mathrm{Re}\sigma_{\perp}$ remains negative up to $\omega \sim \min\{T, \tau^{-1}\}$. The DOS correction changes its sign at $\omega \sim \tau^{-1}$ and then it rapidly decreases. The following high frequency behavior is governed by the Drude law. One can see that the characteristic pseudogap-like behaviour in the frequency dependence of the optical conductivity takes place in the range $\omega \in [T - T_c, \tau^{-1}]$. The depth of the window increases logarithmically with ϵ when T tends to T_c, as shown in Fig. 3.

In the case of the ab-plane optical conductivity the first two positive contributions are not suppressed by the interlayer transmittance, they considerably exceed the negative DOS contribution in a wide range of frequencies and any pseudogap-like behavior is unlikely. The comparison of (15) and (17) shows that the compensation of the two contributions could only take place at $\omega_0 \sim T/\ln\epsilon$ which is out of the range of validity of the AL contribution.

Now we compare the results of our calculations with the available experimental data. The recent measurements [8, 9] of the c-axis reflectivity spectra in the FIR region on $YBa_2Cu_4O_8$ single crystals show the response of a poor metal with the additional contributions from IR active phonon modes. With the decrease of temperature the c-axis optical conductivity decreases showing a transition from Drude-like to pseudogap-like behavior at $\omega \sim 180\ \mathrm{cm}^{-1}$. This gap becomes deeper below 180 K without any abrupt change at the superconducting transition temperature $T_c = 80$ K.

Such experimentally observed behaviour of the optical conductivity is in qualitative agreement with our results. The suppression of the density of states due to the superconducting fluctuations in the vicinity of T_c leads to the decrease of the reflectivity for frequencies up to $\omega \sim \tau^{-1}$. The magnitude of this depression slowly (logarithmically) increases with the decrease of temperature but, evidently, at the edge of the transition it saturates because of the crossover to the 3D regime in fluctuations (where instead of $\ln(1/\epsilon)$ one has $\ln(1/r) - \sqrt{\epsilon}$, see (17)). Thus no singularity is expected in the value of the minimum even in the first order of perturbation theory. Below T_c the fluctuation behavior of $\langle\Delta_{\mathrm{fl}}^2\rangle$ is mostly symmetrical to that above T_c [58] and, with the further decrease of temperature, the fluctuation pseudogap minimum in the optical conductivity

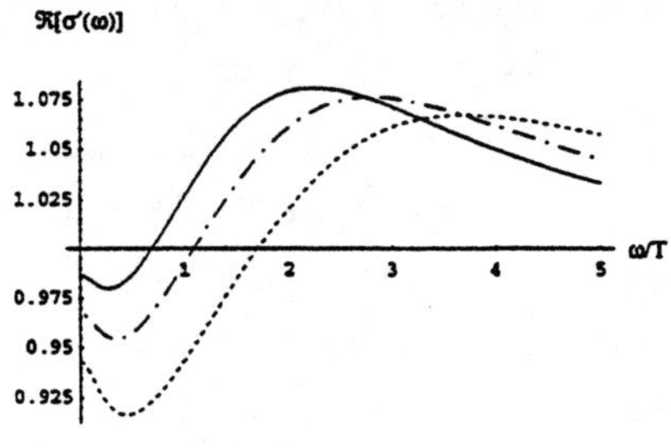

Figure 4: The plot shows the dependence of $\mathrm{Re}\left[\sigma_{\perp}(\omega)/\sigma_{\perp}^{n}\right]$ on ω/T for different values of $T\tau$. The solid line refers to $T\tau = 0.4$; the dot-dashed line refers to $T\tau = 0.3$; the dashed line refers to $T\tau = 0.2$. The other parameters of this plot are the same used in Fig. 2.

smoothly transforms into the real superconducting gap, which opens very sharply in HTS. Let us stress that the independence of the pseudogap threshold from temperature appears naturally in our theory: it is determined by $\omega_0 \sim \tau^{-1}$ (see (19), (20) and Fig. 4). Comparing Fig. 3 and Fig. 4, one can easily see that the threshold does not change with temperature but with the inverse of the scattering rate.

As far as the numerical value of ω_0 is concerned, supposing $T_c\tau = 0.35$ (which is the value for the scattering rate of the sample used in the experiment under consideration [9], that is also in the experimental range of the inverse of the scattering rate $T\tau \approx 0.3 \div 0.7$ [59, 60]), one can see that the pseudogap threshold is of the order of 200 cm^{-1}, in agreement with the experimental data [8, 9].

Our theory is, strictly speaking, valid only in the vicinity of the critical temperature, where $\epsilon \ll 1$. Nevertheless the logarithmic dependence on ϵ of the result obtained gives grounds to believe that it might be qualitatively valid up to $\epsilon = \ln(T/T_c) \sim 1$, so for temperatures up to 200 K in the experiment discussed.

In conclusion we have calculated the optical conductivity tensor for layered superconductors. The pseudogap-like minimum of its c-axis component in a wide range of frequencies for temperatures in the vicinity of T_c is found. Its origin is related with the fluctuation density of states renormalization which can be treated as the opening of the fluctuation pseudogap. These result are qualitatively, and in some aspects quantitatively, in agreement with the recent experiments on $YBa_2Cu_4O_8$ samples.

References

[1] T. Penney et al., *Phys. Rev. B* **38** (1988) 2918.

[2] S. Martin et al., *Phys. Rev. Lett.* **60** (1988) 2194.

[3] G. Briceno et al., *Phys. Rev. Lett.* **66** (1991) 2164.

[4] Y. F. Yan et al., *Phys. Rev. B* **52** (1995) R751.

[5] K. Hashimoto et al., *Phys. Rev. B* **53** (1996) 892.

[6] J. Axnas et al., *Phys. Rev. Lett* **77** (1996) 2280.

[7] C. H. Pennington and C. P. Slichter, in *Physical Properties of High Temperature Superconductors*, ed. by D. M. Ginzberg, World Scientific (1990), Singapore.

[8] D. N. Basov, T. Timusk, B. Dabrowski, H. A. Mook, *Phys. Rev. B* **52** (1995) 13141.

[9] D. N. Basov, T. Timusk, B. Dabrowski and J. D. Jorgensen, *Phys. Rev. B* **50** (1994) 3511.

[10] A. G. Loeser, Z. X. Shen, D. S. Dessau, *Physica C* **263** (1996) 208.

[11] M. Gurvitch et al., *Phys. Rev. Lett.* **63** (1989) 1008.

[12] A. M. Cucolo, C. Noce and A. Romano, *Phys. Rev. B* **46** (1992) 5864.

[13] H. J. Tao, Farun Lu, E. L. Wolf,, *Physica C* **282-287** (1997) 563.

[14] T. Wanatabe et al., *Phys. Rev. Lett.* **79** (1997) 2113.

[15] M. Suzuki, S. Karimoto, K. Namekawa, *Journ. of Phys. Soc. of Japan* **67** (1998) vol. 3.

[16] C. Renner et al., *Phys. Rev. Lett.* **80** (1998) 149.

[17] M. A. Howson et al., *Phys. Rev. B* **41** (1990) 300.

[18] N. V. Zavaritsky, A. A. Samoilov and A. A. Yurgens, *JETP Letters* **55** (1992) 127.

[19] J. M. Harris, Y. F. Yan, N. P. Ong, *Phys. Rev. B* **46** (1992) 14293.

[20] T. R. Chien et al., *Phys. Rev. B* **43** (1991) 6242.

[21] T. R. Chien, Z. Z. Wang, N. P. Ong, *Phys. Rev. B* **46** (1992) 14293.

[22] A. V. Samoilov, *Phys. Rev. B* **49** (1994) 1246.

[23] K. Krishana et al., *Science* **277** (1997) 83.

[24] M. Houssa et al., *Phys. Rev. B* **54** (1996) R6885.

[25] B. G. Levi, *Physics Today* **49** (1996) 17.

[26] V. L. Ginzburg, *Soviet Solid State* **2** (1968) 61.

[27] L. G. Aslamazov and A. I. Larkin, *Soviet Solid State* **10** (1968) 875.

[28] M. Tinkham and W. J. Schockpol, *Progr. Mod. Phys.* **38** (1975) 1061.

[29] E. Abrahams, M. Redi, J.W. Woo, *Phys. Rev. B* **1** (1970) 208.

[30] C. Di Castro, C. Castellani, R. Raimondi, A. Varlamov, *Phys. Rev. B* **49** (1990) 10211.

[31] L. B. Ioffe, A. I. Larkin, A. A. Varlamov and L. Yu, *Phys. Rev. B* **47** (1993) 1693.

[32] V. V. Dorin, R. A. Klemm, A. A. Varlamov, A. I. Buzdin, D. V. Livanov, *Phys. Rev. B* **48** (1993) 12951.

[33] L. G. Aslamazov and A. I. Larkin, *Soviet JETP* **67** (1973) 647.

[34] L. G. Aslamazov and A. A. Varlamov, *Journ. of Low Temp. Phys.* **38** (1980) 223.

[35] B. L. Al'tshuler, M. Yu. Reyzer, A. A. Varlamov, *JETP* **57** (1983) 1329.

[36] K. Maki, *Progr. Theor. Phys* **40** (1968) 193.

[37] R. S. Thompson, *Phys. Rev. B* **1** (1970) 327.

[38] K. E. Gray, D. H. Kim, *Phys. Rev. Lett.* **70** (1993) 1693.

[39] G. Balestrino, M. Marinelli, E. Milani, L. Yu, *Phys. Rev. B* **47** (1993) 6037.

[40] G. Balestrino, E. Milani, A. Varlamov, *Physica C* **210** (1993) 386.

[41] G. Balestrino, E. Milani, C. Aruta and A. Varlamov, *Phys. Rev. B* **54** (1996) 3628.

[42] A. S. Nigmatulin, A. Varlamov, D. Livanov, G. Balestrino and E. Milani *Phys. Rev. B* **53** (1996).

[43] D. Livanov, E. Milani, G. Balestrino and C. Aruta*Phys. Rev. B* **55** (1997) R8701.

[44] W. Lang, *Physica C* **282-287** (1997).

[45] G. Balestrino, E. Milani, and A. A. Varlamov *Soviet JETP Letters* **61** (1995) 833.

[46] A. Varlamov, D. Livanov, F. Federici, *JETP Letters* **65** (1997) 182.

[47] K. Maki, *J. Low Temp. Phys.* **14** (1974) 419.

[48] A. Varlamov and D. Livanov *Sov. Phys. JETP* **71** (1990) 325.

[49] M. Yu Reizer and A. V. Sergeev, *Phys. Rev. B* **50** (1994) 9344.

[50] J. Mosqueira et al., *Physica C* **253** (1997) 1.

[51] M. Randeria and A. A. Varlamov, *Phys. Rev. B* **50** (1994) 10401.

[52] P. Carretta, D. Livanov, A. Rigamonti, A. A. Varlamov *Phys. Rev. B* 54 (1996) R9682.

[53] F. Federici and A. Varlamov, *JETP Letters* **64** (1996) 497.

[54] A. A. Varlamov, G. Balestrino, E. Milani and D. Livanov, *Advances in Phyics* (in press).

[55] L.P.Gor'kov, *Sov. JETP* **9** (1959) 1364.

[56] H. Schmidt, Ann. Phys. Lpz **216** (1968) 336.

[57] L. B. Ioffe, A. I. Larkin, A. A. Varlamov, L. Yu, *Physica C* **235** (1994) 1963.

[58] A. A. Varlamov and V. V. Dorin, *Sov. JETP* **64** (1986) 1159; A. A. Varlamov, V. V. Dorin and I. E. Smoliyarenko *Sov. JETP* **67** (1988) 2536.

[59] D. B. Tanner and T. Timusk, "Optical Properties of High T_c Superconductors" in *Properties of High Temperature Superconductors III*, edited by D. M. Ginsberg, World Scientific Singapore (1992) 428.

[60] P. Calvani, "Infrared Optical Properties of High-T_c Cuprates" in *High T_c Superconductivity: Theory and Experiments*, edited by M. Acquarone, World Pub. Co. (1996), Singapore, p. 233.

Studies of High Temperature
Superconductors
Volume 27

ISBN 1-56072-684-9

PSEUDOGAPS AND MAGNETIC PROPERTIES OF THE TWO-DIMENSIONAL *t-J* MODEL

A. SHERMAN[A] AND M. SCHREIBER[B]

[a]Institute of Physics, University of Tartu, Riia 142, EE-2400 Tartu, Estonia
[b]Institut für Physik, Technische Universität, D-09107 Chemnitz, Germany

I. INTRODUCTION

The photoemission and magnetic properties of cuprate perovskites have been extensively studied during the last few years, both because of their unusual behaviour and in the hope that they might provide insight into the physical origin of high-temperature superconductivity. Among these properties the pseudogap observed in photoemission [1–3] and the magnetic pseudogap revealed in the static susceptibility and in the spin-lattice relaxation rate of normal-state underdoped cuprates [4,5] have attracted considerable attention. A number of different approaches were suggested for the description of the pseudogaps. In particular, in view of the similarity in symmetry and size of the photoemission pseudogap with the superconducting gap, in Refs. [3,6–8] this pseudogap was connected with the superconducting fluctuations existing above T_c. This idea was based on earlier theoretical results of Refs. [9,10]. Another point of view was suggested in Ref. [11] where the energy spectrum of the two-dimensional (2D) t-J model was shown to have a peculiarity which is similar by its properties to the photoemission pseudogap. In accord with Ref. [11] the pseudogap is a consequence of a specific dispersion of the strongly correlated electron system at moderate doping and is not connected with superconducting fluctuations. The discussion of the magnetic pseudogap in doped cuprates is mainly based on scaling arguments [12–14] and on the idea of real-space pairing [15].

In this paper we describe the energy spectrum, including the photoemission pseudogap, and the magnetic properties demonstrating the magnetic pseudogap in a unified approach based on the 2D t-J model widely used for the description of CuO_2 planes of cuprate perovskites (the extensive literature on this model is reviewed in Ref. [16]). For the consideration of the paramagnetic state we extend the spin-wave theory with the constraint of zero staggered magnetization, developed for the Heisenberg model [17,18], to the t-J model. The spectrum is determined by solving numerically a set of self-energy equations for hole and magnon Green's functions in the self-consistent Born approximation with account of the constraint [19]. The constraint can be fulfilled in the ranges of hole concentrations $0.02 \lesssim x \lesssim 0.17$ and temperatures $T \lesssim 100$ K. In this region the obtained hole spectrum differs from a conventional metallic spectrum as the quasiparticle weights of states are less than 1 and change with the hole concentration. This leads to the violation of Luttinger's theorem.

The hole spectrum consists of two essentially different parts: a persistent portion of the narrow spin-polaron band, which is typical for the low-concentration ($x \lesssim 0.02$) spectrum, and a wider part appearing from $x \approx 0.04$ which is characterized by the energy parameter t, the hopping constant. The former part provides the most intensive features in the hole spectral function near the Fermi level. For $x < 0.17$ this part, which is pinned to the Fermi level near $(\pm\pi/2, \pm\pi/2)$, bends upwards (in the hole picture) on approaching $(\pm\pi, 0)$, $(0, \pm\pi)$. In the hole spectral function the crossing of the Fermi level by the second, wider part is completely lost within the foot of a more intensive spin-polaron peak in this region of the Brillouin zone. This looks like the disappearance of a part of the Fermi surface and the opening of a pseudogap near $(\pm\pi, 0)$, $(0, \pm\pi)$. Obtained size, symmetry and concentration dependence of the pseudogap are in agreement with photoemission data in $Bi_2Sr_2CaCu_2O_{8+\delta}$ (Bi2212) [1–3].

Another peculiarity of the calculated hole spectrum is an extended saddle point near $(0, \pi)$. By the energy position and by the extension in the Brillouin zone our results reproduce well the analogous feature of the photoemission spectra. In the case of optimal doping, $x \approx 0.17$, this peculiarity leads to a 2D Fermi surface in the considered 2D system.

A gap in the magnon spectrum of the undoped antiferromagnet appears as a consequence of the constraint of zero staggered magnetization [17,18]. Starting from $x \approx 0.02$ this gap is filled by overdamped magnons. Their increased damping is the consequence of the hole-magnon interaction and at $T = 0$ it indicates the destruction of the long-range antiferromagnetic order by holes [20]. The arising pseudogap leads to the decrease of the static spin susceptibility and the spin-lattice relaxation rate $(T_1T)^{-1}$ with decreasing temperature, as observed experimentally. This behavior is typical for the quantum disordered regime. Calculated values of these quantities are in qualitative and in some cases in quantitative agreement with experiment in underdoped $YBa_2Cu_3O_{6+\delta}$. In some articles the photoemission and magnetic pseudogaps are identified (see, e.g., Ref. [3]). In our opinion these pseudogaps are two different, unconnected peculiarities of the spectra of two well-distinguishable subsystems — holes and magnons.

The outline of the paper is as follows. In Sec. II we discuss the derivation of the t-J Hamiltonian from the extended Hubbard Hamiltonian which is supposed to give a realistic description of CuO_2 planes. This allows us to rewrite spin operators of oxygen and copper ions in terms of operators of the t-J model. The extension of the modified spin-wave approximation with zero staggered magnetization on the t-J model is discussed in Sec. III. The self-energy equations for the hole and magnon Green's functions and the hole and magnon contributions to the magnetic susceptibility in terms of these functions are written out in Sec. IV. Numerical results on the spectrum are considered in Sec. V. The pseudogap in the hole spectrum and magnetic properties are discussed in Sec. VI and VII, respectively. Finally our conclusions are given in Sec. VIII.

II. THE EFFECTIVE HAMILTONIAN

The extended Hubbard model [21] is widely used for the description of CuO_2 planes of cuprate perovskites. The Hamiltonian of the model can be written in the form [22]

$$\begin{aligned} H &= \sum_{\mathbf{m}} H_{\mathbf{m}} + 2t_{pd}\lambda_{\mathbf{a}} \sum_{\mathbf{ma}\sigma} (d^\dagger_{\mathbf{m}\sigma}\phi_{\mathbf{m+a},\sigma} + \text{H.c.}), \\ H_{\mathbf{m}} &= U n_{\mathbf{m},+1} n_{\mathbf{m},-1} + \Delta \sum_\sigma \phi^\dagger_{\mathbf{m}\sigma}\phi_{\mathbf{m}\sigma} + 2t_{pd}\lambda_0 \sum_\sigma (d^\dagger_{\mathbf{m}\sigma}\phi_{\mathbf{m}\sigma} + \text{H.c.}), \end{aligned} \tag{1}$$

where $d^\dagger_{\mathbf{m}\sigma}$ is the creation operator of electrons in the $3d_{x^2-y^2}$ orbitals of copper at the plane site $\mathbf{m}$ with the spin $\sigma = \pm 1$, $\phi^\dagger_{\mathbf{m}\sigma}$ is the Fourier transform of the operator $\phi^\dagger_{\mathbf{k}\sigma} = (\beta_{\mathbf{k}}/2\sqrt{N}) \sum_{\mathbf{ma}} \exp(-i\mathbf{km}) p^\dagger_{\mathbf{m+a}/2,\sigma}$ constructed from the creation operators of electrons in the $2p_\sigma$ orbitals of oxygen $p^\dagger_{\mathbf{m+a}/2,\sigma}$. Complementary linear combinations of these operators, which do not hybridize with the $3d_{x^2-y^2}$ copper orbitals, are omitted in Eq. (1) because their energy is much higher. In Eq. (1), $\mathbf{a} = (\pm a, 0), (0, \pm a)$ where a is the in-plane copper distance which is taken as the unit of length, $\beta_{\mathbf{k}} = \{1 + [\cos(k_x) + \cos(k_y)]/2\}^{-1/2}$, N is the number of sites; U, Δ, and t_{pd} are the Hubbard repulsion on copper, the Cu-O promotion energy and hybridization, respectively, $n_{\mathbf{m}\sigma} = d^\dagger_{\mathbf{m}\sigma} d_{\mathbf{m}\sigma}$, $\lambda_{\mathbf{m}} = N^{-1} \sum_{\mathbf{k}} \exp(i\mathbf{km}) \beta^{-1}_{\mathbf{k}}$, $\lambda_0 \approx 0.96$, $\lambda_{\mathbf{a}} \approx 0.14$. Other components of $\lambda_{\mathbf{m}}$ are small and the respective terms are omitted in Eq. (1).

The splitting of the Hamiltonian into the one- and two-site parts in Eq. (1) provides a good starting point for the perturbation theory, because for parameters [23] of La_2CuO_4 these two parts are characterized by energies differing by one order of magnitude. Notice that the frequently used perturbation expansion in powers of t_{pd} does not work for these parameters, as the hybridization is actually not small in comparison with other energies [22,24]. The prefactor $\lambda_{\mathbf{a}} \sim 0.1$ in Eq. (1) allows one to overcome this difficulty. The zero-order, one-site part $\sum_{\mathbf{m}} H_{\mathbf{m}}$ of the Hamiltonian has two sets of states corresponding to unoccupied and occupied site states of the t-J model

$$\begin{aligned} |\mathbf{m}\rangle &= \left[\frac{c_{21}}{\sqrt{2}}(\phi^\dagger_{\mathbf{m},+1} d^\dagger_{\mathbf{m},-1} - \phi^\dagger_{\mathbf{m},-1} d^\dagger_{\mathbf{m},+1}) + c_{22}\phi^\dagger_{\mathbf{m},-1}\phi^\dagger_{\mathbf{m},+1} + c_{23} d^\dagger_{\mathbf{m},-1} d^\dagger_{\mathbf{m},+1}\right]|v_{\mathbf{m}}\rangle, \\ |\mathbf{m}\sigma\rangle &= (c_{31}\phi^\dagger_{\mathbf{m},-1}\phi^\dagger_{\mathbf{m},+1} d^\dagger_{\mathbf{m}\sigma} + c_{32}\phi^\dagger_{\mathbf{m}\sigma} d^\dagger_{\mathbf{m},-1} d^\dagger_{\mathbf{m},+1})|v_{\mathbf{m}}\rangle, \end{aligned} \tag{2}$$

where $|v_{\mathbf{m}}\rangle$ is the site vacuum state and the coefficients c_{ij} are obtained in the course of the diagonalization of $H_{\mathbf{m}}$. For a given number of holes crystal states $|q\rangle$ constructed as products of site states (2) form the degenerate ground states of the zero-order Hamiltonian $H_0 = \sum_{\mathbf{m}} H_{\mathbf{m}}$. These ground states are separated by a finite gap of the order of $\min(\Delta, t_{pd})$ from excited states. In such conditions one can use the operator form of the perturbation theory [25] to obtain an effective Hamiltonian acting in the subspace of the low-lying states $|q\rangle$. Up to the terms of the second order in the perturbation H_1 [the two-site part of Hamiltonian (1)] this effective Hamiltonian reads

$$H_{\text{eff}} = \mathcal{P}[H_1 - H_1(1-\mathcal{P})(H_0 - E_0)^{-1}(1-\mathcal{P})H_1]\mathcal{P},$$

where $\mathcal{P} = \sum_q |q\rangle\langle q|$ and E_0 is the eigenenergy of H_0 for the ground states $|q\rangle$. Using Eqs. (1) and (2) we obtain the effective t-J Hamiltonian [22]

$$H_{\text{eff}} = t\sum_{\mathbf{ma}\sigma} |\mathbf{m}+\mathbf{a},\sigma\rangle\langle\mathbf{m}+\mathbf{a}||\mathbf{m}\rangle\langle\mathbf{m}\sigma| + \frac{J}{2}\sum_{\mathbf{ma}} \mathbf{S_m S_{m+a}}, \tag{3}$$

where $S^\sigma_\mathbf{m} = S^x_\mathbf{m} + i\sigma S^y_\mathbf{m} = |\mathbf{m}\sigma\rangle\langle\mathbf{m},-\sigma|$, $S^z_\mathbf{m} = \sum_\sigma(\sigma/2)|\mathbf{m}\sigma\rangle\langle\mathbf{m}\sigma|$ are the components of the spin operator $\mathbf{S_m}$, t and J are the effective hopping and superexchange constants which are expressed in terms of the parameters of the extended Hubbard Hamiltonian [see Ref. [22]; in Eq. (3), we omitted three-site (t') terms which give only small corrections in the considered case $J/t \ll 1$]. Using parameters of Ref. [23] we estimated the ratio J/t to lie in the range 0.1–0.5. In the following discussion we use $J/t = 0.2$ and $t = 0.5$ eV.

The Zeeman term of the Hamiltonian can be written in the form

$$H_Z = 2\mu_B\sum_\mathbf{m} \mathbf{s_m H_m} + \mu_B\sum_{\mathbf{ma}} \mathbf{s_{m+a/2}H_{m+a/2}}, \tag{4}$$

where μ_B is the Bohr magneton, $\mathbf{H_m}$ is the applied magnetic field, and $\mathbf{s_m}$ and $\mathbf{s_{m+a/2}}$ are composed of

$$s^\sigma_\mathbf{m} = d^\dagger_{\mathbf{m}\sigma}d_{\mathbf{m},-\sigma}, \quad s^z_\mathbf{m} = \sum_\sigma \frac{\sigma}{2} d^\dagger_{\mathbf{m}\sigma}d_{\mathbf{m}\sigma},$$
$$s^\sigma_{\mathbf{m+a/2}} = p^\dagger_{\mathbf{m+a/2},\sigma}p_{\mathbf{m+a/2},-\sigma}, \quad s^z_{\mathbf{m+a/2}} = \sum_\sigma \frac{\sigma}{2} p^\dagger_{\mathbf{m+a/2},\sigma}p_{\mathbf{m+a/2},\sigma},$$

respectively. Using notations of Eq. (1) the oxygen spin operators can be approximately rewritten as

$$\begin{aligned} s^\sigma_{\mathbf{m+a/2}} &= \frac{\tilde\beta^2}{4}(\phi^\dagger_{\mathbf{m}\sigma} + \phi^\dagger_{\mathbf{m+a},\sigma})(\phi_{\mathbf{m},-\sigma} + \phi_{\mathbf{m+a},-\sigma}), \\ s^z_{\mathbf{m+a/2}} &= \frac{\tilde\beta^2}{8}\sum_\sigma \sigma(\phi^\dagger_{\mathbf{m}\sigma} + \phi^\dagger_{\mathbf{m+a},\sigma})(\phi_{\mathbf{m}\sigma} + \phi_{\mathbf{m+a},\sigma}), \end{aligned} \tag{5}$$

where $\tilde\beta = \beta_0 + \beta_\mathbf{a} \approx 0.96$, $\beta_\mathbf{m}$ being the Fourier transform of $\beta_\mathbf{k}$. In the basis of states (2) the spin operators read

$$\begin{aligned} s^z_{\mathbf{m+a/2}} &= c^2_{21}c^2_{31}\tilde\beta^2\sum_\sigma \frac{\sigma}{16}(|\mathbf{m}\sigma\rangle\langle\mathbf{m}||\mathbf{m}+\mathbf{a}\rangle\langle\mathbf{m}+\mathbf{a},\sigma| \\ &\quad + |\mathbf{m}+\mathbf{a},\sigma\rangle\langle\mathbf{m}+\mathbf{a}||\mathbf{m}\rangle\langle\mathbf{m}\sigma|), \\ s^z_\mathbf{m} &= c^2_{31}\sum_\sigma \frac{\sigma}{2}|\mathbf{m}\sigma\rangle\langle\mathbf{m}\sigma|, \end{aligned} \tag{6}$$

where in the oxygen operator terms containing small coefficients c_{32}, c_{23} were omitted. In the following discussion we set $c_{21} = c_{31} = \tilde\beta = 1$.

III. THE SPIN-WAVE APPROXIMATION FOR ZERO STAGGERED MAGNETIZATION

Hamiltonian (3) can be essentially simplified with the use of the spin-wave approximation. As known [26], at low temperatures and hole concentrations $x \lesssim 0.02$ the CuO_2 planes are antiferromagnetically ordered. For larger x this long-range ordering is destroyed. To describe low-lying magnetic excitations and their interaction with holes in this case we use the version of the spin-wave theory formulated in Refs. [17,18] for the Heisenberg antiferromagnet with zero staggered magnetization. As shown in Refs. [17,18], in the absence of holes this approach reproduces results obtained in Refs. [27,28] with the mean-field Schwinger boson and renormalization group theories and it is remarkably accurate, as follows from the comparison with exact diagonalization and Monte Carlo results. Here we reformulate this approach to simplify the inclusion of holes in the Hamiltonian.

We use the Holstein-Primakoff transformation [25] to introduce boson operators of spin waves $b_{\mathbf{m}}$,

$$S^z_{\mathbf{m}} = e^{i\mathbf{\Pi m}}\left(\frac{1}{2} - b^\dagger_{\mathbf{m}} b_{\mathbf{m}}\right), \quad S^\sigma_{\mathbf{m}} = P^\sigma_{\mathbf{m}} \varphi_{\mathbf{m}} b_{\mathbf{m}} + P^{-\sigma}_{\mathbf{m}} b^\dagger_{\mathbf{m}} \varphi_{\mathbf{m}}, \tag{7}$$

where $\mathbf{\Pi} = (\pi, \pi)$, $P^\sigma_{\mathbf{m}} = [1 + \sigma \exp(i\mathbf{\Pi m})]/2$, and $\varphi_{\mathbf{m}} = (1 - b^\dagger_{\mathbf{m}} b_{\mathbf{m}})^{1/2}$. In Eq. (7), the factors $\exp(i\mathbf{\Pi m})$ and $P^{\pm\sigma}_{\mathbf{m}}$ are introduced to account for alternating directions of spins in the classical Néel state which is used as the reference state in the spin-wave approximation. On substituting Eq. (7) into the Heisenberg part of Hamiltonian (3), expanding $\varphi_{\mathbf{m}}$ and keeping terms up to the quartic order, we use the mean-field approximation in these latter terms

$$H_H = \frac{J}{2} \sum_{\mathbf{ma}} \mathbf{S}_{\mathbf{m+a}} \mathbf{S}_{\mathbf{m}} \approx -\frac{JN}{2} - J\langle b_0 b_{\mathbf{a}} \rangle \left[4 \sum_{\mathbf{m}} b^\dagger_{\mathbf{m}} b_{\mathbf{m}} + \frac{1}{2} \sum_{\mathbf{ma}} \left(b^\dagger_{\mathbf{m+a}} b^\dagger_{\mathbf{m}} + b_{\mathbf{m+a}} b_{\mathbf{m}}\right)\right], \tag{8}$$

where angular brackets denote averaging over the grand canonical ensemble and the four correlations $\langle b_0 b_{\mathbf{a}} \rangle$ are supposed to be equal. On deriving Eq. (8) we took into account the condition

$$\langle b^\dagger_{\mathbf{m}} b_{\mathbf{m}} \rangle = \frac{1}{2} \tag{9a}$$

which follows from the constraint of zero staggered magnetization,

$$\sum_{\mathbf{m}} e^{i\mathbf{\Pi m}} S^z_{\mathbf{m}} = 0 \quad \text{or} \quad \sum_{\mathbf{m}} b^\dagger_{\mathbf{m}} b_{\mathbf{m}} = \frac{N}{2} \tag{9b}$$

and ensures zero site magnetization, $\langle S^z_{\mathbf{m}} \rangle = 0$. To account for this constraint in the subsequent consideration we add the term $2J\nu \langle b_0 b_{\mathbf{a}} \rangle \sum_{\mathbf{m}} b^\dagger_{\mathbf{m}} b_{\mathbf{m}}$ with the Lagrange multiplier ν to Hamiltonian (8).

The deviation of the quartic terms from their mean-field value in Eq. (8) describes the magnon-magnon interaction which leads to the magnon damping [29]. In the t-J model there is another mechanism of the magnon damping connected with the hole-magnon interaction. Estimations [20,29] show that in the considered range of hole concentrations this latter interaction gives the main contribution to the damping. Therefore we do not consider the magnon-magnon interaction below.

The resulting Hamiltonian is diagonalized by the unitary transformation

$$U = \exp\left[\frac{1}{2}\sum_{\mathbf{k}\sigma}{}' \alpha_{\mathbf{k}}\left(b_{\mathbf{k}\sigma}b_{-\mathbf{k},-\sigma} - b^\dagger_{\mathbf{k}\sigma}b^\dagger_{-\mathbf{k},-\sigma}\right)\right] \quad (10)$$

with $\alpha_{\mathbf{k}} = \ln[(1+\eta\gamma_{\mathbf{k}})/(1-\eta\gamma_{\mathbf{k}})]/4$, $\eta = 2/(2-\nu)$, $\gamma_{\mathbf{k}} = \sum_{\mathbf{a}} \exp(i\mathbf{ka})/4$, and the primed sum sign indicates that the summation is restricted to the magnetic Brillouin zone which is half as large as the usual one. In Eq. (10), $b_{\mathbf{k}\sigma} = \sqrt{2/N}\sum_{\mathbf{m}} \exp(-i\mathbf{km})b_{\mathbf{m}}P^\sigma_{\mathbf{m}}$ where due to the projector $P^\sigma_{\mathbf{m}}$ the summation is performed over one sublattice. As a result, we obtain

$$\begin{aligned} \mathcal{H}_H &= U^\dagger H_H U = \sum_{\mathbf{k}\sigma}{}' \omega^0_{\mathbf{k}} b^\dagger_{\mathbf{k}\sigma}b_{\mathbf{k}\sigma}, \quad \omega^0_{\mathbf{k}} = -\frac{4J}{\eta}\langle b_0 b_{\mathbf{a}}\rangle\sqrt{1-\eta^2\gamma^2_{\mathbf{k}}}, \\ \langle b_0 b_{\mathbf{a}}\rangle &= \frac{2}{N}\sum_{\mathbf{k}\sigma}{}' \frac{\gamma_{\mathbf{k}}}{\sqrt{1-\eta^2\gamma^2_{\mathbf{k}}}}\left[\langle b_{-\mathbf{k},-\sigma}b_{\mathbf{k}\sigma}\rangle_U - \eta\gamma_{\mathbf{k}}\left(\langle b^\dagger_{\mathbf{k}\sigma}b_{\mathbf{k}\sigma}\rangle_U + \frac{1}{2}\right)\right], \end{aligned} \quad (11)$$

where we omitted unessential constant terms, and in $\langle b_0 b_{\mathbf{a}}\rangle$ for the following discussion we keep the anomalous correlation $\langle b_{-\mathbf{k},-\sigma}b_{\mathbf{k}\sigma}\rangle_U$ which is nonzero at $x \neq 0$. The subscript U means that the averaging is performed with the Hamiltonian transformed with operator (10). In the absence of holes we have $\langle b^\dagger_{\mathbf{k}\sigma}b_{\mathbf{k}\sigma}\rangle_U = [\exp(\omega^0_{\mathbf{k}}/T) - 1]^{-1}$ and $\langle b_{-\mathbf{k},-\sigma}b_{\mathbf{k}\sigma}\rangle_U = 0$ where T is the temperature in energy units, while for $x > 0$ the correlations are calculated from the magnon Green's function. Condition (9a) which determines η in Eq. (11) acquires the form

$$\frac{2}{N}\sum_{\mathbf{k}}{}' \frac{1}{\sqrt{1-\eta^2\gamma^2_{\mathbf{k}}}}\left(\langle b^\dagger_{\mathbf{k}\sigma}b_{\mathbf{k}\sigma}\rangle_U + \frac{1}{2} - \eta\gamma_{\mathbf{k}}\langle b_{-\mathbf{k},-\sigma}b_{\mathbf{k}\sigma}\rangle_U\right) = 1. \quad (12)$$

Analogous equations (without $\langle b_{-\mathbf{k},-\sigma}b_{\mathbf{k}\sigma}\rangle_U$) for the magnon spectrum of the Heisenberg antiferromagnet without holes were obtained in a somewhat different manner in Refs. [17,18]. As shown in these works, in states without long-range antiferromagnetic ordering and for finite lattices one obtains $\eta < 1$ which introduces a gap in the magnon spectrum (11) near the points $(0,0)$ and (π,π) of the Brillouin zone.

The reference state of the spin-wave approximation discussed above is the classical Néel state $|\mathcal{N}\rangle$. Other states are described via the reference state and magnon creation operators determined for this state. The introduction of holes in this picture leads to two possibilities for the hole movement: there is a magnon or there is no magnon on a site which a hole jumps to. Both these possibilities are described by the following term of the Hamiltonian:

$$H_t = t\sum_{\mathbf{ma}} h_{\mathbf{m}}h^\dagger_{\mathbf{m+a}}(b_{\mathbf{m+a}} + b^\dagger_{\mathbf{m}}), \quad (13)$$

which corresponds to the first term in Eq. (3). In Eq. (13), $h^\dagger_{\mathbf{m}} = \sum_\sigma P^\sigma_{\mathbf{m}}|\mathbf{m}\rangle\langle\mathbf{m}\sigma|$ is the hole creation operator in the Néel state $|\mathcal{N}\rangle = \prod_{\mathbf{m}}(\sum_\sigma P^\sigma_{\mathbf{m}}|\mathbf{m}\sigma\rangle)$.

In spite of the clear physical meaning of the constraint of zero staggered magnetization, let us discuss the approximations made from a somewhat different point of view. Notice that in the case of short-range antiferromagnetic order characterized by the spin correlation length $\xi \gg a$ one can use the usual spin-wave approximation in any crystal region with a linear size of the order of ξ. A Néel state with some local spin quantization axis is used as the reference state for this spin-wave approximation. Additionally one should take into account the finite-size effect due to a finite value of ξ. This is done by applying condition (12). The value of η determined by this condition is directly connected with ξ [17] (recall that $\eta < 1$ both for a finite ξ and a finite lattice). Notice also that only sites neighboring to the hole site are involved in the processes described by Eq. (13). The hole-magnon interaction is of the short-range type. This is the reason why in the case of short-range antiferromagnetic order with $\xi \gg a$ the hole hopping term (13) looks exactly like the same term for the long-range order [30,31]. There is no "bare-hopping" (without magnon operators) term in Eq. (13) because in the case $\xi \gg a$ the direction of the spin quantization axis is practically the same on sites involved in a hole jump.

After unitary transformation (10) the total Hamiltonian reads

$$\mathcal{H} = U^\dagger H_t U + \mathcal{H}_H = \sum_{\mathbf{kk'}\sigma}{}' (g_{\mathbf{kk'}} h^\dagger_{\mathbf{k}\sigma} h_{\mathbf{k-k'},-\sigma} b_{\mathbf{k'}\sigma} + \text{H.c.}) + \sum_{\mathbf{k}\sigma}{}' \omega^0_{\mathbf{k}} b^\dagger_{\mathbf{k}\sigma} b_{\mathbf{k}\sigma}, \tag{14}$$

where $g_{\mathbf{kk'}} = -4t\sqrt{2/N}(\gamma_{\mathbf{k-k'}} u_{\mathbf{k'}} + \gamma_{\mathbf{k}} v_{\mathbf{k'}})$ and $u_{\mathbf{k}} = \cosh(\alpha_{\mathbf{k}})$, $v_{\mathbf{k}} = -\sinh(\alpha_{\mathbf{k}})$. On carrying out the unitary transformation we neglected the noncommutativity of hole and magnon operators which is justified at least for $x \lesssim 0.1$ by comparison with exact diagonalization results [32]. At $\eta = 1$ Eq. (14) reduces to the Hamiltonian obtained in Refs. [30,31] for the case of the long-range antiferromagnetic order. The number of magnons is not conserved by Hamiltonian (14) and at $x > 0$ the anomalous correlation $\langle b_{-\mathbf{k},-\sigma} b_{\mathbf{k}\sigma}\rangle_U$ in Eqs. (11) and (12) is nonzero.

Notice that the used spin-wave approximation is not rotationally invariant and the correlations $\langle S^+_{\mathbf{l}} S^-_{\mathbf{m}}\rangle$ are zero [17,18]. Therefore only the z components of spin operators are considered in the following discussion.

IV. SUSCEPTIBILITY AND SELF-ENERGY EQUATIONS

In the new notations the spin components (6) acquire the form

$$s^z_{\mathbf{m}} = \frac{1}{2} e^{i\mathbf{\Pi m}} \left(\frac{1}{2} - b^\dagger_{\mathbf{m}} b_{\mathbf{m}}\right), \quad s^z_{\mathbf{m+a}/2} = \frac{1}{32} e^{i\mathbf{\Pi m}} \left[h_{\mathbf{m}} h^\dagger_{\mathbf{m+a}} \left(b_{\mathbf{m+a}} - b^\dagger_{\mathbf{m}}\right) + \text{H.c.}\right]. \tag{15}$$

$s^z_{\mathbf{m}}$ and $s^z_{\mathbf{m+a}/2}$ give contributions to the magnetization

$$M^z_{\mathbf{q}} = -2\mu_B s^z_{\mathbf{q}}, \quad s^z_{\mathbf{q}} = \sum_{\mathbf{m}} s^z_{\mathbf{m}} e^{-i\mathbf{qm}} + \sum_{\mathbf{m}} \sum_{\mathbf{a'}} s^z_{\mathbf{m+a'}/2} e^{-i\mathbf{q}(\mathbf{m+a'}/2)},$$

from magnons and holes, respectively. Here $\mathbf{a'} = (a, 0), (0, a)$. The susceptibility is determined by the equation

$$\chi^z(\mathbf{q}\omega) = \frac{i}{N} \int_0^\infty d\tau e^{i\omega\tau} \langle [M^z_{\mathbf{q}\tau}, M^z_{-\mathbf{q}}] \rangle,$$

where $M^z_{\mathbf{q}\tau} = \exp(iH\tau) M^z_{\mathbf{q}} \exp(-iH\tau)$, $H = H_t + H_H - \mu\mathcal{N}$, $\mathcal{N} = \sum'_{\mathbf{k}\sigma} h^\dagger_{\mathbf{k}\sigma} h_{\mathbf{k}\sigma}$, and μ is the hole chemical potential. The susceptibility can be calculated using the simplest decoupling, as the subsequent terms of the perturbation series for the respective Matsubara Green's function are proportional to powers of the small hole concentration and are further decreased by rapidly oscillating coefficients. In this approximation the magnon and hole contributions (indicated by subscripts m and h, respectively) in the susceptibility can be written as

$$\begin{aligned}
\operatorname{Im}\chi^z_m(\mathbf{q}\omega) &= \frac{4\mu_B^2}{N}\sum_{\mathbf{k}}\int_{-\infty}^{\infty}\frac{d\nu}{\pi}[n_B(\nu) - n_B(\nu+\omega)] \\
&\quad\times[K_1(\mathbf{k},\nu)K_1(\mathbf{k}+\boldsymbol{\kappa},\nu+\omega) + K_2(\mathbf{k},\nu)K_2(\mathbf{k}+\boldsymbol{\kappa},\nu+\omega)], \\
\operatorname{Im}\chi^z_h(\mathbf{q}\omega) &= \frac{\mu_B^2}{16N^2}\sum_{\mathbf{k}\mathbf{k}'}\iint_{-\infty}^{\infty}\frac{d\nu d\nu'}{\pi^2}[n_F(\nu) - n_F(\nu+\nu'-\omega)][n_B(\nu') - n_B(\nu'-\omega)] \\
&\quad\times \operatorname{Im}G(\mathbf{k}\nu)\operatorname{Im}G(\mathbf{k}+\mathbf{k}'-\mathbf{q},\nu+\nu'-\omega) \qquad (16) \\
&\quad\times\Big[\operatorname{Im}D_{11}(\mathbf{k}'\nu')\gamma^2\Big(\mathbf{k}-\frac{\mathbf{q}}{2}\Big) - \operatorname{Im}D_{11}(\mathbf{k}',-\nu')\gamma^2\Big(\mathbf{k}+\mathbf{k}'-\frac{\mathbf{q}}{2}\Big) \\
&\quad -2\operatorname{Im}D_{12}(\mathbf{k}'\nu')\gamma\Big(\mathbf{k}-\frac{\mathbf{q}}{2}\Big)\gamma\Big(\mathbf{k}+\mathbf{k}'-\frac{\mathbf{q}}{2}\Big)\Big], \\
\operatorname{Re}\chi(\mathbf{q}\omega) &= \mathcal{P}\int_{-\infty}^{\infty}\frac{d\nu}{\pi}\frac{\operatorname{Im}\chi(\mathbf{q}\omega)}{\nu-\omega},
\end{aligned}$$

where $n_B = [\exp(\omega/T) - 1]^{-1}$, $n_F = [\exp(\omega/T) + 1]^{-1}$, $\boldsymbol{\kappa} = \mathbf{q} - \boldsymbol{\Pi}$,

$$K_1(\mathbf{k}\omega) = u^2_{\mathbf{k}}\operatorname{Im}D_{11}(\mathbf{k}\omega) + 2u_{\mathbf{k}}v_{\mathbf{k}}\operatorname{Im}D_{12}(\mathbf{k}\omega) - v^2_{\mathbf{k}}\operatorname{Im}D_{11}(\mathbf{k},-\omega),$$

$$K_2(\mathbf{k}\omega) = u_{\mathbf{k}}v_{\mathbf{k}}[\operatorname{Im}D_{11}(\mathbf{k}\omega) - \operatorname{Im}D_{11}(\mathbf{k},-\omega)] + (u^2_{\mathbf{k}} + v^2_{\mathbf{k}})\operatorname{Im}D_{12}(\mathbf{k}\omega),$$

and $D_{ij}(\mathbf{k}\omega)$, $G(\mathbf{k}\omega)$ are the Fourier transforms of the magnon and hole Green's functions

$$D_{11}(\mathbf{k}t) = -i\theta(t)\langle[b_{\mathbf{k}\sigma}(t), b^\dagger_{\mathbf{k}\sigma}]\rangle_U, \quad D_{12}(\mathbf{k}t) = -i\theta(t)\langle[b_{-\mathbf{k},-\sigma}(t), b_{\mathbf{k}\sigma}]\rangle_U,$$

$$G(\mathbf{k}t) = -i\theta(t)\langle[h_{\mathbf{k}\sigma}(t), h^\dagger_{\mathbf{k}\sigma}]\rangle_U,$$

$b_{\mathbf{k}\sigma}(t) = \exp[i(\mathcal{H}-\mu\mathcal{N})t]b_{\mathbf{k}\sigma}\exp[-i(\mathcal{H}-\mu\mathcal{N})t]$. These Green's functions do not depend on the spin index. In Eq. (16), summations over wave vectors are performed over the full Brillouin zone. In the second magnetic zone, which together with the first magnetic zone forms this full zone, $D_{11}(\mathbf{k}\omega)$ and $G(\mathbf{k}\omega)$ repeat periodically their values in the first zone, while $D_{12}(\mathbf{k}\omega)$ changes sign.

These Green's functions are determined from the set of self-energy equations. The hole Σ and magnon Π_{11}, Π_{12} self-energies are described by the following diagrams:

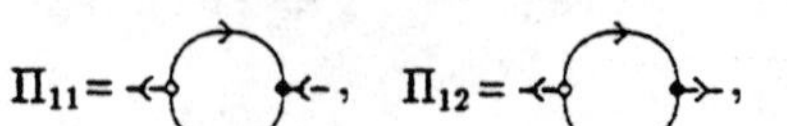

where solid and dashed lines correspond to hole and magnon Green's functions, open and filled circles are bare and full vertices. Dashed lines with two oppositely directed arrows correspond to the anomalous magnon Green's functions $D_{12}(\mathbf{k}t)$ and $D_{21}(\mathbf{k}t) = -i\theta(t)\langle[b^\dagger_{\mathbf{k}\sigma}(t), b^\dagger_{-\mathbf{k},-\sigma}]\rangle_U$. The first correction to the bare vertex $g_{\mathbf{kk}'}$ is exactly zero due to the impossibility to coordinate spin indices in this correction [33]. This suggests the use of the Born approximation in which the full vertices are substituted with the bare ones. In this approximation the real-frequency self-energy equations read

$$\begin{aligned}
&G(\mathbf{k}\omega) = [\omega + \mu - \Sigma(\mathbf{k}\omega)]^{-1},\\
&\mathrm{Im}\,\Sigma(\mathbf{k}\omega) = -2\sum_{\mathbf{k}'}{}' \int_{-\infty}^{\infty} \frac{d\omega'}{\pi}\Big[g^2_{\mathbf{kk}'}\mathrm{Im}\,D_{11}(\mathbf{k}'\omega') - g^2_{\mathbf{k}-\mathbf{k}',-\mathbf{k}'}\mathrm{Im}\,D_{11}(-\mathbf{k}',-\omega')\\
&\qquad +2g_{\mathbf{kk}'}g_{\mathbf{k}-\mathbf{k}',-\mathbf{k}'}\mathrm{Im}\,D_{12}(\mathbf{k}'\omega')\Big][n_B(\omega') + n_F(\omega'-\omega)]\mathrm{Im}\,G(\mathbf{k}-\mathbf{k}',\omega-\omega'),\\
&\mathrm{Re}\,\Sigma(\mathbf{k}\omega) = \mathcal{P}\int_{-\infty}^{\infty}\frac{d\omega'}{\pi}\frac{\mathrm{Im}\,\Sigma(\mathbf{k}\omega')}{\omega'-\omega},\\
&D_{11}(\mathbf{k}\omega) = \frac{R^*(\mathbf{k},-\omega)}{R(\mathbf{k}\omega)R^*(\mathbf{k},-\omega) - \Pi^2_{12}(\mathbf{k},\omega)},\quad D_{12}(\mathbf{k}\omega) = \frac{\Pi_{12}(\mathbf{k},\omega)}{R(\mathbf{k}\omega)R^*(\mathbf{k},-\omega) - \Pi^2_{12}(\mathbf{k},\omega)},\\
&\mathrm{Im}\,\Pi_{11}(\mathbf{k}\omega) = 2\sum_{\mathbf{k}'}{}' g^2_{\mathbf{k}'\mathbf{k}}\int_{-\infty}^{\infty}\frac{d\omega'}{\pi}\,\mathrm{Im}\,G(\mathbf{k}'\omega')\,\mathrm{Im}\,G(\mathbf{k}'-\mathbf{k},\omega'-\omega)[n_F(\omega') - n_F(\omega'-\omega)],\\
&\mathrm{Im}\,\Pi_{12}(\mathbf{k}\omega) = 2\sum_{\mathbf{k}'}{}' g_{\mathbf{k}'\mathbf{k}}g_{\mathbf{k}'-\mathbf{k},-\mathbf{k}}\int_{-\infty}^{\infty}\frac{d\omega'}{\pi}\,\mathrm{Im}\,G(\mathbf{k}'\omega')\,\mathrm{Im}\,G(\mathbf{k}'-\mathbf{k},\omega'-\omega)\\
&\qquad \times[n_F(\omega') - n_F(\omega'-\omega)],\\
&\mathrm{Re}\,\Pi_{ij}(\mathbf{k}\omega) = \mathcal{P}\int_{-\infty}^{\infty}\frac{d\omega'}{\pi}\frac{\mathrm{Im}\,\Pi_{ij}(\mathbf{k}\omega')}{\omega'-\omega},
\end{aligned} \tag{17}$$

where $R(\mathbf{k}\omega) = \omega - \omega^0_{\mathbf{k}} - \Pi_{11}(\mathbf{k}\omega)$. Equations (17) and (12) form a self-consistent set and can be solved iteratively. The calculation procedure is the following: for given values of μ and T some starting value $\eta < 1$ was selected; after the convergence of

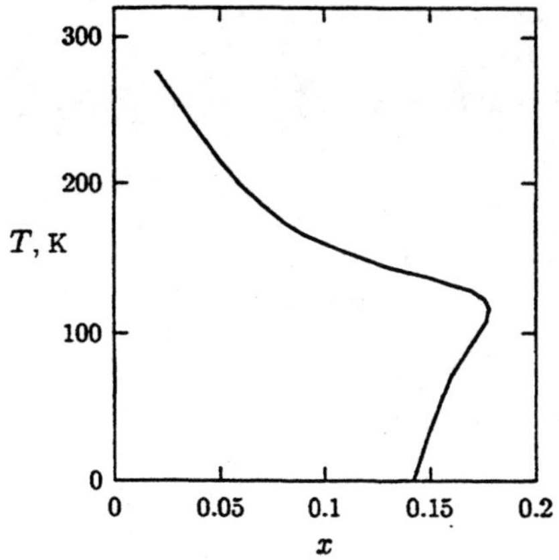

Fig. 1. The curve encloses the region where condition (12) can be fulfilled.

the iterations condition (12) is checked and η is appropriately changed for the next iteration cycle, until the condition is fulfilled with the accuracy of 10^{-3} (some other details of the calculation procedure can be found in Ref. [34]). In the calculations a 20×20 lattice was used. Green's functions were computed on a mesh of frequency points equally spaced with the step $\Delta\omega \approx 0.022t \approx 11$ meV. We found that condition (12) can be satisfied only in a limited region of the T-x plane, namely below the curve shown in Fig. 1.

V. THE ENERGY SPECTRUM

The evolution of the calculated hole spectral function $A(\mathbf{k}\omega) = -\mathrm{Im}\,G(\mathbf{k}\omega)$ with the concentration

$$x = -\frac{2}{\pi N}\sum_{\mathbf{k}}\int_{-\infty}^{\infty} d\omega\, n_F(\omega)\,\mathrm{Im}\,G(\mathbf{k}\omega) \tag{18}$$

is shown in Fig. 2 for two points of the Brillouin zone. We use the hole picture where

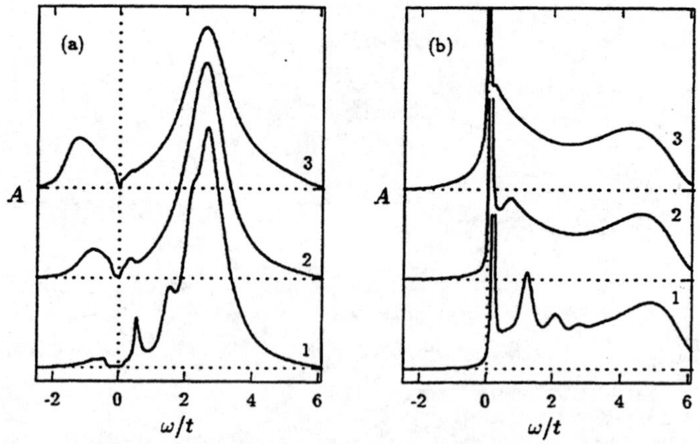

Fig. 2. The hole spectral function $A(\mathbf{k}\omega)$ for $\mathbf{k} = (0,0)$ (a) and $(0,\pi)$ (b). $T = 0$. Curves 1, 2, and 3 correspond to $x = 0.016$, 0.059, and 0.133, respectively.

states below the Fermi level $\omega = 0$ are filled by holes. Since our description is based on the spin-wave approximation with the magnetic Brillouin zone which is twice smaller than the full Brillouin zone, the spectral functions in the points $\mathbf{k}$ and $\mathbf{k} + (\pi,\pi)$ are identical. For long-range antiferromagnetic ordering when these points are equivalent such description does not lead to any loss of information. In the case of short-range order the use of the smaller Brillouin zone leads to a somewhat coarsened description. The points $\mathbf{k}$ and $\mathbf{k}+(\pi,\pi)$ are no longer equivalent — the respective spectral functions contain similar maxima which however have essentially different intensities and widths [35]. In our approach, where the maxima in the two points appear together in one spectral function for the momentum in the first magnetic Brillouin zone, we cannot determine whether a selected maximum is more intensive in the first or in the second magnetic Brillouin zone (which form the full zone). In other words we cannot determine where is the usual band and where is the shadow band [35]. However, we can distribute the maxima between the two magnetic zones by drawing additional information from experiment as we shall do in the following discussion.

At $x \lesssim 0.04$ the spectra contain series of peaks and the hole-magnon scattering continuum (see curves 1 in Fig. 2). With increasing x only the lowest and most intensive of these peaks is retained in the spectrum for wave vectors near the boundary of the magnetic Brillouin zone [everywhere in this region the spectrum is similar to that for $\mathbf{k} = (0, \pi)$]. This peak corresponds to the so-called spin-polaron band in the hole spectrum. Other peaks are washed away, forming a broad dispersive maximum above the Fermi level for momenta in the central part of the magnetic Brillouin zone. Simultaneously a maximum develops below the Fermi level (compare curves 2 and 3 in Fig. 2). As seen in Fig. 3, this maximum possesses dispersion and is comparatively narrow near the Fermi level.

The energy positions of the spectral maxima discussed above as functions of momentum are shown in Fig. 4 for heavily underdoped and moderately doped cases [as

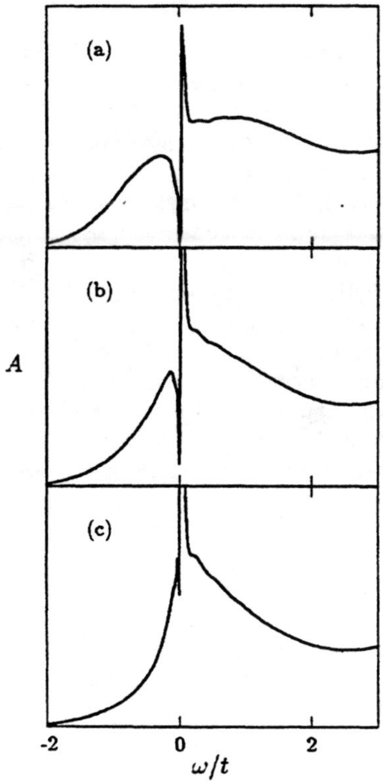

Fig. 3. The hole spectral function for $\mathbf{k} = (0.5\pi, \pi)$ (a), $(0.4\pi, \pi)$ (b), and $(0.3\pi, \pi)$ (c). $x = 0.133$, $T = 0$.

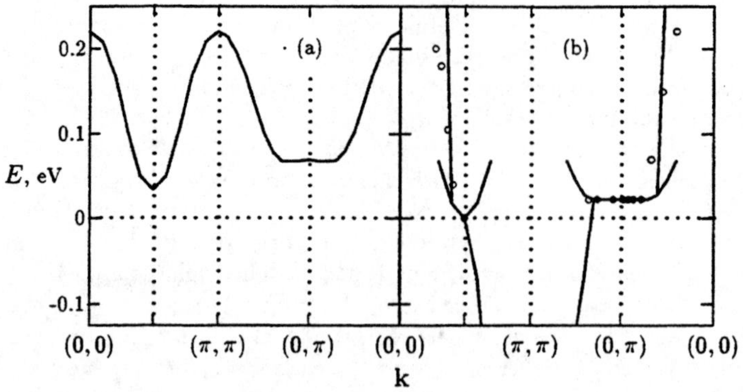

Fig. 4. Energy vs. momentum relationships calculated for $x = 0.021, T = 0$ (a) and $x = 0.121$, $T = 0.02t = 116$ K (b, solid line). In part (b), circles indicate positions of quasiparticle peaks in the photoemission experiment [40] carried out at $T = 100$ K in a Bi2212 crystal with $T_c = 85$ K.

discussed above, we have used the experimental fact that hole pockets are positioned around $(\pm\pi, \pm\pi)$ to relate the portion of the energy band below the Fermi level to this part of the full Brillouin zone]. Figure 4a demonstrates the well-known spin-polaron band discussed in a large number of works devoted to the case of low doping (see, e.g., [32,33,36–39]). The width of this band is of the order of J, i.e. much less than the hole hopping constant t. This is connected with the above discussed fact that in the rigorous antiferromagnetic order the hole movement requires the emission and absorption of magnons. In such conditions the slower subsystem — magnons — will determine the bandwidth of the combined quasiparticle. As mentioned, a part of the spin-polaron band is retained near the boundary of the magnetic Brillouin zone for moderate doping. As seen in Fig. 4b, this part retains, with some distortion, main features of the spin-polaron band in this region. Among these features is the large nearly flat region which is visible around $(0, \pi)$ in Fig. 4b. In this figure we have compared the calculated energy band with the normal-state photoemission data [40] in Bi2212 with $T_c = 85$ K which corresponds to the hole concentration in the range $0.11 - 0.15$. In Ref. [40] the energy position of the flat region — the so-called extended van Hove singularity — is estimated to be $\pm 30 - 50$ meV relative to the Fermi level. We positioned the experimental flat region at +20 meV (in the hole picture), in accordance with later more exact measurements [3]. As seen in Fig. 4b, with respect to both the energy position and the extension in the Brillouin zone the calculations reproduce well the experimental van Hove singularity. Notice that also the general shape of the band, as seen in photoemission (which tests the region $\omega \geq 0$), is well reproduced by the calculations. That the flat portion of the spin-polaron band can correspond to the photoemission extended saddle point was apparently first indicated in Ref. [41].

As follows from Fig. 4, considerable changes occur in the hole band shape on moving from light to moderate dopings, as was first indicated in Refs. [39,34]. The narrow, with the width of the order of J, spin-polaron band is transformed to a much wider band characterized by the energy parameter t. The general shape of this band resembles a considerably distorted 2D nearest-neighbor band produced by the kinetic term of the t-J Hamiltonian (3). Analogous changes in the band shape are observed in the photoemission of Bi2212 [2]. These changes point to a certain weakening of correlations for $x > 0.04$, however, some features of the strongly correlated spectrum are retained: as mentioned, near the Fermi level around the boundary of the magnetic Brillouin zone the spectrum contains a persistent part of the spin-polaron band and widths of spectral maxima grow steeply with distance from the Fermi level.

These changes in the hole spectrum are connected with changes in the magnon subsystem. For $T = 0$ starting from $x \approx 0.02$ in the central part of the magnetic Brillouin zone magnons become overdamped. The overdamped magnons manifest themselves in a perceptible intensity of the magnon spectral function $B_{11}(\mathbf{k}\omega) = -\mathrm{Im}\, D_{11}(\mathbf{k}\omega)$ in the nearest vicinity and on both sides of $\omega = 0$ (see Fig. 5a where together with the structure corresponding to an overdamped magnon the maximum of a usual magnon is also visible; notice that overdamped magnons do not form maxima in B_{11} because this quantity changes sign at the central frequency $\omega = 0$ of these magnons). The appearance of the overdamped magnons points to the destruction of the long-range antiferromagnetic order by holes [20,42] which, in contrast to the destruction due to thermal fluctuations, occurs also at zero temperature. Due to a finite intensity in B_{11}, produced by these magnons in the range $\omega < 0$, the magnon occupation number $n_{\mathbf{k}} = -\int_{-\infty}^{\infty} d\omega\pi^{-1} n_B(\omega) B_{11}(\mathbf{k}\omega)$ is finite at $T = 0$ which leads to a finite zero-temperature correlation length ξ in the spin correlation function $\langle s_{\mathbf{l}}^z s_{\mathbf{m}}^z \rangle$ (in the considered finite lattice this phase transition is smeared; fortunately for relevant small x an analytic consideration for an infinite lattice is possible [20,42]). The overdamped magnons can be identified with relaxational modes describing relative rotations of magnetic quantization axes in regions of size ξ. In the hole spectrum the destruction of the long-range antiferromagnetic order manifests itself in the mentioned change of the shape and characteristic energy of the spectrum from J to t at $x \approx 0.04$. Qualitatively this can be understood in the following way: after the destruction of the long-range

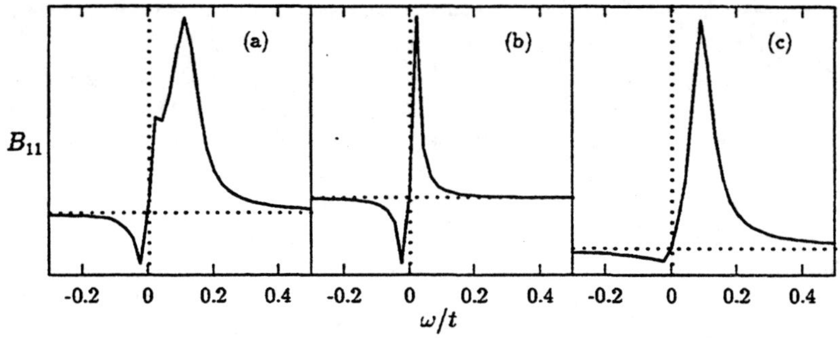

Fig. 5. The magnon spectral function $B_{11}(\mathbf{k}\omega)$ for $\mathbf{k} = (0, \pi/5)$, $T = 0$, $x = 0.059$ (a), $\mathbf{k} = (0,0)$, $T = 58$ K, $x = 0.1$ (b), and $\mathbf{k} = (\pi/2, \pi/2)$, $T = 116$ K, $x = 0.172$ (c).

order holes can move without introducing additional disorder in the magnon subsystem and, as a result, the larger characteristic energy, t, reveals itself in the spectrum.

Apparently nearly simultaneously with the appearance of overdamped magnons η becomes finite and a gap opens in the magnon spectrum. The low-frequency overdamped magnons transform this gap to a pseudogap. This pseudogap is most evident in $B_{11}(\mathbf{k}=0,\omega)$ by the asymmetry of the spectrum around $\omega = 0$ (Fig. 5b). In spite of the appearance of overdamped magnons, even at $x \approx 0.17$ and $T \approx 100$ K usual magnons with essentially softened frequencies and increased damping are retained at the periphery of the magnetic Brillouin zone indicating persistent antiferromagnetic correlations (see Fig. 5c).

Let us return to the hole spectrum. The hole Fermi surfaces calculated for moderate dopings are shown in Figs. 6a and 6b. In part (a), line segments along the boundary of the magnetic Brillouin zone are connected with the spin-polaron band. After touching the Fermi level (which occurs at $x \approx 0.01$) the bottom of this band remains pinned to the Fermi level and the band flattens with increasing x. Originating from work [43] it is widely believed that for small hole concentrations the Fermi surface consists of small hole pockets around $(\pm\pi/2, \pm\pi/2)$. Our calculations do not support this point of view. The Fermi level does not cross the bottom of the spin-polaron band but is rather pinned to this bottom and the mentioned hole pockets do not arise [notice however that the line segments near $(\pm\pi/2, \pm\pi/2)$ in Fig. 6 can have a finite width provided that it is much less than our momentum resolution $\pi/10$].

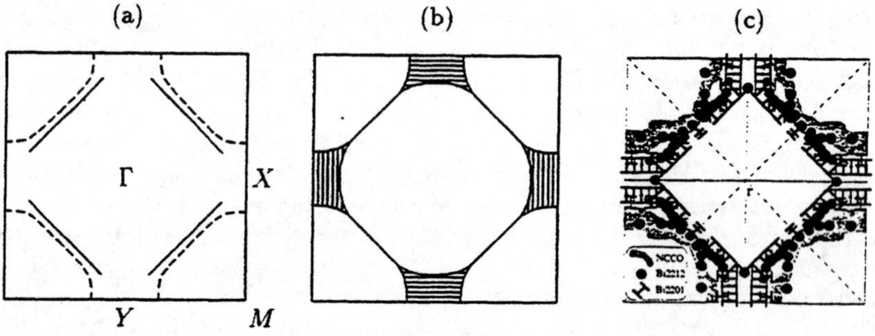

Fig. 6. The calculated hole Fermi surface for $T \approx 100$ K, $0.07 \lesssim x < 0.17$ (a), $x = 0.172$ (b), and experimental Fermi surface for several cuprates (c, from Ref. [44]). Dashed lines in (a) and hatched regions in (b) indicate hidden and two-dimensional parts of the surface. The points X, Y, and M correspond to $\mathbf{k} = (\pi, 0)$, $(0, -\pi)$, and (π, π), respectively.

In Fig. 6a, dashed curves indicate the crossings of the Fermi level by the part of the energy band which arises with growing x below the bottom of the spin-polaron band (see Figs. 2–4). This part forms hole pockets around $(\pm\pi, \pm\pi)$ and determines the hole concentration (18). The pockets start to form from small x and their extent in the Brillouin zone grows with x; however up to $x \approx 0.07$ the pockets do not reach the Fermi level — all their states are positioned below the Fermi level. Thus, for $x \lesssim 0.07$ the Fermi surface consists of only the line segments along the boundary of the magnetic Brillouin zone and no closed Fermi surface exists. For larger hole concentrations the hole pockets reach the Fermi level and the crossings depicted by the dashed curves in Fig. 6a arise. However. as seen in Fig. 3, just at this crossing the weaker maximum corresponding to the pocket is completely lost within the foot of a much more intensive spin-polaron peak which is located somewhat above the Fermi level for the temperature, hole concentration and wave vectors of Fig. 3. Thus, the dashed curves in Fig. 6a correspond to hidden parts of the Fermi surface. If like in photoemission experiments the spectrum is not tested below the Fermi level (in the hole picture), the respective crossings reveal themselves only as a finite spectral intensity at the Fermi level.

As mentioned, with growing x the persistent part of the spin-polaron band flattens. As a consequence, the extended saddle points approach the Fermi level and at $x = 0.172$ they fall on it. The Fermi surface of the considered two-dimensional fermions becomes two-dimensional, as shown in Fig. 6b. The mentioned hole concentration is close to optimal doping which corresponds to the highest T_c. As observed in photoemission of Bi2212 [2], in this case the saddle points do lie, within the experimental accuracy, on the Fermi level. Fig. 6c demonstrates Fermi surfaces deduced from photoemission in $Nd_{2-x}Ce_xCuO_4$ (NCCO), Bi2212, and $Bi_2(Sr_{0.97}Pr_{0.03})_2CuO_{6+\delta}$ (Bi2201). Contrasting this figure with Figs. 6a and 6b, we conclude that our calculations reproduce satisfactorily the main features of the experimental Fermi surface in crystals with significantly different hole concentrations.

For Fig. 6a we indicated the concentration range where the Fermi surface remains practically unchanged. In particular, it means that the size of the $(\pm\pi, \pm\pi)$ hole pockets varies only slightly in the concentration range $0.07 \lesssim x \lesssim 0.17$. This result of our calculations agrees with experiment [1] and points to the substantial violation of Luttinger's theorem [45]. In accord with this theorem the area enclosed by the Fermi surface in the Brillouin zone should vary linearly with x. As seen in Fig. 2, quasiparticle weights of states (spectral intensities) which form the hole pockets grow with increasing x. It is this growth of quasiparticle weights, rather than the growing size of these pockets, which leads to the increase of the hole concentration in Eq. (18).

As follows from the above discussion, the energy spectrum of the considered fermions differs essentially from the Fermi liquid behavior of conventional metals. To this we can add the linear, rather than quadratic, frequency dependences of the hole decay widths near the Fermi level in the case of moderate doping [39]. This result resembles the marginal Fermi liquid [46], however, in contrast to this concept our calculated $\mathrm{Im}\,\Sigma(\omega)$ has markedly different slopes below and above the Fermi level and a strong momentum dependence.

VI. PSEUDOGAP IN THE HOLE SPECTRUM

As follows from Fig. 3, the spin-polaron peak is the most prominent feature of the hole spectrum near the Fermi level for wave vectors in the vicinity of the Fermi surface. The hole spectral function is directly related to the photoemission spectrum. Hence the spin-polaron peak will determine the position of the leading edge of the photoemission

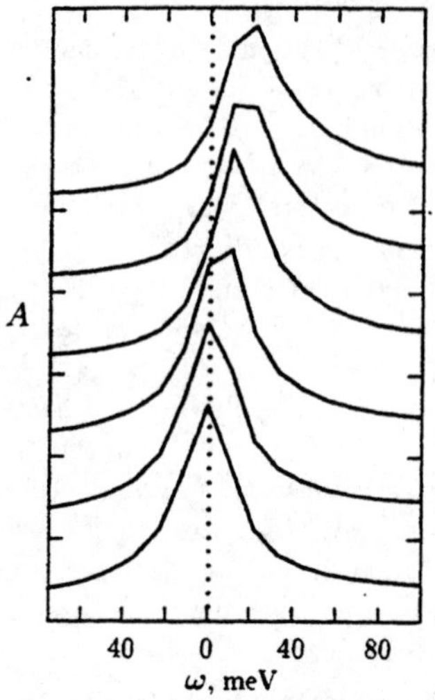

Fig. 7. The hole spectral function for wave vectors on the Fermi surface. Curves from top to bottom correspond to $\mathbf{k} = (0.2\pi, \pi)$, $(0.2\pi, 0.9\pi)$, $(0.2\pi, 0.8\pi)$, $(0.3\pi, 0.7\pi)$, $(0.4\pi, 0.6\pi)$, and $(0.5\pi, 0.5\pi)$, respectively. $T = 116$ K, $x = 0.121$.

spectrum. For several wave vectors on the Fermi surface the hole spectral function is shown in Fig. 7 for the underdoped case. As seen from this figure, the spin-polaron maximum, which lies on the Fermi level near $(\pi/2, \pi/2)$, is shifted upwards on approaching $(\pi/5, \pi)$. Recall that the part of the Fermi surface near $(\pi/5, \pi)$ is connected with another, broader and weaker maximum which is completely lost at the foot of the spin-polaron peak on crossing the Fermi level (see Fig. 3). As a consequence, the situation in Fig. 7 looks like a part of the Fermi surface disappears and a gap opens between the hole energy band and the Fermi level near $(\pi/5, \pi)$. Due to the mentioned hidden crossing of the Fermi level in this point there remains a finite intensity at $\omega = 0$ which transforms the gap to the pseudogap. The same behavior of the leading edge is observed in photoemission of underdoped cuprates which led to the idea of the photoemission pseudogap [1–3].

In Fig. 8 we compare our calculated position of the spin-polaron peak and the experimentally measured position of the photoemission leading edge [3] as functions of momentum along the Fermi surface shown in the insets of both parts of the figure (some differences in the Fermi surfaces shown may be connected both with the experimental resolution which produces some uncertainty in the position of the Fermi surface especially in the case of narrow bands and with the influence of terms not included in the t-J Hamiltonian). In part (b), the location on the Fermi surface is determined by the angle measured from the line $(\pi, \pi) - (\pi, 0)$. At $T = 14$ K experimental curves for the 83 K and 87 K samples in Fig. 8b correspond to superconducting gaps. As indicated in Ref. [3], in the former, underdoped sample the shape of the curve and the magnitude of the gap remain practically unchanged when the temperature increases and somewhat exceeds T_c, while the gap is closed in the latter, optimally doped sample. Taking into account these experimental facts we conclude from the comparison of Figs. 8a and 8b that the calculations reproduce satisfactorily the general shape and the magnitude of

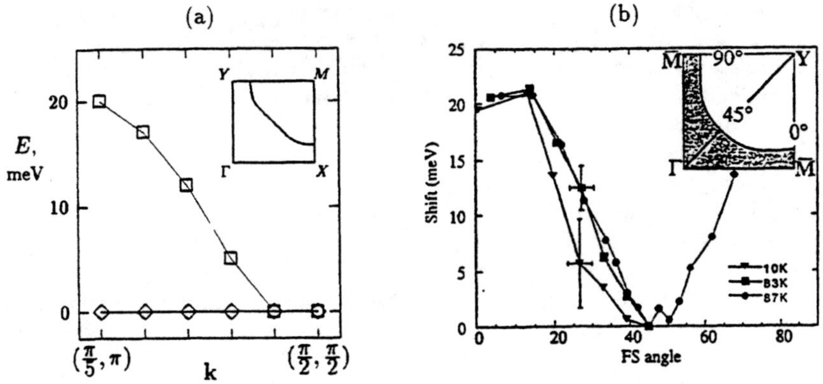

Fig. 8. (a) The position of the spin-polaron peak along the Fermi surface, shown in the inset, for $x = 0.121$ (□) and $x = 0.172$ (◇) at $T = 116$ K. The points M, X, and Y are defined in the caption of Fig. 6. (b) The position of the leading edge of the photoemission spectrum vs. momentum along the Fermi surface in the inset for samples with $T_c = 10$ K (heavily underdoped, triangles), 83 K (underdoped, squares), and 87 K (optimally doped, circles). Measurements in Ref. [3], where this figure were taken from, were carried out for Bi2212 at $T = 14$ K. The points $\overline{M}$ and Y correspond to the X, Y and M points in the square Brillouin zone.

the normal-state pseudogap in the underdoped case. Moreover, as seen from Fig. 8a, in agreement with experiment the pseudogap is closed in the case of optimal doping.

In Ref. [3] the similarity of symmetries of the superconducting gap and the normal-state pseudogap and their smooth evolution into each other with temperature served as the basis for the supposition that the pseudogap is the normal-state precursor of the superconducting gap. In accord with this supposition the pseudogap arises above T_c due to superconducting fluctuations. We did not include these fluctuations in our present calculations and thus the pseudogap shown in Fig. 8a is not connected with the fluctuations. In our calculations the pseudogap arises due to the specific dispersion of the spin-polaron band, a part of which is retained near the Fermi level at moderate doping and gives the most intensive maxima in the spectral function. The existence of this band is a consequence of strong electron correlations. We do not exclude the possibility that the superconducting fluctuations do contribute to the pseudogap, however, based on the satisfactory agreement between our estimate and the observed pseudogap magnitude we suppose that the main contribution is provided by strong electron correlations. Besides, with the superconducting fluctuation mechanism it is difficult to understand why the pseudogap appears only on one side of the Fermi level and why the fluctuations disappear abruptly in a small concentration range near optimal doping when the pseudogap is closed. For the 2D t-J model various calculations (see, e.g., Refs. [34,47–49]) give the $d_{x^2-y^2}$ symmetry for the superconducting gap in the case of moderate doping. This gap looks similar to the pseudogap in Fig. 8a, as the symmetries of both of them are determined by the hole-magnon interaction and by short-range antiferromagnetic ordering. This ensures smooth evolution of the pseudogap into the superconducting gap with lowering temperature below T_c.

As observed in Ref. [3], in slightly underdoped samples the pseudogap is closed when temperature exceeds some T^*. This characteristic temperature increases steeply with decreasing hole concentration. We believe that this behaviour is connected with crossing the boundary shown in Fig. 1. Outside of this boundary for $x \gtrsim 0.12$ we found a hole energy spectrum which is similar to the spectrum of the usual metal and does not contain any pseudogap.

Concluding this section let us mention two differences we see between our calculated and the experimental results. First, in our calculations the magnitude of the pseudogap increases slightly with decreasing hole concentration, while in the experiment [3] it remains unchanged, within experimental errors, for samples with markedly different x (see Fig. 8b). Second, in the normal-state photoemission spectra of underdoped Bi2212 the linewidth increases dramatically on moving from $(\pi/2, \pi/2)$ to the vicinity of $(0, \pi)$ [2]. Though the photoemission line shape is not well understood [50], an analogous behavior of linewidths could be expected in the hole spectral function. However, in our results in Fig. 7 the change of the linewidth does not look so dramatic. This contradiction points either to the experimental pseudogap being somewhat larger than that reported in Ref. [3] [in this case the overdamped magnons wash away the $(0, \pi)$ maximum, as they did with the $(0,0)$ maximum in Fig. 2a, curve 2] or to some decay process with low-frequency excitations not included in the t-J model.

VII. MAGNETIC PROPERTIES

The spin correlation function $C_{\mathbf{l}-\mathbf{m}} = \langle s^z_{\mathbf{l}} s^z_{\mathbf{m}} \rangle$ is given by

$$C_{\mathbf{l}-\mathbf{m}} = -\frac{1}{4}\delta_{\mathbf{ml}} + \left\{\frac{2}{N}\sum_{\mathbf{k}}{}' \frac{e^{i\mathbf{k}(\mathbf{m}-\mathbf{l})}}{\sqrt{1-\eta^2\gamma^2_{\mathbf{k}}}}\left[\langle b^\dagger_{\mathbf{k}\sigma} b_{\mathbf{k}\sigma}\rangle_U + \frac{1}{2} - \eta\gamma_{\mathbf{k}}\langle b_{-\mathbf{k},-\sigma} b_{\mathbf{k}\sigma}\rangle_U\right]\right\}^2 \qquad (19a)$$

when $\mathbf{l}$ and $\mathbf{m}$ belong to the same sublattice and

$$C_{\mathbf{l}-\mathbf{m}} = -\left\{\frac{2}{N}\sum_{\mathbf{k}}{}' \frac{e^{i\mathbf{k}(\mathbf{m}-\mathbf{l})}}{\sqrt{1-\eta^2\gamma^2_{\mathbf{k}}}}\left[\langle b_{-\mathbf{k},-\sigma} b_{\mathbf{k}\sigma}\rangle_U - \eta\gamma_{\mathbf{k}}\left(\langle b^\dagger_{\mathbf{k}\sigma} b_{\mathbf{k}\sigma}\rangle_U + \frac{1}{2}\right)\right]\right\}^2 \qquad (19b)$$

when $\mathbf{l}$ and $\mathbf{m}$ are on different sublattices. In the considered region of the T-x plane the decay of spin correlations (19) with the distance $|\mathbf{l}-\mathbf{m}|$ is nonexponential (see Fig. 9) which may be partly connected with finite-size effects. To estimate the spin correlation length we used the formula

$$\xi^2 = \sum_{\mathbf{l}} |\mathbf{l}|^2 e^{i\Pi\mathbf{l}} \langle s^z_{\mathbf{l}} s^z_{\mathbf{0}} \rangle / (2\sum_{\mathbf{l}} e^{i\Pi\mathbf{l}} \langle s^z_{\mathbf{l}} s^z_{\mathbf{0}} \rangle).$$

For $T = 116$ K the product $\xi\sqrt{x}$ is nearly constant and approximately equal to the lattice spacing in the range $0.017 \lesssim x \lesssim 0.09$, in agreement with experiment in $La_{2-x}Sr_xCuO_4$ [26]. For larger x at this temperature, ξ becomes of the order of the

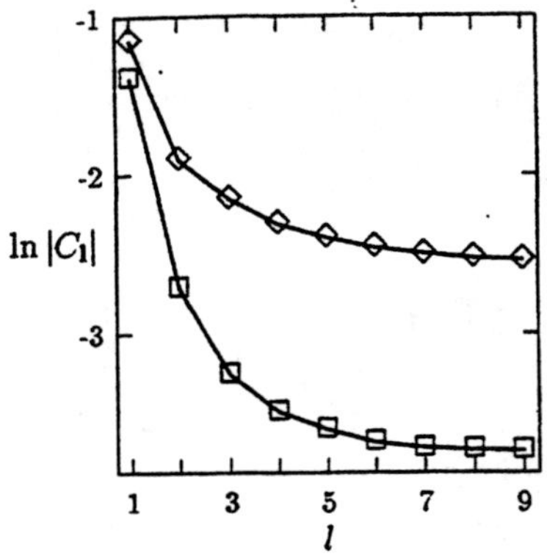

Fig. 9. The spin correlation function along the lattice axis [$\mathbf{l} = (l, 0)$] for $x = 0.027$ (◇) and $x = 0.1$ (□) at $T = 0$.

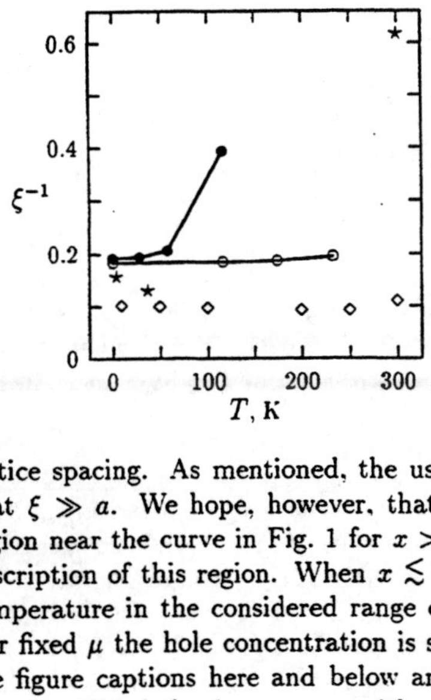

Fig. 10. The inverse correlation length in units of the inverse lattice spacing for $x \approx 0.03$ (open circles) and $x \approx 0.1$ (filled circles). Values obtained from the neutron-scattering experiments in $La_{1.86}Sr_{0.14}CuO_4$ [51] and in $La_{1.96}Sr_{0.04}CuO_4$ [26] are shown by stars and diamonds, respectively.

lattice spacing. As mentioned, the use of the spin-wave approximation (7) assumes that $\xi \gg a$. We hope, however, that our results obtained for the case $\xi \approx a$ (the region near the curve in Fig. 1 for $x > 0.09$) may give at least qualitatively a correct description of this region. When $x \lesssim 0.06$, our calculated ξ is nearly independent of temperature in the considered range of T, as seen in Fig. 10 for the case $x \approx 0.03$ (for fixed μ the hole concentration is somewhat changed with T; values of x given in the figure captions here and below are mean values for the considered temperature ranges). This behaviour agrees with experimental data in $La_{1.96}Sr_{0.04}CuO_4$ [26], also shown in Fig. 10. For larger x values ξ^{-1} are also weakly temperature-dependent at low T and increase more rapidly as the boundary in Fig. 1 is approached (see the data for $x \approx 0.1$ in Fig. 10). This behaviour is also in agreement with experimental results in $La_{1.86}Sr_{0.14}CuO_4$ by G. Aeppli et al. reported in Ref. [51] (stars in Fig. 10). Notice, however, that the growth of ξ^{-1} predicted by the theory is somewhat more rapid than that observed in experiment. The saturation of ξ with decreasing T, demonstrated by Fig. 10, is the distinctive property of the quantum disordered regime [14,28] in which the system resides in the considered region of the T-x plane.

In this region the hole contribution χ_h^z to the susceptibility is negligibly small in

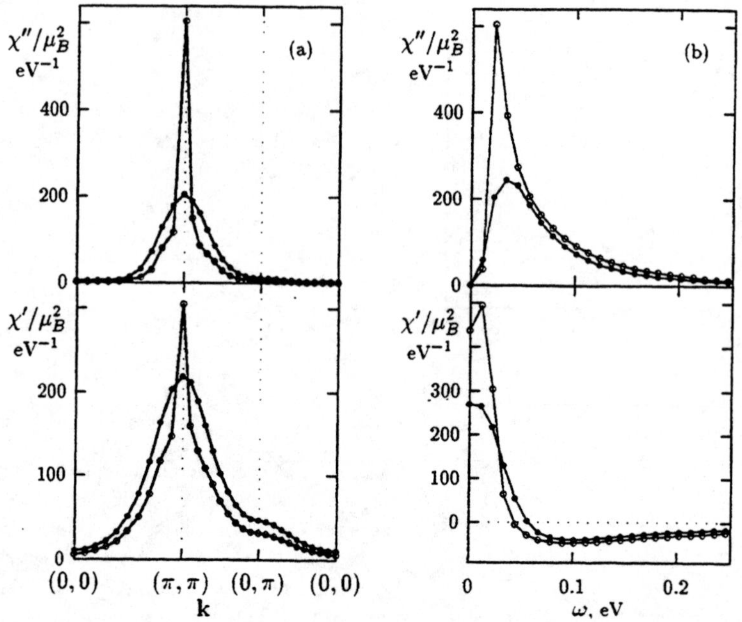

Fig. 11. Imaginary χ'' and real χ' parts of the magnetic susceptibility as functions of wave vector along the symmetry lines in the Brillouin zone for $\omega \approx 0.022$ eV (a) and frequency for $\mathbf{k} = (\pi, \pi)$ (b). $x \approx 0.11$. Open and filled circles correspond to $T = 58$ K and 116 K, respectively.

comparison with the spin contribution χ^z_m. As seen in Fig. 11, the magnetic susceptibility (16) is strongly peaked around (π, π). This demonstrates strong antiferromagnetic fluctuations which persist even in the case of comparatively short correlation lengths of the order of the lattice spacing. As known, low-frequency incommensurate spin fluctuations are observed in the normal state of Sr-doped La_2CuO_4 [52]. This becomes apparent in a four-peaked structure of $\mathrm{Im}\,\chi(\mathbf{q}\omega)$, the peaks being displaced from the commensurate position to the points $\mathbf{q}_i = (\pi, \pi \pm \delta), (\pi \pm \delta, \pi)$. To investigate whether this incommensurability is connected with the hole-magnon interaction in CuO_2 planes a more sophisticated spin-wave approximation than that given in Eq. (7) is needed. We do not consider this point in the present paper. Notice that the frequency dependence of $\mathrm{Im}\,\chi(\mathbf{q}\omega)$ in Fig. 11b is close to that observed in normal-state $La_{1.86}Sr_{0.14}CuO_4$ at wave vectors $\mathbf{q}_i$ [51]. Both the total peak intensity at these wave vectors, the position of the peak, and its temperature dependence are close to those shown in this figure.

We used the obtained magnetic susceptibility for calculating the spin-lattice relaxation times at the Cu and O sites ${}^{67}T_1$ and ${}^{17}T_1$ and the Cu spin-echo decay time T_{2G} by using the equations [14]

$$\frac{1}{{}^{\alpha}T_1T} = \frac{1}{2\mu_B^2 N}\sum_{\mathbf{q}} {}^{\alpha}F(\mathbf{q})\frac{\operatorname{Im}\chi(\mathbf{q}\omega)}{\omega}, \quad \omega \to 0,$$

$$\frac{1}{T_{2G}} = \sqrt{\frac{0.69}{128}}\left({}^{63}\gamma_n\right)^2\left\{\frac{1}{N}\sum_{\mathbf{q}} F_e^2(\mathbf{q})\left[\operatorname{Re}\chi(\mathbf{q}0)\right]^2 - \left[\frac{1}{N}\sum_{\mathbf{q}} F_e(\mathbf{q})\operatorname{Re}\chi(\mathbf{q}0)\right]^2\right\}^{1/2}, \quad (20)$$

$${}^{63}F(\mathbf{q}) = \left[A_\perp + 4B\gamma_{\mathbf{q}}\right]^2, \quad F_e(\mathbf{q}) = \left[A_\parallel + 4B\gamma_{\mathbf{q}}\right]^2, \quad {}^{17}F(\mathbf{q}) = 2C^2\left[1+\cos(q_x)\right]^2,$$

where ${}^{63}\gamma_n$ is the Cu nucleus gyromagnetic ratio, $B = 3.82 \cdot 10^{-7}$ eV, $A_\perp = 0.84B$, $A_\parallel = -4B$, and $C = 0.91B$. The spin-lattice relaxation times in Eq. (20) correspond to the applied static magnetic field perpendicular to the CuO_2 plane. Results are shown in Fig. 12 together with the calculated $\chi^0 = \chi(0,0)$ and the respective experimental results obtained in $YBa_2Cu_3O_{6.63}$ [14,53,54]. From our results for different hole concentrations we selected for this figure those which appeared to be closest to the experimental data.

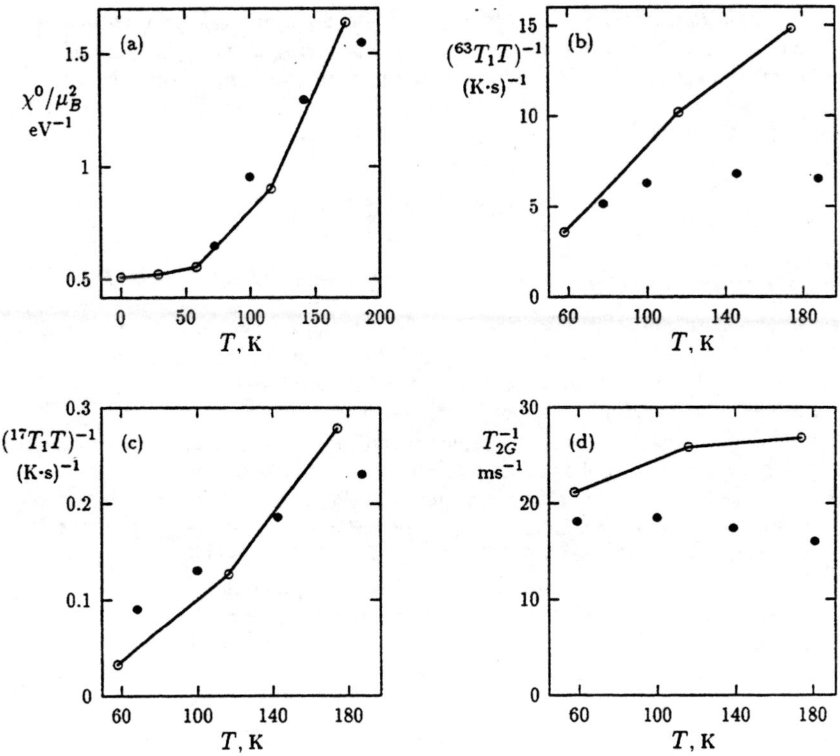

Fig. 12. The static spin susceptibility (a), $1/(T_1T)$ at the Cu (b) and O (c) sites for $\mathbf{H}||\mathbf{c}$, and $1/T_{2G}$ (d) calculated for $x \approx 0.05$ (open circles). The experimental data for $YBa_2Cu_3O_{6.63}$ are shown by filled circles. χ^0 was inferred from the Knight shift data [14], $1/(T_1T)$ and $1/T_{2G}$ are from Refs. [53] and [54], respectively.

Those results are for $x \approx 0.05$ which is apparently somewhat smaller than the hole concentration in $YBa_2Cu_3O_{6.63}$. With increasing x our calculated χ^0 and $(^{\alpha}T_1T)^{-1}$ increase, remaining of the same order of magnitude as those shown in Fig. 12, while T_{2G}^{-1} slightly decreases. These concentration dependences of χ^0 and T_{2G}^{-1} agree with experimental observations [14,54–56], though for χ^0 the theoretical dependence is stronger than that observed experimentally. The situation is apparently more difficult for $(^{63}T_1T)^{-1}$. In underdoped $YBa_2Cu_3O_{6+y}$ this quantity decreases with doping [57], while in $HgBa_2CuO_{4+\delta}$, it increases [58]. Apparently a more elaborate model is necessary for the description of this concentration dependence. Analyzing Fig. 12 we conclude that the t-J model is able to describe correctly the temperature dependences of the depicted quantities and to give their proper orders of magnitude in the quantum disordered regime.

As seen in Fig. 12. $(T_1T)^{-1}$ and χ^0 decrease with decreasing temperature. Such behaviour observed for $T > T_c$ in underdoped cuprates [4,5] is considered as an indication of the pseudogap in the spectrum of magnetic excitations [4,5,13,14]. Our results corroborate this point of view — analyzing Eq. (16) and our numerical data we came to the conclusion that the mentioned temperature dependence is mainly connected with the occupation of low-frequency magnons, rather than the temperature variation of the magnon spectral intensities. Due to the pseudogap this occupation decreases with temperature.

VIII. SUMMARY

In this work we applied the modified spin-wave theory with the additional constraint of zero staggered magnetization to the two-dimensional t-J model in the paramagnetic state. In the Born approximation the constraint equation (12) and the self-energy equations (17) for the hole and magnon Green's functions form the self-consistent set which was solved numerically for finite hole concentrations x and temperatures T. The constraint can be fulfilled in the region of the T-x plane below the curve in Fig. 1.

A number of unusual features of photoemission spectra in cuprate perovskites are satisfactorily reproduced by the obtained results. Among these features are the general shape of the electron energy spectrum and its evolution from the narrow spin-polaron band at small doping to the much wider band for moderate doping. Both by the energy position and by the extension in the Brillouin zone our calculated extended saddle point reproduces well the van Hove singularity of photoemission spectra. Also the obtained Fermi surface with hidden and two-dimensional parts is close to that observed experimentally. In the calculated Fermi surface the size of the hole pockets varies only slightly with the growth of the hole concentration. This growth is mainly connected with an increase of the quasiparticle weights of states occupied by holes. In our calculated hole spectrum the pseudogap has the magnitude, symmetry and the concentration dependence which are similar to those observed in photoemission. This pseudogap is not connected with superconducting fluctuations which were not included in the calculations. It arises due to the specific dispersion of the spin-polaron band a part of which is retained near the Fermi level at moderate doping and gives the most intensive maxima in the spectral function. The persistence of this band is an indication of strong electron correlations retained at moderate doping.

We calculated also a number of magnetic characteristics of the t-J model. We found that in the region shown in Fig. 1 the temperature variation of the spin correlation length is typical for the quantum disordered regime and that this dependence as well as the concentration dependence of the correlation length are close to those observed in cuprates. The magnon spectrum contains the pseudogap which manifests itself in the temperature dependence of the static spin susceptibility and spin-lattice relaxation rates at the Cu and O sites. Our calculated values of these quantities and the Cu spin-echo decay rate, their temperature and concentration dependences are in qualitative and in some cases in quantitative agreement with experiment.

The considered phase with the above-discussed properties differs essentially from the conventional metal. As mentioned, this phase exists in the region bounded by the curve in Fig. 1. Outside of this region for $x \gtrsim 0.12$ we found the energy spectrum of the usual metal.

ACKNOWLEDGMENTS

This work was partially supported by the ESF grant No. 2688 and by the WTZ grant (Project EST112.1) of the BMBF.

REFERENCES

[1] A. G. Loeser, D. S. Dessau, and Z.-X. Shen, Physica C 263 (1996) 208.
[2] D. S. Marshall, D. S. Dessau, A. G. Loeser, C.-H. Park, A. Y. Matsuura, J. N. Eckstein, I. Bozovic, P. Fournier, A. Kapitulnik, W. E. Spicer, and Z.-X. Shen, Phys. Rev. Lett. 76 (1996) 4841.
[3] H. Ding, T. Yokoya, J. C. Campuzano, T. Takahashi, M. Randeria, M. R. Norman, T. Mochiku, K. Kadowaki, and J. Giapintzakis, Nature 382 (1996) 51.
[4] T. Imai, H. Yasuoka, T. Shimizu, Y. Ueda, K. Yoshimura, and K. Kosuge, Physica C 162-164 (1989) 169.
[5] J. Rossat-Mignod, L. P. Regnault, P. Bourges, P. Burlet, C. Vettier, and J. Y. Henry, Physica B 192 (1993) 109.
[6] J. Maly, K. Levin, and D. Z. Lin, Phys. Rev. B 54 (1996) R15657.
[7] R. S. Markiewicz, J. Phys. Chem. Solids 58 (1997) 1179.
[8] N. Kristoffel and T. Örd, Physica C 298 (1998) 37.
[9] N. Trivedi and M. Randeria, Phys. Rev. Lett. 75 (1995) 312.
[10] V. Emery and S. A. Kivelson, Nature 374 (1995) 434.
[11] A. Sherman and M. Schreiber, Phys. Rev. B 55 (1997) R712.
[12] A. V. Chubukov and S. Sachdev, Phys. Rev. Lett. 71 (1993) 169.
[13] A. Sokol and D. Pines, Phys. Rev. Lett. 71 (1993) 2813.
[14] V. Barzykin and D. Pines, Phys. Rev. B 52 (1995) 13585.
[15] V. M. Loktev and S. G. Sharapov, preprint cond-mat 9706285.
[16] Yu. A. Izyumov, Uspekhi Fiz. Nauk 167 (1997) 465 [Phys.–Usp. (Russia) 40 (1997) 445].
[17] M. Takahashi, Phys. Rev. B 40 (1989) 2494.
[18] S. Tang, M. E. Lazzouni, and J. E. Hirsch, Phys. Rev. B 40 (1989) 5000.
[19] A. Sherman and M. Schreiber, Phys. Lett. A 238 (1998) 303; Physica C, in press.
[20] A. Sherman and M. Schreiber, Phys. Rev. B 48 (1993) 7492.
[21] V. J. Emery, Phys. Rev. Lett. 58 (1987) 2794.
[22] A. V. Sherman, Phys. Rev. B 47 (1993) 11521; Physica C 211 (1993) 329.
[23] A. K. McMahan, J. F. Annett, and R. M. Martin, Phys. Rev. B 42 (1990) 6268.
[24] J. H. Jefferson, H. Eskes, and L. F. Feiner, Phys. Rev. B 45 (1992) 7959.
[25] S. V. Tyablikov, Methods of the Quantum Theory of Magnetism (Plenum Press, New York, 1967).
[26] B. Keimer, N. Belk, R. G. Birgeneau, A. Cassanho, C. Y. Chen, M. Greven, M. A. Kastner, A. Aharony, Y. Endoh, R. W. Erwin, and G. Shirane, Phys. Rev. B 46 (1992) 14034.
[27] D. A. Arovas and A. Auerbach, Phys. Rev. B 38 (1988) 316.
[28] S. Chakravarty, B. I. Halperin, and D. R. Nelson, Phys. Rev. B 39 (1989) 2344.
[29] S. Tyč and B. I. Halperin, Phys. Rev. B 42 (1990) 2096.
[30] S. Schmitt-Rink, C. M. Varma, and A. E. Ruckenstein, Phys. Rev. Lett. 60 (1988) 2793.
[31] C. L. Kane, P. A. Lee, and N. Read, Phys. Rev. B 39 (1989) 6880.
[32] F. Marsiglio, A. E. Ruckenstein, S. Schmitt-Rink, and C. M. Varma, Phys. Rev. B 43 (1991) 10882.
[33] G. Krier and G. Meissner, Ann. Phys. 2 (1993) 738.

[34] A. Sherman, Phys. Rev. B 55 (1997) 582.
[35] A. P. Kampf and J. R. Schrieffer, Phys. Rev. B 42 (1990) 7967.
[36] A. V. Sherman, Physica C 171 (1990) 395.
[37] G. Martinez and P. Horsch, Int. J. Mod. Phys. B 5 (1991) 207.
[38] N. M. Plakida, V. S. Oudovenko, and V. Yu. Yushankhai, Phys. Rev. B 50 (1994) 6431.
[39] A. Sherman and M. Schreiber, Phys. Rev. B 50 (1994) 12887.
[40] Z.-X. Shen and D. S. Dessau, Phys. Repts. 253 (1995) 1.
[41] E. Dagotto, A. Nazarenko, and M. Boninsegni, Phys. Rev. Lett. 73 (1994) 728.
[42] F. Onufrieva, V. Kushnir, and B. Toperverg, Physica B 194-196 (1994) 1449.
[43] B. I. Shraiman and E. D. Siggia, Phys. Rev. Lett. 60 (1988) 740.
[44] D. M. King, Z.-X. Shen, D. S. Dessau, D. S. Marshall, C. H. Park, W. E. Spicer, J. L. Peng, Z. Y. Li, and R. L. Greene, Phys. Rev. Lett. 73 (1994) 3298.
[45] J. M. Luttinger and J. C. Ward, Phys. Rev. 118 (1960) 1417; J. M. Luttinger, Phys. Rev. 119 (1960) 1153.
[46] C. M. Varma, P. B. Littlewood, S. Schmitt-Rink, E. Abrahams, and A. E. Ruckenstein, Phys. Rev. Lett. 63 (1989) 1996.
[47] D. J. Scalapino, Phys. Repts. 250 (1995) 329.
[48] A. Sherman and M. Schreiber, Phys. Rev. B 52 (1995) 10621; Physica C 253 (1995) 23.
[49] N. M. Plakida, Phil. Mag. B 76 (1997) 771; N. M. Plakida, V. S. Oudovenko, P. Horsch, A. I. Liechtenstein, Phys. Rev. B 55 (1997) R11997.
[50] L. Z. Liu, R. O. Anderson, and J. W. Allen, J. Phys. Chem. Solids 52 (1991) 1473.
[51] Y. Zha, V. Barzykin, and D. Pines, Phys. Rev. B 54 (1996) 7561.
[52] G. Aeppli, S. M. Hayden, H. A. Mook, T. E. Mason, A. D. Taylor, K. N. Clausen, T. G. Perring, S.-W. Cheong, Z. Fisk, and D. Rytz, Physica B 192 (1993) 103.
[53] M. Takigawa, A. P. Reyes, P. C. Hammel, J. D. Thompson, R. H. Heffner, Z. Fisk, and K. C. Ott, Phys. Rev. B 43 (1991) 247.
[54] M. Takigawa, Phys. Rev. B 49 (1994) 4158.
[55] R. E. Walstedt, R. F. Bell, L. F. Schneemeyer, J. V. Waszczak, and G. P. Espinosa, Phys. Rev. B 45 (1992) 8074.
[56] T. Imai and C. P. Slichter, Phys. Rev. B 47 (1993) 9158.
[57] C. Berthier, M.-H. Julien, O. Bakharev, M. Horvatić, and P. Ségransan, Physica C 282-287 (1997) 227.
[58] H. Yasuoka, Physica C 282-287 (1997) 119.

Studies of High Temperature
Superconductors
Volume 27

ISBN 1-56072-684-9

CHARGE DYNAMICS VIA THE BLOCKING LAYER AND THE PSEUDO GAP OF HIGH T_c-SUPERCONDUCTORS (HTS)

J. HALBRITTER

Forschungszentrum Karlsruhe
Institut für Materialforschung I
Postfach 3640, D-76021 Karlsruhe, Germany

1. Introduction

Superconducting cuprates are layered compounds with correlated conduction mainly confined to the CuO_2-planes. The CuO_2-planes are separated by quasi-insulating blocking layers depicted in Fig. 1 which dope the CuO_2-planes [1]. In the in-plane charge- or spin-exchange or in the specific heat a 'pseudo gap kT*' has been found [2], given by exchanges declining below T*. This 'in-plane pseudo gap kT*' is often related to in-plane spin interaction [3] because of the accepted spin correlations in HTS-CuO_2-planes. But chemistry wise, HTS's are not typical for the Cu-O bonds. In contrast, the O-1s core level shift is more typical for Y-, Ba-, Sr-, Ca,- or La-oxides [4,5] and the anion bonds adjacent to the apex oxygen change strongly from insulating to (super)-conducting cuprate [5]. This hints to the blocking layer, i.e., to the quasi-insulating layer reaching from apex-oxygen to apex-oxygen, not only as the source of static doping of the CuO_2-planes, but also as the source for dynamic charge exchanges yielding the correlated, metallic in-plane conduction. Also, the blocking layer as 'insulator' and the accepted importance of the metal-insulator transition for HTS [1,6,7] highlights to charge exchanges with the blocking layer

In the superconducting state most charge exchange mechanisms are concealed by superconducting coherence. Hence, this paper concentrates on the normal conducting state charge transfer, especially across the blocking layer. Along this line, evidence is presented for the experimental blocking layer Coulomb charging energy ΔU^*_{PS} agreeing quantitatively with the in-plane pseudo gap kT*. Because of their inertness, blocking layers act as HTS surface termination and may degrade and impress surface spectroscopic methods [5,8-10] most strongely. The out-of-plane conduction $\sigma^{\perp}(T,\omega)$ changes with doping [11,12] from 'activated' to 'metallic' and is related to kT* by resonant tunneling with ΔU^*_{PS} = kT* as Coulomb charging energy of quasi-localized stripe states of the blocking layer midst, where the stripe length increases with doping and therewith ΔU^*_{PS} decreases. Aside of such transport information, higher energy charge exchange processes with the blocking layer can be detected by spectroscopic methods of the bulk or at surfaces, where for the latter intrinsic surface relaxation or extrinsic corrosion and sorption processes have to be considered.

The paper is organized as follows: In Sect. 2 some basic equations are repeated needed to analyze tunneling in Sect. 3, where the correlated, in-plane CuO_2 conduction is taken as given. In Sects. 3.1 and 3.2 bulk exchange processes are discussed, i.e. direct and resonant tunneling across the blocking layer able to explain $\sigma^{\perp}(T,\omega)$, $j_c^{\perp}(T)$ and $\Delta U^*_{PS} \approx kT^*$ with accepted parameters. In Sect. 3.3 information on the blocking layer is summarized and in Sect. 3.4 surface degradations and surface spectroscopies. Consequences of blocking layer states near E_F (≤ 1 eV) are discussed in Sect. 4 reaching from incoherent exchanges above T_c to superconducting interaction.

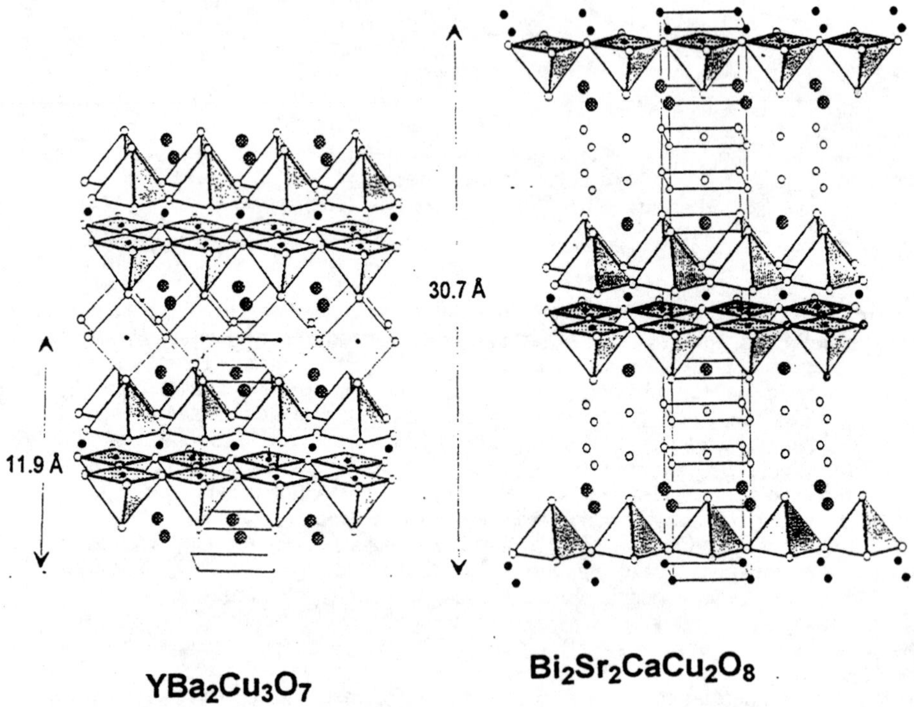

Fig. 1: Between the conducting CuO_2 planes perpendicular tunnel exchange via the insulating blocking layer occurs enhanced by intermediate state tunneling obstructed by off-site Coulomb charging ΔU^*_{PS}. With overdoping ΔU^*_{PS} diminishes and the extended stripe states at the Fermi energy E_F show superconductivity with $\Delta^{\perp} \leq \Delta_0$ weakened by on-site Coulomb repulsion ΔU_c. The stripe states in the midst of the blocking layer, dominate the perpendicular charge transfer by resonant tunneling. a) $YBa_2Cu_3O_{7-\delta}$ (YBCO) has CuO chains, where the localized states become extended for $\delta < 0.2$ b) $Bi_2Sr_2CaCu_2O_{8+\delta}$ (BSCCO) shows stripe states at E_F in the Bi-planes which extend with overdoping ($\delta > 0.2$)

2. Tunnel spectroscopy and charging [13]

Direct tunneling through the blocking layer between the CuO_2-planes of HTS's (Fig. 1), i.e. tunneling between two parallel plates in distance d at voltages eU well below the barrier height ϕ_o yields the conductance G_o with c_M as density of tunnel channels

$$G_o^{-1} \cong \frac{13k\Omega}{2\,c_M} \exp(2\kappa d) \tag{1a}$$

where ϕ_o relates to $\kappa = \sqrt{2 m \phi_o} / \hbar$ and 13 k Ω is the quantum resistance. Throughout the paper $\phi_o \approx 2$ eV is used determining the decay constant to $\kappa = 7$/nm. Resonant tunneling is largest for intermediate states (density n_L, energy ε_L relative to E_F, x_L as distance to the left metal bank depicted in Fig. 2) at the Fermi energy E_F in the midst $x = d/2$ of the tunnel barrier with a spread of some 1/κ. If tunnel paths contain n > 1 intermediate states of uniform density $n_L(\varepsilon_L, x) \equiv n_L$ the distance dependence of G_o weakens further yielding as conductance:

$$G_n \propto \left[\frac{n_L\, deV_L\, n^2}{\kappa^2}\right]^n \left[\frac{E_o}{eU} \lambda^{\frac{n-1}{2}} e^{-\kappa d}\right]^{\frac{2}{n+1}} \ldots \tag{1b}$$

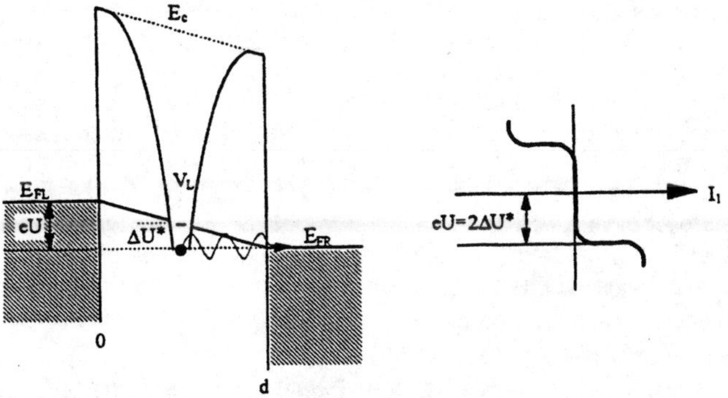

Fig. 2: Localized states in the midst of the barrier dominate resonant tunneling and show a Coulomb gap $\Delta U^*_{PS} \propto 1/\varepsilon_r d$. The situation shown is a state at $E_F - \Delta U^*$ allowing resonant tunneling $I_1(kT < \Delta U^*, U)$ for $|eU/2| > \Delta U^*$.

with E_o the depth of the potential well (Fig. 2) housing the state and with λ as electron - phonon (plasmon) interaction constant describing the energy transfer to the tunnel path. To note is $G_1 \propto \exp(-\kappa d)$ being exponentially large compared to direct tunneling $G_o \propto \exp(-2\kappa d)$ and so its current dominates for large d-values. This is often described by a lowered effective barrier height $\phi_{eff} = \phi_o/4$ [13a] and so Eq. (1b) yields the tunnel distance spectroscopy (TDS). In direct tunneling in Eq. (1a) no simple 'tunnel time' τ exists whereas localization yields a well defined life time τ [13]. By atomic-like localization at V_L for about $x_L \geq 0.2$ nm incoherent tunneling dominates [13c] with a decay width (Eq. 4' of [13a])

$$\Gamma(x) = \hbar/2\tau(x) \propto \exp(-2\kappa x) \tag{1c}$$

Coherent and incoherent tunneling via intermediate states depends on coherence of the metallic banks and, crucially, on the charging ΔU at the intermediate site. For applications discussed below, two charging energies ΔU^* and ΔU_c are important. ΔU^* is the off-site (image charge), Coulomb energy and ΔU_c is the on-site, Coulomb charging energy. Electrons localized atomically long enough at an intermediate site at x, i.e. $\Delta U^* > \hbar/2\tau(x) = \Gamma(x)$, yield with the barrier dielectric constant $\varepsilon_r\varepsilon_o$ ((Eq. A 1 of [13a])

$$\Delta U^* = -\frac{0.28\,eV \cdot dnm\,eV}{\varepsilon_r x\,(d-x)} \tag{2a}$$

as off-site Coulomb charge energy and activated, T-dependent incoherent resonant tunneling described in detail in [11,13a]. The on-site Coulomb charging energy

$$\Delta U_c \cong e^2 / t^* 4\pi\varepsilon_r\varepsilon_o \tag{2b}$$

is the repulsion energy for a second electron localized in a distance t* to the first one. The repulsion energy ΔU_c causes pair weakening described by the ratio

$$c_w = \Delta U_c/\Gamma \tag{2c}$$

Any delocalization of the charge over an area A > $(d/2)^2$ decreases $\Delta U^* = e^2/2C$ and ΔU_c of Eqs. (2a) and (2b), as shown by the mirror charge capacitance increase: $C = 4\pi\varepsilon_r\varepsilon_o d/2 \rightarrow C = \varepsilon_r\varepsilon_o A/d/2$. That is, $\Delta U^*=2d/2/(\varepsilon_r\varepsilon_o A)$ substitutes Eq. (2a). In Eq. (2b) $\Delta U_c \propto 1/t^* \propto 1/\sqrt{A}$ decreases also with A. Maximal charge transfer favors minimal ΔU-values, i.e., 'stripe-like' delocalization with maximal t*-values. Such incoherent charging effects slow the tunnel process down, i.e. reduce the conductance G_1 in Eq. (1b) by a factor $g(\Delta U) \cong 1 - 1000$[11]. $g \cong 10^3$ may hold for states close to a surface with $\Delta U^* \approx$ eV, where strong surface plasmon excitation is needed and $\Delta U^* \approx 10^{-2}$ eV seems to correspond to $g \approx 100$, i.e. $G^*_1 = G_1/100$ [13c]. For ΔU^* tending to zero g approaches 1.

With the above concepts the spectroscopies VTS and DTS can be sketched. Voltage tunnel spectroscopy is a well known method to deduce in direct tunneling via I(U) κ(U) of Eq. (1a), the density of states, the barrier shapes $\phi(x,y)$ and the distributions and density of intermediate tunnel states $n_L(x_L,\varepsilon_L)$ with the help of the logarithmic derivative $g^*(U)$ [13], which shows sharp maxima at

$$\varepsilon^*_L = \varepsilon_L + eUx/d + \Delta U^* + \Delta U_c \tag{2d}$$

with ΔU^* and ΔU_c given above. The distance tunnel spectroscopy (DTS) uses Eq. (1b).

3. Tunnel Conduction Perpendicular to the CuO_2-Planes

The tunnel charge transfer through the blocking layer is dominated by its thickness $d^\perp$, barrier height $\phi \approx 2$ eV, density of intermediate states $n_L(\varepsilon,x)$ and their charging energies ΔU. This paper concentrates on the best studied n-type HTS YBCO and BSCCO. Whereas $d^\perp$, ϕ or n_L are well accepted parameters [7,11] ΔU^* needs some clarification. $\varepsilon_r \cong 24$ as typical perovskite value is appropriate in Eq. (2a) and for the distance $d^\perp + 2\lambda^\perp$ has to be used with $\lambda^\perp \sim 1/\sqrt{n_s} \approx 0.5$ nm describing the electric field throughput of CuO_2-planes [13c,d]. This yields for the Cu-chain states ($d^\perp$ =.9 nm) of YBCO,

$$\Delta U^*_{PS} = \frac{1.12\,eV\,nm}{\varepsilon_r(d^\perp + 2\lambda^\perp)} = 22\,meV \quad and \quad \Delta U^*_s \approx 11\ meV \quad \text{for } d \gg d^\perp/2 \tag{2e}$$

at surfaces with the second electrode far away. Hence, incoherent tunneling dominates for $x \approx 0.2$ nm < $d^\perp/2$ (Eq. (1c)) for short stripes.

Some consequences of ΔU_{PS}^* on bulk conduction, in addition to [7,11], are mentioned in Sect. 3.1. In Sects. 3.2 and 3.3 superconducting and spectroscopic, bulk information on the blocking layer are summarized followed by surface blocking layer corrosion and surface spectroscopies.

3.1 Effects of the blocking layer on bulk transport

As obvious by geometry, the blocking layer defines $\rho^{\perp}(T, \omega)$, e.g., the highest normal resistances $\rho^{\perp}(T \approx 300\ K, \omega)$ of LSCO, YBCO, BSCCO or TlCCO [6,9,12-14] scale with $d^{\perp}$ and $\phi \cong 2$ eV, i.e. they are given by direct tunneling through the blocking layer. For example with the Sharvin resistance $R_{sh} \approx 10^{-11}\Omega cm^2$ the lowest resistivity across the blocking layer is

$R^{\perp}_0(BSCCO) \cong 10^{-6}\ \Omega cm^2$ and $R^{\perp}_0(YBCO) \cong 10^{-8}\ \Omega cm^2$ (3a)

in line with direct tunneling. With doping $R^{\perp}_0$ is reduced by resonant tunneling $R^{\perp}_1$ and for optimally doped YBCO with $n_L(d/^{\perp}/2) \approx 10^{21}/cm^3$ deduced from anisotropy

$R^{\perp}_0 / R^{\perp}_1 \cong 50$ (3b)

is obtained confirming again the above simple tunnel model. The $\rho^{\perp}(T,0)$ activation energy fits to Eqs. (2a) and (2e) quantitatively and in its $d^{\perp}$-dependence, i.e. Coulomb charging ΔU^*_{PS} defines incoherent, activated tunneling via states at E_F in the blocking layer [11]. Doping the stripes lessens ΔU^*_{PS} further yielding a distribution with ΔU^*_{max} given by atomic localization (Eq. (2e)) and ΔU^*_{min} by maximal stripe delocalization. Whereas rf methods average over the ΔU^* distribution in dc the actual current path minimizes the dc resistance and, thus, states with $\Delta U^* \geq \Gamma^{\perp}$ will be shunted by transport channels with $\Delta U^* < \Gamma^{\perp}$. In BSCCO or TlCCO $d^{\perp}$ is larger than in YBCO or LSCO and thus $\Delta U^* > \Gamma^{\perp}$ holds, where always some current paths with $\Delta U^* \approx \Delta U^*_{max}$ show up above T_c decreasing in amount with doping [14-16]. In YBCO or LSCO $d^{\perp}$ is small enough to allow $\Delta U^* < \Gamma^{\perp}$ yielding metallic dependencies $\rho^{\perp}(T) = \rho^{\perp}(0) + p\alpha T$ by zig-zag conduction via CuO_2-planes ($\rho^{\parallel}(T) = \alpha T$) by locally confined perpendicular tunnel channels in mean distances $a^{\perp} \cong 5$ - 100 nm, depending on cuprate and O-content [7b]. For $T > T^*$ these channels are open and yield p(YBCO) ≥ 30 and p(BSCCO) $> 10^4$ as percolation factors around optimal doping, in line with the densities n_L of intermediate states [11]. That is, in '$\rho^{\perp}(T)$ dependencies' $\rho^{\parallel}(T)$ enters percolatively as zig-zag current by 'ab-plane shorts' with $\rho^{\perp}(0) = R^{\perp}/a^{\perp}$. The cross-over 'activated - metallic' in $\sigma^{\perp}(T)$ is governed by the exponential dependence $\Gamma^{\perp} \propto \exp(-2\kappa d^{\perp})$ and, thus, scales with $d^{\perp}$ and $\kappa \cong 7$/nm in comparing different cuprate classes [16a]. The counterpart of $\rho^{\perp}(T,\omega)$, the in-plane resistance $\rho^{\parallel}(T,\omega)$ along the CuO_2-double planes may scatter at those ΔU^*_{PS} exchange processes which yields $\rho^{\parallel}(T)$ linearely depending on T above T^* assigned to electron-electron interactions [16a]. In YBCO mainly the perpendicular tunnel exchange measured by $\rho^{\perp}(T)$ seems to scatter and to reduce $\rho^{\parallel}(T)$, as evidenced by a mean free path $l^{\parallel}(100\ K) \approx 10$ nm $\cong a^{\perp}$ for optimally doped YBCO [7b, 17]. Hence, the above interface plasmon exchange ΔU^*_{PS} is proposed as reason for the electron electron interaction yielding above T^* $\rho^{\parallel}(T) \propto T$ [18]. With deoxygenation T^* grows and, hence, e.g., $l^{\parallel}(100K)$ increases describing also the [17b] bottleneck in photo induced carrier relaxation. The strong $\rho^{\perp}$ - $\rho^{\parallel}$ coupling is also shown spectroscopically by bending mode changes due to plasmon exchange – see Sect. 3.2 and [12b]. In underdoped cuprates this scatter process dies out for $T < \Delta U^*_{PS}/k$ yielding then $\delta\rho^{\parallel}(T) \propto -\exp(-\Delta U^*_{PS}/kT)$ [2d]. This is one [2] definition of an in-plane pseudo gap T^*, which quantitatively yields [11]

$$kT^* \cong \overline{\Delta U^*_{PS}} \tag{4}$$

The averaging in $\rho^{\|}(T)$ and in $\rho^{\perp}(T,\omega \to O)$ yields similar ΔU^*_{PS}-value. Remarkable in this connection is 248- YBCO which is underdoped in the CuO_2 planes [16b] but has ordered chains. In this case, $T^* \cong 170$ K $\cong \Delta U^*_{min}/k$ is encountered, where $\rho^{\|}(T)$ and $\rho^{\perp}(T)$ decrease together by $\Delta U^* < \Gamma^{\perp}$. For similar doping of 123, $\rho^{\perp}(T)$ is activated by short Cu-chain stripes as intermediate states with $\Delta U^* > \Gamma^{\perp}$ [16a]. If YBCO is optimally doped but disordered into the tetragonal phase [6], the 'atomization' of stripes yields insulating YBCO hinting to the need of chain segments, i.e. stripes, for superconductivity.

In summary, the blocking layer Coulomb gap $\Delta U^*_{PS} = kT^*$ yields the charge transfer gaps in $\rho^{\|}(T,\omega)$ and in $\rho^{\perp}(T,\omega)$ and, hence, in spin exchange. The perpendicular exchange causes in-plane scattering by ΔU^*_{PS} exchanges which describes the HTS- electron-electron interaction $l^{\|}$ (100K) $\approx a^{\perp}$ [17], excellently, at least in the case of YBCO where data are available. In the above normal conducting state transport only ΔU^*_{PS} of blocking layer states at $d^{\perp}/2$, e.g., Cu-chain stripes in YBCO, are important. The apex-O holes discussed below are off the midst $d^{\perp}/2$, i.e. they reduce $\rho^{\perp}(T)$ negligibly [13a] and have, according to Eq. (2a), much larger ΔU^*-values (.> 0.1 – 1 eV) not showing up in $\rho^{\perp}(T,\omega)$ transport below 0.1 eV. They seem responsible for spectrosopic features above 0.1 eV, discussed below..

3.2 Superconductivity and superconducting transport $j^{\perp}_c(T)$

The transition from one-particle, incoherent transport to coherent exchanges corresponds to the transition to superconductivity for all states at the Fermi energy by yet unknown mechanisms. Hence, starting from minimal $j^{\perp}_c$-, i.e. maximal $R^{\perp}$-, values [11] the $j^{\perp}_c$-ratio 100 between 123 and 2212 agrees with direct, i.e. Josephson tunneling (Sects. 2 and 3.1). Then by O-doping [14-16] ($j^{\perp}_c$) $\sigma^{\perp}$ grow by (superconducting) intermediate states in the Cu-chains or Bi-planes. This superconductivity is due to the coherent coupling $\Gamma^{\perp} > \Delta U^*_{PS}$ with the plane states. The value $\Gamma^{\perp}(T_c = 92$ K, 123) $\cong 50$ meV $> \Delta U^*_{PS} \approx 20$ meV decreases by deoxygenation to $\Gamma^{\perp}(T_c = 65$ K) < 5 meV [14]. The $\Gamma^{\perp}$-ratio scales excellently with $R^{\perp}_o/R^{\perp}_1$ of Eqs. (3). For 2212 [15] the analysis yields $\Gamma^{\perp} \approx 2$ meV allowing coherent coupling for Bi-plane stripes with $\Delta U^* < \Gamma^{\perp}$ with $j^{\perp}_c(123)/j^{\perp}_c(2212) \approx \Gamma^{\perp}(123)/\Gamma^{\perp}(2212)$ for negligible n_L-densities [11].

To estimate the 'superconductivity' in the YBCO-blocking layer stripes their pair weakening has to be quantified: According to Eq (2c), for 123 with $\Gamma^{\perp} \cong 50$ meV, $t^* \cong 1$ nm and $\Delta U_c \le 1$ meV ($\varepsilon_r \cong 24$) $c_w \cong 0.5$ and $\Delta^{\perp}/\Delta_o \approx 0.5$ is obtained as gap in the Cu-chains. With deoxygenation $\Gamma^{\perp}$ and t^* shrink and, hence ΔU^* increases and $\Delta^{\perp}$ seems to disappear for $T_c \le 80$ K, where $j^{\perp}_c R^{\perp} \propto 1/R^{\perp}$ is found [14], in line with normal conducting intermediate states [7]. With the growth of the chain gap $\Delta^{\perp}$ below T_c, the in-plane scattering length $l^{\|}(T) = v_F\, \tau^{\|}(T)$ grows till the grain boundary relaxation processes set in [17]. This $l^{\|}(T<T_c) = v_F\, \tau^{\|}(T)$ increase below T_c diminishes with deoxygenation and for $T_c \le 80$ K $\tau^{\|}(T)$ and $l^{\|}(T)$ reach their maximum already at the pseudo gap T^* playing then, e.g., the role of the bottle-neck for relaxation processes. The larger $d^{\perp}$-values yield for BSCCO stripes $c_w \le 0.01$ and $\Delta^{\perp} \le$ meV, able to enhance $j_c^{\perp}$, but not likely to interfere with CuO-plane ARPES data.

Whereas YBCO-surfaces degrade easily, BSCCO seems stable if reaction with water is avoided as discusses in Sect. 3.4.1. Hence, 2212 point contact spectroscopy may yield proper superconducting information not overshadowed by 'surface degradation problems', as will be discussed below.

3.3 Bulk spectroscopies of blocking layer states at E_F

In Sect. 3.1 intermediate strip states $n_L(\varepsilon, d^{\perp}/2)$ at E_F and their off-site Coulomb charging energy ΔU^*_{PS} have been identified by transport measurements, i.e., for $\varepsilon = E - E_F < 50$ meV. Higher ε-information is obtained by X-ray absorption (XAS) [19], by infrared spectroscopy (IR) [12], by photoelectron spectroscopy (XPS or ARPES) [5,8], by point contact (PCS) [10] or tunnel-spectroscopies (STS) [9, 20-22]. In $Y_{1-x}Ba_2Ca_xCu_3O_{7-\delta}$ the holes in the chain-O/apex-O and plane-O can be varied independently, which has been measured by XAS [19]. There it has been shown that n_L(chain-O) ≅ n_L(apex-O) holds and that T_c larger 10 K has been obtained for n_L(chain-O/apex-O)) > 0 only, i.e. the tunnel exchange between CuO_2-plane and blocking layer states seems essential for superconductivity. By IR the energy of those exchanges are measured [12]. As discussed in Sect. 3.1 $\Delta U^* \approx 20$ meV of $n_L(d^{\perp}/2)$ holes in 123 and 2212 have been identified by $\sigma^{\parallel}(T,\omega)$ as pseudo gap. The exchange plane-O apex-O with $\Delta U^*_{AP} > 0.1$ eV seem to show up as mid-infrared peak, which, in strength, moves together with the ΔU^*_{PS} [12c], in good agreement with the above XAS-result n_L(chain-O) ≅ n_L(apex-O) [19]. The direct observation of the perpendicular exchange by $\sigma^{\perp}(T,\omega > 10$ meV) is overshadowed by the strong IR active bending phonons [12c]. Using the O-1 and O-2 bending phonons (Fig. 3) as probe, Schützmann [12b] found strong changes of those modes in frequency (≤ 5 %) and oscillator strength (≤ 50 %) around kT*, changing with O-doping. This result confirms the model of perpendicular charge transfer via O-holes changing those perpendicular vibrations and yielding strong $\rho^{\parallel}$-$\rho^{\perp}$-coupling freezing out below $\{\hbar\omega, kT\} \cong \Delta U^*$, where the oscillator strength is shifted to $\hbar\omega \geq 2\,\Delta U^*_{PS}$. The above bulk results have to be compared with surface spectroscopies, which depend on degradations discussed in Sect. 3.4.1.

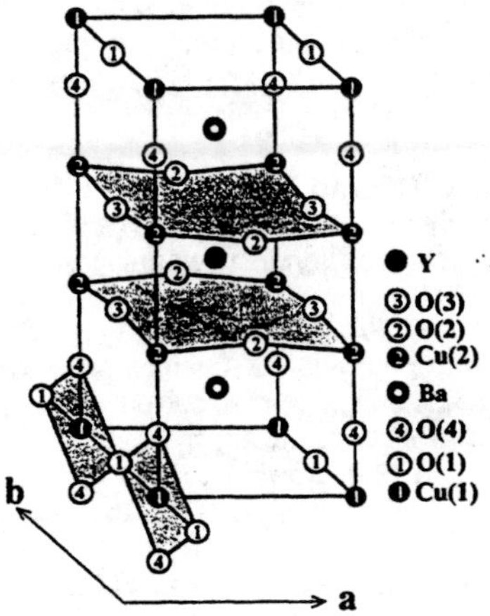

Fig. 3: Unit cell of $Y_{1-x}Ba_2Ca_xCu_3O_{7-\delta}$. Between the conducting CuO_2 planes perpendicular tunnel exchange may occur enhanced by intermediate state tunneling via Cu-chain states obstructed by off-site Coulomb charging ΔU*. This charging interacts with out-of-plane O-1 and O-2 vibrations changing their spectra at $\hbar\omega \approx \Delta U^*$. Static charging, i.e., holes at O-1 have been found for superconducting 123 only, as identified by Ba-core level shifts [5] and X-ray absorption spectroscopy [19]. With overdoping ΔU* diminishes and the chain states show superconductivity [14] with $\Delta^{\perp} < \Delta_o$ weakened by on-site Coulomb repulsion ΔU_C.

But by ARXPS one can separate bulk and true surface properties and the bulk core level shifts give information about the local hole concentration [5]. For example, superconducting YBCO shows a Ba-4d line shift of 1.5 eV to lower binding energy reflecting the apex-O hole (O – 4 in Fig.3) This shift is not found in insulating YBCO or at relaxed surfaces [5a, b]. Similar shifts have been identified in BSCCO [5c]. ARPES and PCS have an information depth between 1 and 0.1 nm and, hence in-situ cleaved surfaces for spectroscopic studies are essential (Sect. 3.4.1). ARPES measures the two-dimensional Fermi surface [8], where a (pseudo) gap is found separated by features above about 100 meV. Both features change with 2212-doping in the way discussed above [8,20,21]. In contrast to IR and PCS, ARPES shows a large background [20], making quantitative estimates, especially about the minimum, difficult. The PCS-results show the least background and a minimum approaching zero for overdoped and optimally doped BSCCO. Because of the coherence in direct tunneling and the observation of the closing superconducting gap $\Delta(T)$ at T_c, this minimum contains as crucial information, that the low energy features ($\leq$ 50 meV) and the high energy features ($\geq$ 100 meV) are out of phase.

3.4 Surface studies of the blocking layer

Surface methods, like XPS(X-ray photo electron spectroscopy), STS (scanning tunnel spectroscopy) and PCS (point contact spectroscopy) have information depths shrinking from 5 to below 1 nm with carrier energy shrinking from 1 keV to below eV. The combined use of XPS or STM with ARPES or STS is essential because chemistry, morphology and spectroscopy are needed to quantify surface reconstruction or aging. HTS, as layered compounds, show 'surfaces' in the blocking layer by cleaving or crystal growth, which are more or less stable in UHV or air depending on temperature and humidity. Thus spectroscopic information on bulk HTS may be obtained if the transmission from the bulk through the surface blocking layer into the detector is properly accounted for. In the following the surface degradation of YBCO and BSCCO is discussed, before in Sect. 3.4.2 spectroscopy on such surfaces is summarized.

3.4.1 Surface degradation of YBCO and BSCCO

YBCO surfaces degrade already by cleaving in UHV below 50 K as shown in XPS by insulating plaques [5b], which degrade further by warming up to 300 K, as shown in STM and STS by the lost atomic resolution, by the linearly growing tunnel conductivity dI/dU, and by the leakage tunnel current [20 – 22]. Handling in lab air yields reaction with H_2O and CO_2 yielding 1 – 4 nm reaction cinder [23], which still allows superconducting STS measurements with even more leakage tunnel current [22,23]. Distance spectroscopy quantifies [13c] this intermediate state tunneling by revealing one intermediate state for in-situ surfaces held below 50 K [20] growing to two or more intermediate states by warming up to 300 K and water adsorption [22,23] with a 'barrier height' $\phi_o/(n+1)^2$ (Eq. (1b)) below 0.3 eV.

BSCCO surfaces are assumed to be stable because of the atomic STM resolution after cleaving at 300 K in air [9]. But the observed barrier height $\phi_o/(n+1)^2 \leq 0.2$ eV by distance spectroscopy [22] reveals adsorbates in the form of a BiOH-H_2O layer, which act as a floating electrode with a Coulomb barrier $\Delta U^* \approx 0.2$ eV [13d, 22] if not properly biased. According to [22] both tunnel channels have the same conductance $G(|eU| > \Delta U^*)$ and show atomic resolution in line with hydroxylation of the BiO-surface layer [13d].

3.4.2 Surface spectoscopy of YBCO and BSCCO

YBCO, cleaved in UHV below 50 K reveales by ARPES [5b] insulating plaques by the Ba-5d-level shifts and atomic order by STS [20]. Both methods are compatible with localized states showing up by $\Delta U^*_s \cong 13$ meV in PES [5b] and by $\Delta U^*_{PS} \cong 20$ meV in STS [20] in the resonant tunnel channel [13a]. Worth mentioning is the finding in [5b] that for clean surfaces ΔU^*_s mask gap and Fermi surface information in ARPES of the CuO_2-planes underneath. If this is not resolvable for 'clean' surfaces, degraded surfaces with stronger ΔU^*_{PS}-features make any separation hopeless. Handled at room temperatures degraded surface layer [23] with $n \geq 2$ intermediate state tunneling ($R_{STM} > 10^9\ \Omega$) show up. Only by closer approach, penetrating into the YBCO surface ($R_{STM} < 5 \cdot 10^8\ \Omega$) a superconducting tunnel gap $\Delta^\perp$ with negligible leakage current is obvious in perpendicular tunneling [21].
The BiO-surface layer of BSCCO does not reconstruct fast at 300 K in air, at least according to STM [9,22] showing atomic resolution for $R_{STM} > 10^9\ \Omega$ with $\phi_o/(n+1)^2 \cong 0.2$ eV, which according to Eq. (1.2) corresponds to tunneling via two intermediate states. As a matter of fact, those tunnel channels image the BiO plane atomically resolved and show also $\Delta U^*_{BiO} \cong 20$ meV features in the intermediate tunnel channel according to the temperature dependence [9]. To explain the ΔU^*_{BiO}- feature bound to the BiO-plane in the n = 2 channel, the water plaques on top of BiO-(OH) should be mentioned as chemisorption state [23]. The plaques acts as intermediate electrode if insulated against the BiO-intermediate states [13d]. Because of the distances involved and the throughputs of CuO_2-planes and of the H_2O-OH-electrode (Eq. (2e)) $\Delta U^*_{PS} \cong \Delta U^*_{BiO}$ holds, as found in [9,10]. One feature not explainable by resonant tunneling is the dip in dI/dU at about 2 ΔU^*_{PS} deepening with quality of the surface [9], i.e., being especially deep at 3 ΔU^*_{PS} in PCS [10]. This dip disappearing at T_c is the leading indicator for the superconducting state, e.g., in flux lattice imaging [22b] or in ARPES [24]. In STS, and specially in PCS, the tunnel dip approaches even zero being a strong indication for two tunnel channels out of phase: ΔU^*_{PS} or $\Delta^\perp$ and ΔU^*_{AP} above 0.1 eV. Aside of the ARPES background [24a], the STS-spectra below 10 K [9] and the PCS-spectra up to T_c [10] fit the ARXPS-spectra [9,24] in all features astoundingly well, even in doping dependence, asking questions about the common origin and the transmission via the blocking or an adsorption layer. At this point the above results on clean YBCO surface [5b] are worth mentioning: there the ΔU^*_S-(ΔU^*_{PS}-adsorbate?) features mask superconducting gap and Fermi surface information. The same may be true for BSCCO.
Because ARPES reveals k-dependencies, e.g. the Fermi surface, some words about the different k-dependencies of the ΔU^*_{PS}- and ΔU^*_{AP}-features are in order: In YBCO the CuO-chain holes favor exchanges k || b, i.e. $(0,\pi)$. Similar selection rules hold for BSCCO, because the stripe-like organization of the holes in BiO-planes, where the strip length grows with oxigenation, i.e. ΔU^*_{PS} shrinks [24]. Those ΔU^*_{PS}-exchanges modulate the k-dependence of the CuO_2-plane Fermi surface, which shift for $T > T_c$ due to 'pairing order' close to π/a [24]. The closeness of ΔU^*_{PS} and the energy gap $\Delta(O)$ is made obvious by PCS [10] showing $\Delta^\perp(T)$ with the proper T-dependence being close to ARPES results, below 10 K, to STS [9] and to the above bulk $\rho^\perp(T,\omega)$-observations summarized in Sect. 3.1. The $\Delta U^*_{PS} \approx 20$ meV $\cong \Delta^\perp$ signatures have in STS and PCS the largest amplitude because of the exponential transmission dependencies on energy (Eqs. (1b)), but agree quantitatively with bulk ΔU^*_{PS}-processes and ARPES. Hence, $\Delta U^*_{PS} \approx \Delta^\perp$ is not only a surface artifact but also a property of the bulk below T_c, i.e. hints strongly toward bosonic ΔU^*_{PS}-exchanges as one cause for coherence. Those exchanges, governing the three-

dimensional metal-insulator-transition, interfere with the ΔU^*_{AP}-exchanges for momenta k along (O,O)-(π,π) above 0.1 – 1 eV.

4. Summary and Discussion

In Sects. 3.1 and 3.2 evidence was presented that $\rho^{\perp}(T,\omega)$, $\rho^{\parallel}(T,\omega)$ and $j^{\perp}_c(T)$ are governed by resonant tunneling via blocking layer states $n_L(d^{\perp}/2)$ showing a Coulomb gap ΔU^*_{PS} agreeing quantitatively with the transport pseudo gap as function of doping [2,11]. In Sect. 3.4 it was shown that this Coulomb gap explains also the 'pseudo gap' observed by surface methods if proper account for surface degradation is taken. In the superconducting states an energy gap $\Delta(T)$ approaching 0 at T_c is observed, e.g., by PCS [10] or ARPES [8,24]. For relaxed [5b] or degraded [9] surfaces a temperature independent $\Delta U^*_S/\Delta U^*_{PS}$ Coulomb gap is observed, which masks or interferes [5b] with the superconducting gap $\Delta(T)$. To separate the gaps ΔU^* and $\Delta(T)$ temperature dependent and k-sensitive measurements are needed.

But the high T_c-values, the observation [25] that ΔU^*_{PS} scales T_c with doping, and the two components $\Delta U^*_{PS}/\Delta U^*_{AP}$ above and in [26] ask for clarification. One answer can be found in the XAS [19] and IR [12c] results where $n_L(d^{\perp}/2)$ and n_L(apex) change with doping synchronously. Thus, the T_c-ΔU^*_{PS}-scaling [25] carries also the strength of the ΔU^*_{AP}-n_L(apex)-exchange, where the latter is needed to explain $T_c > 20$ K. The above analysis envisions the crucial role of the apex-O showing up in the Fermi surface symmetry and in $\Delta U^*_{AP} > 0.1$ eV, but evenly important seems that a missing apex-O in NCCO allows $T_c \leq 20$ K only [1]. In the above two component system the symmetry and interference of both exchanges is crucial as observed, e.g., in PCS and in ARPES energy and momentum wise. The symmetry yields via ΔU^*_{PS} stripes, which minimize ΔU-energies, and via ΔU^*_{AP} d-wave symmetry. But the popularity of ΔU^*_{PS}-exchanges based on their dominance in the easily measured transport in the normal conducting state, e.g., in $\delta\rho^{\parallel} \propto T$ or $\rho^{\perp}(T,\omega)$ [2,11,12,18], and, especially, in the superconducting state, e.g., in $\Delta U^*_{PS} \approx \Delta(0)$, being separable by their different k- and T-dependencies, only. Hence, $T_c(n_L)$ diminishes with doping by the ΔU^*_{PS}-decrease leading to a three dimensional metal. On the other side of optimal doping, $T_c(n_L)$ decreases by the $n_L(d^{\perp}/2)$ decrease by ΔU^*_{PS} becoming larger than $\Delta(0)$.

Acknowledgement

The author thanks M. Beasley, V. Emery, A. Freimuth, R. Gross, R. Kleiner, M. Merz, Ch. Renner, W. Prusseit, Z. X. Shen and Y. De Wilde for helpful discussions.

REFERENCES

[1] Physical properties of High-Temperature Superconductors, Vol. I – VI (Ed. D. M. Ginsberg, World Scientific, Singapore)

[2] J.W. Loram et al., J. Superconductivity 7, 243 (1994)
b) B. Batlogg et al., Physica C 235 - 240, 130 (1994)
c) B. Wuyts et al., Phys. Rev. B 53, 9418 (1996)
d) S.K. Tolpygo et al., Phys. Rev. B 53, 12454 (1996)

[3] e.g., W.W. Warren et al., Phys. Rev. Lett. 62, 1193 (1993)

[4] L. Barr and C. R. Brundle, Phys. Rev. B 46, 9199 (1992)

[5] J. Halbritter et al., AIP Conf. Proc. No 182 (AVS, 1988), p. 208;
b) M. Schabel, et al., Phys. Rev. B 57, 6090 and 6107 (1998)
c) O. Tjernberg et al., Phys. Rev. Lett. 79, 499 (1997)

[6] G. S. Boebinger et al. in: Adv. in Superconduct. IX (Springer Verlag, Tokyo, 1997) and Phys. Rev. Lett. 77, 2065 (1996)

[7] J. Halbritter, Phys. Rev. B 46, 14861 (1992) and references therein
b) J. Halbritter, Phys. Rev. B 48, 9735 (1993)

[8] D.S. Marshall et al., Phys. Rev. Lett. 76, 4841 (1996); H. Ding et al., Nature 382, 51 (1996);

[9] Ch. Renner et al., Phys. Rev. Lett. 80, 149 (1998); Y. de Wilde et al., ibid, 153

[10] N. Miyakowa et al., Phys. Rev. Lett. 80, 157 (1998)

[11] J. Halbritter, Physica C 302, 221 (1998)
b) J. Halbritter, J. Superconductivity 11, 237 (1998)

[12] D. N. Basov et al., Phys. Rev. Lett. 77, 4090 (1996) and J. Phys.: Condens. Matter 8, 10049 (1996)
b) J. Schützmann et al., Phys. Rev. B 52, 13665 (1995)
c) D. Mihailovic et al., Phys. Rev B 57, 6116 (1998)

[13] J. Halbritter, Surface Science 122, 80 (1982)
b) J. Halbritter, J. Appl. Phys. 58, 1320 (1985)
c) J. Halbritter, Proc. Adriatico Research Conf. on: Electron and Ion Transfer in Condensed Media, Trieste, July, 1996 (World Scientific, Singapore, 1997), p. 278
d) J. Halbritter, Appl. Phys. A 67, 1 (1998)

[14] M. Rapp et al., Phys. Rev. Lett 77, 928 (1996); J. D. Hettinger et al., Phys. Rev. Lett. 74, 4726 (1995)

[15] R. Kleiner and P. Müller, Phys. Rev. B 49, 1327 (1994); T. Watanabe et al., Phys. Rev. Lett. 79, 2113 (1997)
b) N. E. Hussey et al., Phys. Rev. B 56, R 11423 (1997)

[16] S. I. Cooper, K. E. Gray, in: Physical Properties of High Temperature Sperconductors IV; (Ed. D. M. Ginsberg, World Scientific, Singapore, 1995)
b) D. H. Kim et al., Physica C177, 431 (1991) and V. Hardy et al., Phys. Rev. B56, 130 (1997)

[17] T. Jacobs et al., IEEE Trans Appl. Supercond. 7 1917 (1997);
E. Keskin et al., ibid 9, (1999)
b) C. J. Stevens et al., Phys. Rev. Lett. 78, 2212 (1997) D. Mihailovie et al., J. Phys. Chem. Sol. 59, 1997(1998)

[18] J. C. Phillips, Phys. Rev. B 46, 8542 (1992)
b) A. S. Alexandrov et al., Phys. Rev. Lett 77, 4796 (1996)

[19] M. Merz et al., Phys. Rev. Lett 80, (1998)

[20] L. Edwards et al., Phys. Rev. Lett. 69, 2967 (1992) and ibid 73, 1154 (1994)

[21] M. Kawasaki, and M. Nentoh, MRS Bulletin, Sept. 1994, p. 33, J. Appl. Phys. 75, 5227 (1994); T. Hasegawa et al., J. Phys. Chem. Solids 54, 1351 (1993)

[22] Ch. Renner et al., Phys. Rev. B 51, 9208 (1995)

[23] U. Hubler et al., Appl. Phys. A 66, S1219 (1988); M. Regier et al, IEEE Trans Appl. Superconduct. 9 (1999)

[24] Z. X. Shen et al., Phys. Rev. Lett. 78, 1721 (1997) and Phys. Rep. 253, 1 (1995)
b) Z. X. Shen et al., Science 280, 259 (1988)

[25] G. V. M. Williams et al., Phys. Rev. Lett 78, 721 (1997)

[26] D. Mihailovic, K. A. Müller in: High T_c Superconductivity 1996: Ten years after the Discovery (E. Kaldis et al., Eds, Kluwer, Netherlands, 1997), p. 243

Studies of High Temperature
Superconductors
Volume 27

ISBN 1-56072-684-9

SUPERCONDUCTING PAIRING, AND THE COLLECTIVE MAGNETIC EXCITATION IN THE EXTENDED 2-DIMENSIONAL *t-J* MODEL

OLEG SUSHKOV

School of Physics, University of New South Wales,
Sydney 2052, Australia

1 Introduction

To investigate the non-Fermi liquid behavior we consider the extended two-dimensional $t-J$ model which includes additional hopping t''. In the regime $t, J \ll t''$ we were able to solve the model analytically. It has a very rich phase diagram including antiferromagnetic (AF) insulator and AF strange metal with different kinds of pseudospin-singlet superconducting pairings (p,d,g-waves). We also demonstrate a collective triplet excitation with energy below the superconducting gap.

It is now widely accepted that superconductivity of cuprates is closely related to their unusual magnetic properties, and it is increasingly clear that magnetic pairing is the most realistic mechanism of cuprate superconductivity. However the mechanism of pairing as well as other unusual properties are far from completely understood. The problem has been attacked along several directions. First we have to mention the empirical or semi-empirical approach which allows one to relate different characteristics measured experimentally. This approach is to a large extent based on the Hubbard model. For a review see article [1]. In the low energy limit the Hubbard model can be reduced to the $t-J$ model. Another approach to cuprates is based on numerical studies of the $t-J$ model (see review [2]). Our studies are also based on this model. We used the ordered Neel state at zero doping as a starting point to develop the spin-wave theory of pairing [3]. The method we used was not fully satisfactory, since it violated spin-rotational symmetry, nevertheless it allowed us to calculate from first principles all of the most important properties including the critical temperature, the spin-wave pseudogap and the low energy spin triplet excitations [4].

A sharp collective mode with very low energy has been revealed in YBCO in spin polarized inelastic neutron scattering [5, 6, 7]. A number of theoretical explanations have been suggested for this effect [8, 4], all of these are based on the idea that the system is close to AF instability. However all known explanations use some uncontrolled approximations and assumptions.

In the present work we investigate close to half filling regime for the 2D $t-J$ model, where it can be solved analytically without any uncontrolled approximations. It can be done for the region of parameters where long-range AF order is preserved under doping. This is the regime where non Fermi liquid behavior can be studied in detail. We analyze the superconducting pairing in this regime and consider the spin triplet collective excitation. It is demonstrated that close to the point of AF instability energy of this excitation is very small. The excitation exists only at very small momenta. The idea of this work is somewhat similar to that of our previous paper [9], however here we investigate different regime.

2 Hamiltonian and single hole dispersion

Let us consider a $t-J-J''-V$ model defined by the Hamiltonian

$$H = -t\sum_{\langle ij\rangle\sigma} c_{i\sigma}^{\dagger}c_{j\sigma} - t''\sum_{\langle ij_2\rangle\sigma} c_{i\sigma}^{\dagger}c_{j_2\sigma} + \sum_{\langle ij\rangle}\left[J\left(\mathbf{S}_i\mathbf{S}_j - \frac{1}{4}n_in_j\right) + Vn_in_j\right]. \quad (1)$$

$c_{i\sigma}^{\dagger}$ is the creation operator of an electron with spin σ ($\sigma=\uparrow,\downarrow$) at site i of the two-dimensional square lattice. The $c_{i\sigma}^{\dagger}$ operators act in the Hilbert space with no double electron occupancy. The $\langle ij\rangle$ represents nearest neighbor sites, and $\langle ij_2\rangle$ represents next next nearest sites. The spin operator is $\mathbf{S}_i = \frac{1}{2}\sum_{\alpha,\beta} c_{i\alpha}^{\dagger}\sigma_{\alpha\beta}c_{i\beta}$, and the number density operator is $n_i = \sum_\sigma c_{i\sigma}^{\dagger}c_{i\sigma}$. In addition to the minimal $t-J$ model (see Ref. [2]) we have introduced additional next next nearest hopping t'', and Coulomb repulsion V at nearest sites. Note that we do not introduce next nearest neighbor hopping t' (diagonal) because we do not need it for the purposes of this study.

In the paper [9] we analyzed the model defined by the Hamiltonian (1) in the limit $t, t'' \ll J$. In the present work we consider limit

$$t, J \ll t''. \quad (2)$$

It is well known that the $t-J$ model at half filling describes the Mott insulator. It is equivalent to the 2D Heisenberg model, and the ground state of the model has long range AF order. At small doping the holes are concentrated near the points

$(\pm\pi/2, \pm\pi/2)$ where single hole dispersion has minima. In leading approximation the dispersion is of the form (we take energy at the minimum as a reference point)

$$\epsilon_k = \beta\left(\gamma_{\mathbf{k}}^2 + (\gamma_{\mathbf{k}}^-)^2\right), \qquad (3)$$
$$\beta \approx 0.8 \times 8t'' = 6.4t'',$$

$\gamma_{\mathbf{k}} = \frac{1}{2}(\cos k_x + \cos k_y)$, $\gamma_{\mathbf{k}}^- = \frac{1}{2}(\cos k_x - \cos k_y)$. Calculation of the dispersion (3) is straightforward because it is due to hopping within the same magnetic sublattice. Coefficient 0.8 appears because of spin quantum fluctuations: $0.8 = 1 - 0.2$, where 0.2 is the spin flip probability in the Heisenberg model. Alon with quasimomentum the hole in the AF background has an additional quantum number: pseudospin. We denote the hole creation operator by $h^\dagger_{\mathbf{k}\sigma}$, where $\sigma = \pm 1/2$ is pseudospin. The relation between pseudospin and usual spin is discussed in the paper [10].

We will consider the case of very small doping, $\delta \ll 1$, with respect to half filling (total filling is $1 - \delta$). In this case all holes are concentrated in small pockets around the points $\mathbf{k_0} = (\pm\pi/2, \pm\pi/2)$. Single hole dispersion (3) can be expanded near each of these points

$$\epsilon_k = \frac{1}{2}\beta\mathbf{p}^2, \qquad (4)$$

where $\mathbf{p} = (p_1, p_2)$ is deviation from the center of the pocket: $\mathbf{p} = \mathbf{k} - \mathbf{k_0}$, p_1 is orthogonal to the face of the magnetic Brillouin zone, and p_2 is parallel to the face (see Fig. 1). The Fermi energy and Fermi momentum for the holes equal $\epsilon_F \approx \frac{1}{2}\pi\beta\delta$, $p_F \approx (\pi\delta)^{1/2}$.

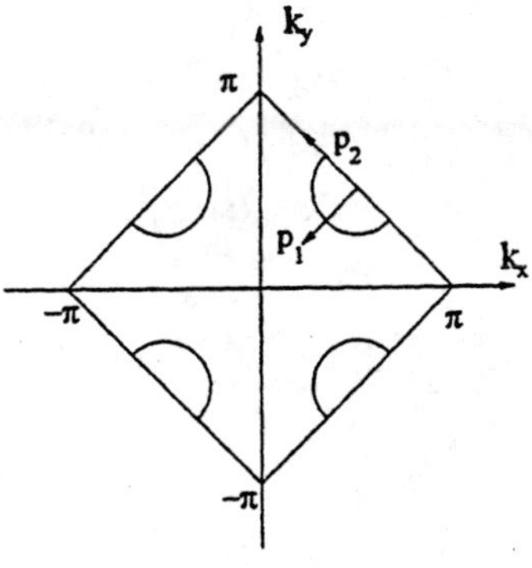

Figure 1: *Magnetic Brilloun zone and single hole dispersion*

3 Hole-spin-wave interaction and instability of the Neel state

Spin-wave excitations on an AF background are usual spin waves with dispersion $\omega_{\mathbf{q}} = 2J\sqrt{1-\gamma_{\mathbf{q}}^2} \approx \sqrt{2}Jq$, at $q << 1$, see Ref. [11] for review. The hole-spin-wave interaction is well known (see, e.g. Ref.[12])

$$H_{h,sw} = \sum_{\mathbf{k},\mathbf{q}} g_{\mathbf{k},\mathbf{q}} \left(h^\dagger_{\mathbf{k}+\mathbf{q}\downarrow} h_{\mathbf{k}\uparrow} \alpha_{\mathbf{q}} + h^\dagger_{\mathbf{k}+\mathbf{q}\uparrow} h_{\mathbf{k}\downarrow} \beta_{\mathbf{q}} + \text{H.c.} \right), \tag{5}$$
$$g_{\mathbf{k},\mathbf{q}} = 4t\sqrt{2}(\gamma_{\mathbf{k}} U_{\mathbf{q}} + \gamma_{\mathbf{k}+\mathbf{q}} V_{\mathbf{q}}),$$

where $h^\dagger_{\mathbf{k}\sigma} = c_{\mathbf{k},-\sigma}$ is the hole creation operator with pseudospin σ, $\alpha^\dagger_{\mathbf{q}}$ and $\beta^\dagger_{\mathbf{q}}$ are the spin wave creation operators for $S_z = \mp 1$, and $U_{\mathbf{q}} = \sqrt{\frac{J}{\omega_{\mathbf{q}}} + \frac{1}{2}}$ and $V_{\mathbf{q}} = -sign(\gamma_{\mathbf{q}})\sqrt{\frac{J}{\omega_{\mathbf{q}}} - \frac{1}{2}}$ are parameters of the Bogoliubov transformation diagonalizing the spin-wave Hamiltonian, see Ref.[11]. Virtual spin wave emission gives a correction to the hole dispersion, see Fig.2. However this correction is small $\delta\epsilon \sim t^2/t''$ and therefore can be neglected compared with (3).

Figure 2: *Spin-wave correction to the single hole dispersion. Solid line corresponds to the hole and dashed line corresponds to the spin wave.*

To describe renormalization of the spin wave under doping, it is convenient to introduce the set of Green's functions [13]

$$\begin{aligned}
D_{\alpha\alpha}(t,\mathbf{q}) &= -i\langle T[\alpha_{\mathbf{q}}(t)\alpha^\dagger_{\mathbf{q}}(0)]\rangle, \\
D_{\alpha\beta}(t,\mathbf{q}) &= -i\langle T[\alpha_{\mathbf{q}}(t)\beta_{-\mathbf{q}}(0)]\rangle, \\
D_{\beta\alpha}(t,\mathbf{q}) &= -i\langle T[\beta^\dagger_{-\mathbf{q}}(t)\alpha^\dagger_{\mathbf{q}}(0)]\rangle, \\
D_{\beta\beta}(t,\mathbf{q}) &= -i\langle T[\beta^\dagger_{-\mathbf{q}}(t)\beta_{-\mathbf{q}}(0)]\rangle.
\end{aligned} \tag{6}$$

In the present work we consider only the long-range dynamics: $q \sim k \sim p_F \ll 1$. In this limit all possible polarization operators coincide [4] $P_{\alpha\alpha}(\omega,\mathbf{q}) = P_{\alpha\beta}(\omega,\mathbf{q}) = P_{\beta\alpha}(\omega,\mathbf{q}) = P_{\beta\beta}(\omega,\mathbf{q}) = \Pi(\omega,\mathbf{q})$, where $\Pi(\omega,\mathbf{q})$ is given by the diagram presented at Fig. 3.

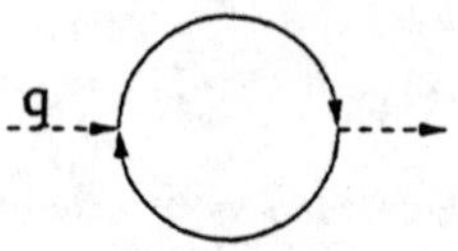

Figure 3: *Spin-wave polarization operator. Solid line corresponds to the hole and dashed line corresponds to the spin wave.*

For stability of the system the condition (Stoner criterion)

$$\omega_q + 2\Pi(0,\mathbf{q}) > 0 \tag{7}$$

must be fulfilled [14]. Otherwise the Green's functions (6) would possess poles with imaginary ω. Considering holes as a "normal Fermi liquid" [15] one can easily calculate the polarization operator at $q \ll p_F$: $\Pi(0,\mathbf{q}) \approx -4t^2\sqrt{2}q/\pi\beta$, Ref. [14]. Relatively weak pairing, which we consider below, does not influence this result. Then the condition of stability can be rewritten as

$$\beta = 6.4t'' > \frac{8t^2}{\pi J}. \tag{8}$$

To provide stability of the AF order we have to choose

$$t'' > t''_c \approx 0.4t^2/J. \tag{9}$$

If $t < J$ or $t \sim J$ the stability condition is automatically fulfilled since in the present work we consider $t, J \ll t''$. However at $t \gg J$ one can violate the condition (8). In this case we will assume that $t'' > t''_c$. If t'' is close to t''_c it is convenient to introduce the parameter η

$$\eta^2 = 1 - \frac{8t^2}{\pi J\beta} = (t'' - t''_c)/t'' \tag{10}$$

as a measure of this closeness. The criterion (7) is proportional to this parameter.

4 Spin-singlet p-wave pairing caused by the short-range attraction

It is not convenient to consider the superconducting pairing in the magnetic Brillouin zone with four half-pockets (see Fig. 1). Because of this we translate the picture to the shifted zone with two whole pockets, Fig. 4. We stress that this is question of convenience only, the representations are absolutely equivalent because of the translational invariance.

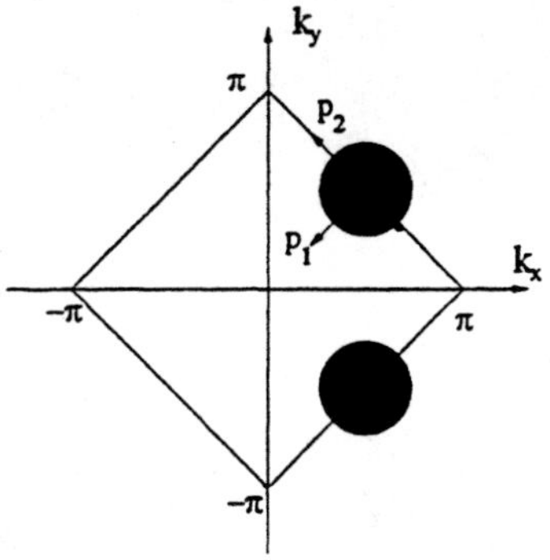

Figure 4: *Shifted zone with two whole pockets. Shadowed area corresponds to occupied hole states.*

There are two mechanisms for the superconducting pairing: short-range attraction and long-range attraction. First we consider the short-range effect. Attraction between holes at nearest sites (short-range) is due to the reduction in number of missing AF links. The value of this attraction immediately follows from eq.(1)

$$U = J\langle \mathbf{S_i S_j} - \frac{1}{4} + V\rangle \approx -0.58J + V. \tag{11}$$

Strong enough Coulomb repulsion ($V > 0.58J$) kills this mechanism. In the momentum representation the interaction (11) can be rewritten as

$$H_U = 8U \sum_{\mathbf{k_1,k_2,k_3,k_4}} \gamma_{\mathbf{k_1-k_3}} h^\dagger_{\mathbf{k_3}\uparrow} h^\dagger_{\mathbf{k_4}\downarrow} h_{\mathbf{k_2}\downarrow} h_{\mathbf{k_1}\uparrow} \delta_{\mathbf{k_1+k_2,k_3+k_4}}. \tag{12}$$

For scattering inside a hole pocket the interaction is practically momentum independent because $\mathbf{k_1} \approx \mathbf{k_2} \approx \mathbf{k_3} \approx \mathbf{k_4} \approx (\pi/2, \pi/2)$, and hence $\gamma_{\mathbf{k_1-k_3}} \approx 1$. Such interaction gives "s-wave pairing" with the gap without nodes at the Fermi surface. The value of the superconducting gap one can easily find using the results of papers [16, 17]. This gives

$$\Delta = Ct''\sqrt{\delta}e^{\pi\beta/4U} = Ct''\sqrt{\delta}e^{-5t''/(0.58J-V)}, \tag{13}$$

where $C \sim 10$ is some dimensionless constant. The solution is valid only if $V < 0.58J$, for stronger Coulomb repulsion the pairing disappears. It is important to stress the peculiar symmetry properties of the above pairing. This peculiarity comes from the presence of long-range AF order. As we already mentioned, the gap has no nodes at the Fermi surface and from this point of view it is "s-wave pairing". However we remind that we have considered the pairing in the shifted zone and in this zone it is not easy to classify the states by parity. For well defined parity we have to return to the magnetic Brillouin zone, so we have to translate the outside parts of the Fermi surface by the inverse vector of the magnetic lattice $\mathbf{G} = (\pi, \pi)$, see Fig. 5.

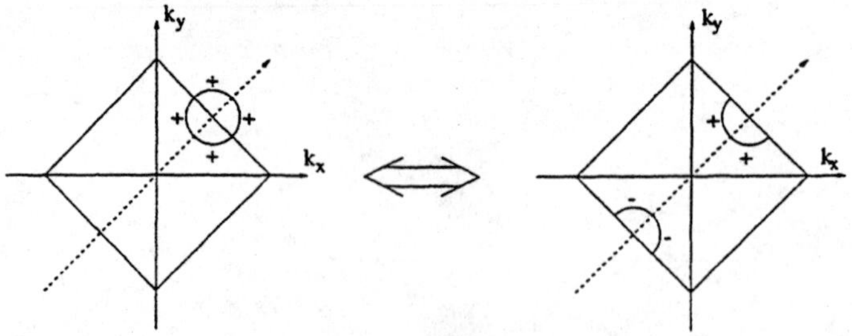

Figure 5: *Translation from the shifted zone to the magnetic Brillouin zone. The superconducting gap has no nodes at the Fermi surface. The gap changes sign under this translation.*

The point is that under such translation the superconducting gap changes the sign as it is shown at Fig. 5. This property follows from the fact that the coefficient in the interaction (12) changes sign under such translation: $\gamma_{\mathbf{k_1}-\mathbf{k_3}+\mathbf{G}} = -\gamma_{\mathbf{k_1}-\mathbf{k_3}}$ (for details see paper [18]).

Thus in reality we have negative parity pairing which is usually called p-wave. The above consideration was relevant to the hole pocket centered at $(\pi/2, \pi/2)$. Similar construction is valid for another pocket centered at $(\pi/2, -\pi/2)$. Existence of two solutions corresponds to the double degeneracy of the E-representation of the C_{4v} group. Taking linear combinations of the single pocket solutions we find two degenerate solutions for the entire Brillouin zone with lines of nodes $\mathbf{k_x} = 0$ or $\mathbf{k_y} = 0$ well outside the Fermi surface. We would like to stress that we have considered the spin-singlet (more exactly pseudospin-singlet) pairing! This situation is very much different from the usual one when p-wave pairing implies spin triplet. We repeat that the peculiarity is due to the presence of long-range AF order.

5 D- and g-wave pairings caused by the long-range attraction

The long range attraction comes from the spin-wave exchange shown on Fig. 6. In this exchange the typical spin-wave momenta are $q \sim p_F \sim \sqrt{\delta}$, and hence the typical distances are $r \sim 1/q \sim 1/\sqrt{\delta} \gg 1$.

Figure 6: *Spin-wave exchange mechanism of attraction. Solid line corresponds to the hole and dashed line corresponds to the spin wave. The arrow shows the hole pseudospin.*

Similarly to the previous section, it convenient to consider first the pairing inside a hole pocket, say centered at $(\pi/2, \pi/2)$, see Fig. 4. This pairing has been considered in detail in our previous work [3]. It has been shown that for the case of "isotropic" dispersion (4) the only solution is the one with a single node line in the pocket. The gap at the Fermi surface ($\epsilon_F = \frac{1}{2}\pi\beta\delta$) is of the form

$$\Delta(\phi) = \Delta_0 \sin\phi, \qquad (14)$$
$$\Delta_0 = C\epsilon_F\, e^{-\pi J\beta/2t^2} \approx 10Ct''\delta\, e^{-10Jt''/t^2},$$

where $\sin\phi = p_2/p_F$, $p_F^2 = p_1^2 + p_2^2$, and $C \sim 1$ is some constant.

The eqs.(14) describe pairing within a single pocket of the shifted zone. Translation of this solution to the magnetic Brillouin zone is shown at Fig. 7. This is absolutely identical to what we did in the previous section (change of sign at the translation).

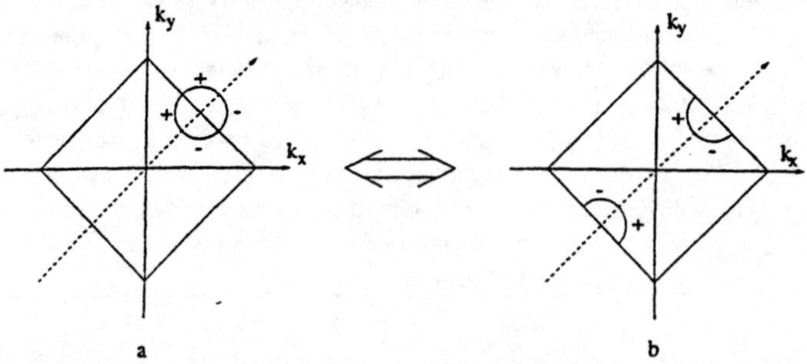

Figure 7: *Translation from the shifted zone to the magnetic Brillouin zone. The superconducting gap has line of nodes. The gap changes sign under the translation.*

There are effectively two pockets in the Brillouin zone, see Fig. 4. Taking symmetric and antisymmetric combinations between the pockets, we get the d- and g-wave pairings respectively. The symmetries of the corresponding superconducting gaps are shown at Fig. 8. It is clear that the d-wave belongs to the B_1 representation of the C_{4v} group and the g-wave belongs to the A_2 representation.

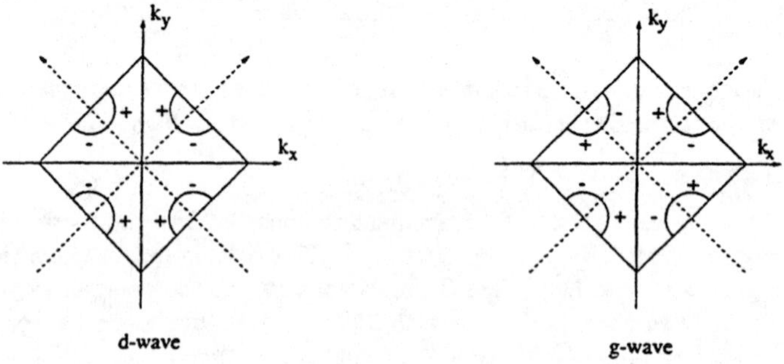

Figure 8: *Symmetry of the superconducting gap corresponding to the d- and g-wave pairings.*

Both solutions originate from (14), therefore they are close in energy. Nevertheless the constant C in eq. (14) is smaller for the g-wave. This is the price for additional lines of nodes ($\mathbf{k_x} = 0$ and $\mathbf{k_y} = 0$). The above consideration did not include short range interaction (12). This is absolutely correct for g-wave pairing which is not sensitive to the interaction (12) at all. However the d-wave is sensitive. Therefore at $V < 0.58J$ the d-wave pairing is enhanced because of (12), while, on the contrary, at larger Coulomb repulsion $V > 0.58J$ the d-wave is suppressed and can even disappear. To avoid misunderstanding we stress that in the limit under consideration ($t'' \gg t, J$) the short range interaction (12) is too weak (even at $V = 0$) to produce d-wave pairing without spin-wave exchange. However the short-range interaction influences the dimensionless constant C (see eq. (14)) which arises in spin-wave exchange mechanism.

6 The phase diagram

The phase diagram of the model under consideration is given on Fig. 9. To be specific we present the case of the not too strong Coulomb repulsion at the nearest sites: $V < 0.58J$. At stronger V the p-wave superconductivity disappears, see eq. (13). Comparing eqs. (13) and (14) we see that the p-wave pairing is stronger at $t < t_c$, while at $t > t_c$ the d-g-wave pairing dominates. At $V = 0$ the critical value is $t_c \approx J$. In the p-wave phase the gap, as well as the critical temperature, is proportinal to square root of the hole concentration: $\Delta \sim T_c \propto \sqrt{\delta}$. But in the d-g-wave phase they are proportional to the first power of concentration: $\Delta \sim T_c \propto \delta$

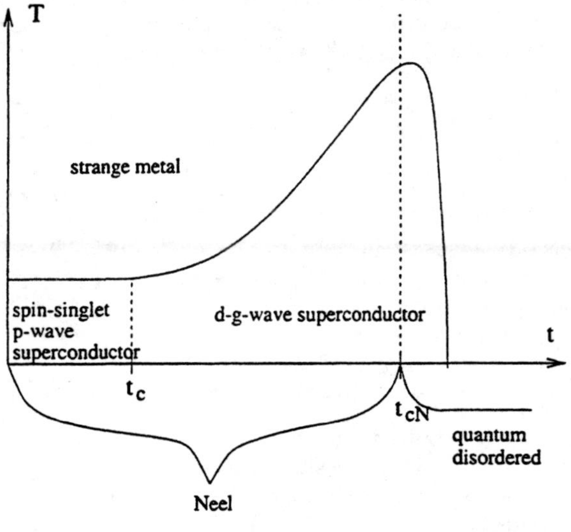

Figure 9: *The phase diagram of the extended 2D* $t - t'' - J - V$ *model.* t_c *is transition point from the p-wave to the d-g-wave superconductor.* t_{cN} *is transition point from the Neel state to the spin quantum disordered state.*

According to eq. (9) at $t < t_{cN} \approx 1.6\sqrt{t''J}$, the long range AF order at zero temperature is preserved under doping, so we have coexistence of the superconductivity and the Neel order. At $t > t_{cN}$ the Neel order is destroyed by the doping and one gets a transition into the quantum disordered phase. However as soon as the magnetic correlation length is larger than the superconducting correlation length the mechanism of pairing is valid and one still has the d-g-wave superconductor. At a temperature higher than the critical one the system behaves as a metal with very strong scattering of mobile holes on spin-wave excitations. Following the tradition we call this state "strange metal".

7 The spin-wave collective excitation

We will see that the spin-wave collective excitation has nontrivial behaviour in the vicinity of the quantum phase transition from the Neel to the disordered phase. Therefore we study this excitation only in the d-g-wave superconducting phase at $T = 0$. The energy spectrum and Bogoliubov parameters are given by the usual BCS formulas

$$\begin{aligned} E_{\mathbf{k}} &= \sqrt{(\epsilon_k - \epsilon_F)^2 + \Delta_{\mathbf{k}}^2}, \\ u_{\mathbf{k}}^2, v_{\mathbf{k}}^2 &= \frac{1}{2}\left(1 \pm \frac{\epsilon_{\mathbf{k}} - \epsilon_F}{E_{\mathbf{k}}}\right) \end{aligned} \tag{15}$$

with gap $\Delta_{\mathbf{k}}$ from eq. (14). The spin wave polarization operator due to mobile holes is given by diagram on Fig. 3 plus a similar diagram with anomalous fermionic Green's functions. Straightforward calculation gives (see e.g. Ref.[4])

$$\Pi(\omega, \mathbf{q}) = \sum_{\mathbf{k},\mathbf{k_0}} g_{\mathbf{k_0 q}}^2 \frac{2(E_{\mathbf{k}} + E_{\mathbf{k+q}})}{\omega^2 - (E_{\mathbf{k}} + E_{\mathbf{k+q}})^2} \left(u_{\mathbf{k}}^2 v_{\mathbf{k+q}}^2 + u_{\mathbf{k}} v_{\mathbf{k}} u_{\mathbf{k+q}} v_{\mathbf{k+q}}\right). \tag{16}$$

This equation includes summation over pockets $\mathbf{k_0} = (\pi/2, \pm\pi/2)$. In these pockets the vertex (5) is $g_{\mathbf{k_0,q}} \approx 2^{5/4} t(q_x \pm q_y)/\sqrt{q}$. Let us consider the case of very small momenta and frequencies: $v_F q < \Delta_0$, and $\omega < \Delta_0$. In this limit one can put $q = 0$ in eq. (16) everywhere except at the vertex and therefore the polarization operator can be evaluated analytically

$$\Pi(\omega, \mathbf{q}) = -\frac{4t^2 \omega_{\mathbf{q}}}{\pi J \beta}\left(1 + i\frac{\pi\omega}{8\Delta_0}\right) \tag{17}$$

Note that the the imaginary part is nonzero even at $\omega < 2\Delta_0$ because the gap (14) has a line of nodes. Any of the Green's functions (6) have a denominator $\omega^2 - \omega_{\mathbf{q}}^2 - 2\omega_{\mathbf{q}}\Pi(\omega, \mathbf{q})$, see e.g. Refs. [13, 4]. The zero of this denominator gives the energy and width of the spin-triplet collective excitation. Using eqs.(17) and (10) we find

$$\begin{aligned} o_{\mathbf{q}} &= \eta\omega_{\mathbf{q}}, \\ \Gamma_{\mathbf{q}} &= \frac{\pi}{8}\frac{1-\eta^2}{\eta}\frac{\omega_{\mathbf{q}}}{\Delta_0} o_{\mathbf{q}}. \end{aligned} \tag{18}$$

In essence this is the renormalized spin-wave. Far from the point of AF instability the parameter $\eta \approx 1$, therefore the renormalization is relatively weak and the decay width is small. The situation is different when approaching the point of instability $t \to t_{cN} \approx 1.6\sqrt{t''/J}$. Here, according to eq. (10), $\eta \to 0$ and therefore the energy of the renormalized spin wave is much smaller than the energy of the bare spin-wave,

$o_\mathbf{q}/\omega_\mathbf{q} = \eta \ll 1$. Moreover this collective excitation exists as a narrow peak only at very small q, when

$$\pi\omega_\mathbf{q}/8\eta\Delta_0 < 1. \tag{19}$$

At higher q the width is larger than its frequency because of decay to particle-hole excitations. We stress that the closer to the point of instability, the smaller is η, and therefore the smaller is the region of q where the excitation exists.

8 Conclusions

We have considered a close to half filling $t - t'' - J - V$ model at $t'' \gg t, J$. We restrict our consideration to the case of small doping $\delta \ll 1$. It is demonstrated that at $t < t_{cN} \approx 1.6\sqrt{t''J}$ the Neel order is preserved under the doping, and at $t > t_{cN}$ the order is destroyed and the system undergoes a transition to the quantum spin disordered phase, see phase diagram at Fig. 9.

If the hole-hole Coulomb repulsion at nearest sites is not too strong ($V < 0.58J$), then at small t the model has psedospin-singlet p-wave superconductivity. As t increases, at the some point t_c (at $V = 0$ the critical point is $t_c \approx J$) the system undergoes a phase transition from the p-wave to the d-g-wave superconductor, see Fig. 9. Which state is realized (d- or g-wave) crucially depends on the Coulomb repulsion V. If V is small the d-wave is preferable, while at larger V the g-wave superconductivity is realized.

In the Neel state we found the collective spin triplet excitation (renormalized spin wave). In the vicinity of the quantum phase transition to the spin disordered state the excitation exists as a narrow mode only at very small momenta and its energy is substantially below the energy of the bare spin wave.

References

[1] A. V. Chubukov and D. K. Morr, Phys. Rep. **288**, 355 (1997) and reference therein.

[2] E. Dagotto, Rev. Mod. Phys. **66**, 763 (1994).

[3] V. V. Flambaum, M. Yu. Kuchiev, and O. P. Sushkov, Physics C **227**, 267 (1994); V. I. Belinicher, A. L. Chernyshev, A. V. Dotsenko, and O. P. Sushkov, Phys. Rev. B **51**, 6076 (1995).

[4] O. P. Sushkov, Phys. Rev. B **54**, 9988 (1996).

[5] J. Rossat-Mignot *et al.*, Physica C **185-189**, 86 (1991).

[6] P. Dai *et al.*, Phys. Rev. Lett., **70**, 3490 (1993); **77**, 5425 (1996).

[7] H. F. Fong *et al.*, Phys. Rev. Lett., **75**, 316 (1996); **78**, 713 (1997).

[8] E. Demler ans S. C. Zhang, Phys. Rev. Lett., **75**, 4126 (1995); D. Z. Liu *et al.*, *ibid.* **75**, 4130 (1995); I. I. Mazin and V. M. Yakovenko, *ibid.* **75**, 4134 (1995); V. Barzykin and D. Pines, Phys. Rev. B **52**, 13585 (1995); G. Blumberg *et al.*, *ibid.* **52**, R15741 (1995); N. Bulut and D. J. Scalapino, *ibid.* **53**, 5149 (1996).

[9] D. Marinaro and O. P. Sushkov. Phys. Rev. B **58**, 14934 (1998).

[10] O. P. Sushkov, G. A. Sawatzky, R. Eder, and H. Eskes, Phys. Rev. B **56**, 11769 (1997).

[11] E. Manousakis, Rev. Mod. Phys. **63**, 1 (1991).

[12] C. L. Kane, P. A. Lee, and N. Read, Phys. Rev. B **39**, 6880 (1989).

[13] J. Igarashi and P. Fulde, Phys. Rev. B **45**, 12357 (1992).

[14] O. P. Sushkov and V. V. Flambaum, Physica C **206**, 269 (1993).

[15] "Normal Fermi liquid" is a somewhat misleading term because we consider a system which is not a normal Fermi liquid from the common point of view. In this case "Normal Fermim liquid" means that we consider an ideal gas of Fermions with dispersion (3). At zero temperature all states inside the semicircles at the Fig. 1 are occupied.

[16] M. Randeria, J.-M. Duan, and L.-Y.Shieh, Phys. Rev. Lett., **62**, 981 (1989).

[17] M. Yu. Kuchiev and O. P. Sushkov, Phys. Rev. B **53**, 443 (1996).

[18] M. Yu. Kuchiev and O. P. Sushkov, Physica C **218**, 197 (1993).

SUBJECT INDEX
VOLUME 27